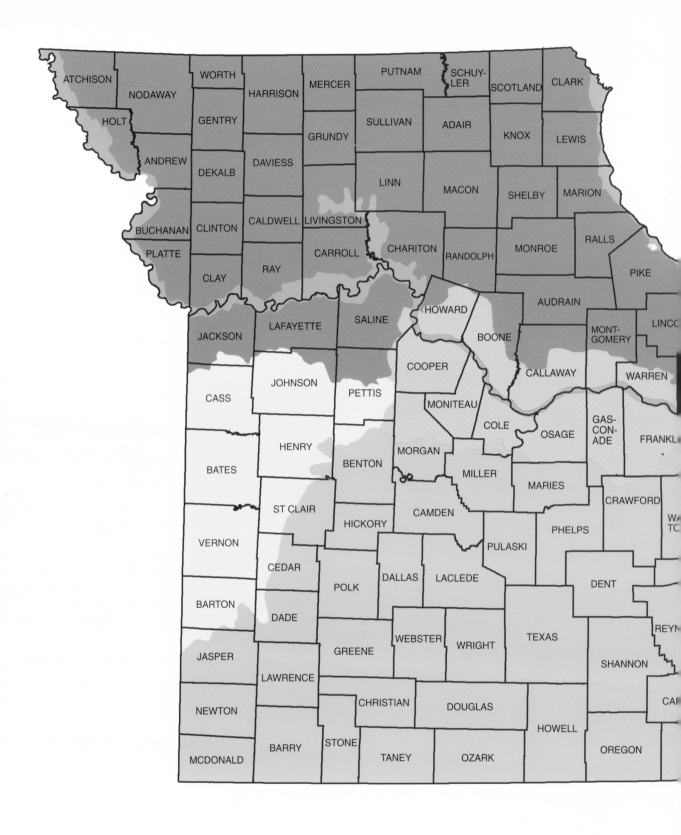

The Natural Divisions of Missouri

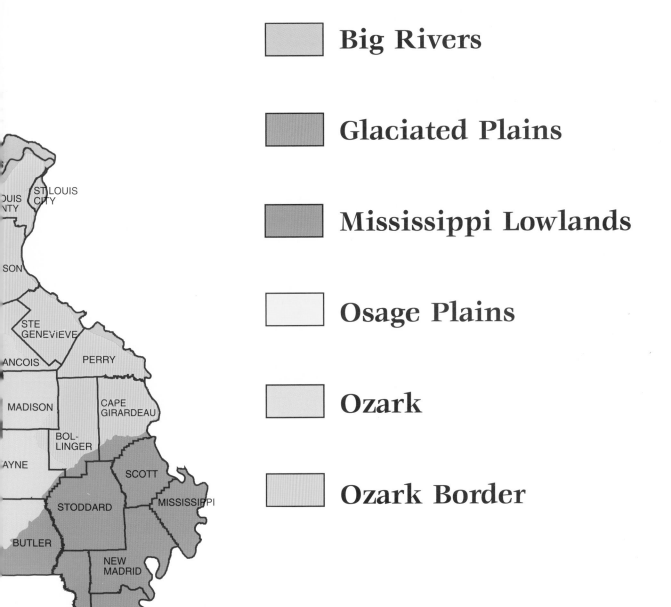

Big Rivers

Glaciated Plains

Mississippi Lowlands

Osage Plains

Ozark

Ozark Border

Cover: The setting sun silhouettes Missouri's champion bur oak, as it has for nearly 500 years. Located near McBaine, in the Missouri River floodplain, the majestic tree measures 272 inches in circumference, stands 84 feet tall and has a crown spread of 116 feet. A survivor of many floods throughout the centuries, it is admired by fellow Boone Countians and all who pass by. Don Kurz photographed the tree on a late November day.

Trees of Missouri

*This book is dedicated
to those who have
climbed trees, planted trees,
and saved trees in their lifetime.*

Today I have grown taller from walking with the trees.

—Karle Wilson Baker, a Texas poet (1878–1960)

Disclaimer

Medicinal uses for plants described in this book are for informational purposes only, and should not be read as promotions for medical or herbal prescriptions for self healing.

Trees of Missouri

by
Don Kurz

illustrations by Paul Nelson

Charlotte Overby, editor
Ara Clark, designer
Libby Block, production assistant

Acknowledgments

I want to thank the staff of the Natural History Division, Missouri Department of Conservation, for their interest and support of my project. I especially appreciate the encouragement and backing provided by Richard H. Thom, Natural History Administrator, and Kim Reilmann, Natural History Office Administrator.

The technical review of the tree book manuscript was done by Tim Smith, Botanist, Natural History Division, and Bruce Palmer, Forestry Education Coordinator, Outreach & Education Division. Their edits and comments are greatly appreciated.

Appreciation goes to Charlotte Overby for editing of the manuscript; Libby Block for entering the editorial changes; Ara Clark for designing the book; and Bernadette Dryden for overall coordination and support.

The Natural Divisions of Missouri and North American maps were created by Niki Aberle and Jason Jett; while the county distribution maps were produced in Arcview by Chris Wieberg with coding accomplished by Kevin Borisenko. A special thanks goes to George Yatskievych, author of the *Flora of Missouri*, for the updated county distribution maps and comments on taxonomic nomenclature.

Thanks also goes to Greg Haas, Tim Smith, Mark Pelton, Mike Skinner, Clint Dalborn, and George Yatskievych for providing locations and, sometimes, plant material for a few of the more uncommon trees.

In following the philosophy of my book *Shrubs and Woody Vines of Missouri*, I felt that it was important to illustrate this book with line drawings rather than use color photographs. To photograph every leaf, twig, flower, and fruit for all 170 trees would have been very time consuming and costly, leading to a much more expensive book. As in the shrub and woody vine book, the tree book is exquisitely illustrated by Paul Nelson. What a combination, with a graduate degree in botany and an artist's eye, Paul has portrayed these tree illustrations in exacting detail and with graceful presentation. I might add, as in the shrub and woody vine book, Paul collected most of the material that he illustrated. He certainly has a gift for illustrating and I am again fortunate and honored to have his work appear in this book.

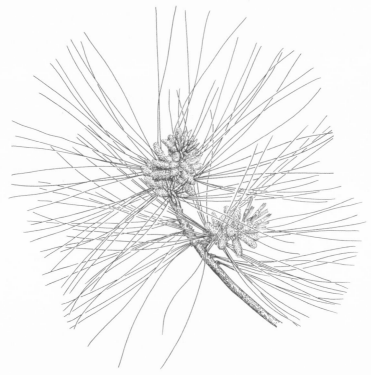

Contents

Introduction
6
How to use this book
Landscaping with native trees
Landscaping to help bring wildlife to your backyard
Planting and maintenance
Propagation

Keys to the Trees
16

Tree Descriptions
40

Oak Leaves
374

Oak Acorns
378

Oak Reproductive Cycle
380

Hickory Reproductive Cycle
382

List of Families, Genera, and Species
384

Other Tree Species
387

Nursery Sources for Native Trees
389

Selected References
391

Index to Scientific and Common Names
393

Introduction

Trees affect everyone's lives in some way every day. Whether providing comfort and shelter in our homes through wood products, aesthetic beauty in our yards, or producing oxygen for us to breathe, trees are important to our quality of life. Trees also provide a host of other benefits, including providing food and shelter for wildlife, reducing soil erosion, influencing weather patterns, providing a "roof" over other plants, and sequestering carbon from the air thus helping to reduce global warming.

The purpose of this book is to provide information on the identification, uses, care, and propagation of trees; its goal is to foster an increased understanding and appreciation of these important plants. Trees of special conservation concern are also described and illustrated with the hope that new locations of them will be found.

There are various definitions that differentiate trees from shrubs. The American Forestry Association describes a tree as a woody plant with a single stem or trunk at least 3 inches in diameter at breast height (4 1/2 feet above ground). A tree is also at least 13 feet tall, with a definite crown of foliage. In comparison, a shrub has multiple stems arising from the ground and is generally smaller than a tree.

Most trees need to form canopies so that their leaves will have maximum exposure to direct sunlight, which enables energy to be harnessed through photosynthesis to produce sugar needed for new growth, including the ability to flower and fruit. On the other hand, there are some trees that live in the understory, such as flowering dogwood, redbud, hop hornbeam, and serviceberry that are well adapted to exist with less light.

There are 149 native tree species in Missouri. For the purpose of discussion in this book, a native tree is one that occurred in Missouri prior to the arrival of European settlers. This is a tree species that is well adapted to living and reproducing in the same soil, topography, and climate for thousands of years. Also, wildlife has evolved to depend on selected trees or types of trees for food and cover. In contrast, a naturalized tree, often referred to as nonnative, exotic, or alien, is one that has escaped into a new habitat due to human influence. Many of these nonnative trees spread from their original plantings and invade nearby natural communities, often spreading prolifically and reducing the diversity of the natural community. These exotic species are so successful because their natural predators in their original homeland did not make the journey with them to their new environment. These nonnative trees often become a nuisance, with eradication proving costly and time-consuming. There are 35 species of trees that have naturalized in the state with origins primarily in Europe and Asia. These exotic trees disrupt the natural balance of forests, savannas, and woodlands in Missouri, and the planting of these species known to be invasive should be discouraged.

The native trees of Missouri are found in a variety of habitats or natural communities. Some of these woody species, however, are restricted to certain regions of the state. These regions or natural divisions (see inside front cover for a map) are based on geologic history, soils, topography, plant and animal distribution, and other natural features. There are six major regions and 18 subregions, which are termed natural divisions and sections.

Ozark Natural Division: This is a region of extensive forested hills and valleys that covers about 40 percent of Missouri's surface. The division has an ancient geological history, which included several periods of slow uplift, accompanied by deep erosion by its streams. This land mass has been exposed for more than 250 million years, while surrounding regions were repeatedly covered by glaciers, seas, or floods. This long exposure, together with a diversity of bedrock and soil types, has created habitats for more species of plants and animals than exist in any other part of the state.

Ozark Border Natural Division: This is a transition zone between the Ozarks and other regions of the state and covers about 12 percent of Missouri's surface. The landscape is Ozarklike, but the soils are deeper and more productive. Plant and animal ranges in the Ozarks and Glaciated Plains overlap in this natural division.

Glaciated Plains Natural Division: Covering about 30 percent of the state's land surface, the landscape of this natural division has been dramatically affected by major glacial events that ended approximately 500,000 years ago. The glaciers leveled north Missouri and deposited silts, sands, gravels, and boulders. Erosion throughout time has produced rolling plains that once were home to extensive prairies, interrupted only by scattered savannas and forested river valleys.

Osage Plains Natural Division: Like the Ozarks, this region is also unglaciated. It covers about 8 percent of the state's land surface. The gently rolling hills and plains once were dominated by prairie. Although the deeper soils have been plowed for row crops and the thinner soils pastured, there are still areas of prairie—although measured in acres instead of square miles.

Big Rivers Natural Division: The Missouri and Mississippi rivers and their flood plains and terraces occupy this natural division, which covers about 5 percent of the state's surface. Although greatly altered today by locks and dams, levees, and agriculture, the remaining forested land and aquatic features provide important habitat for a variety of plants and animals.

Mississippi Lowlands Natural Division: Comprising about 5 percent of the surface of the state, this region was the northern boundary of the Gulf of Mexico more than 24 million years ago. Much later, during the time of the glaciers, meltwater from the retreating ice formed the Ohio and Mississippi river systems, which scoured and deposited sediments, and reshaped the land to what it is today. Up until about 100 years ago, extensive bottomland forests and swamps dominated the region. Today, massive ditches and extensive agriculture have eliminated most of the habitat for unique plants and animals that have a southern coastal plain origin.

(Note: For a technical discussion of this subject, see "The Natural Divisions of Missouri" by R.H. Thom and J.H. Wilson in "Transactions of the Missouri Academy of Science," Vol. 14, 1980, pp. 9–23; or, for a more general description, obtain a copy of the "Directory of Missouri Natural Areas," Missouri Conservation Department, 1996, which is available at Conservation Department offices.)

How to Use This Book
PLANT NAMES

Common names for plants are easy to learn, but they sometimes lead to confusion and misunderstanding because one species may have several names, and one name sometimes can be applied to more than one plant. Eastern witch hazel, for example, also is called common witch hazel, witch hazel, hamamelis, long boughs, pistachio, snapping hazel, snapping hazelnut, southern witch hazel, spotted alder, striped tobacco, white hazel, winterbloom, and wood tobacco. These names are frequently local and vary from place to place, but there is only one scientific name, *Hamamelis virginiana*, and that is used worldwide. An example of a common name that is used for more than one plant is bowman's root. It is a synonym for hemp dogbane, spotted spurge, and Culver's root—three completely different plants.

Scientific names are in classical Latin or Greek and are adopted throughout the world, regardless of spoken language. Scientific names are governed by the International Code of Botanical Nomenclature, a detailed set of rules adopted by systematic botanists. Scientific names are also binomial, composed of the genus name followed by the specific name. The genus name is a noun, often commemorating noted botanists, or is simply the classical name for the group. The first letter of the genus is always capitalized, for example Quercus, and is always in italics, *Quercus*. The species name is an adjective, modifying the noun, and is always written in lower case letters such as *alba*. Therefore, the scientific name for white oak is *Quercus alba*. The scientific name for every tree covered in this book has an explanation for the derivation of the genus and species name. The origin of the common name is also presented.

Following the scientific name is the name, usually abbreviated, of the botanist who originally described and named the species; if two botanists are responsible for the binomial combination, the first is placed in parenthesis. For example, the proper citation for white oak is *Quercus alba* L. The "L." is for Linnaeus (1707–1778) a Swedish botanist, who is often called the Father of Taxonomy. His basic system for naming, ranking, and classifying plants and animals is what is in use today (of course with many changes). The common and scientific names used in this book follow either Julian A. Steyermark's *Flora of Missouri* or George Yatskievych and Joanna Turner's *Catalogue of the Flora of Missouri*.

USE OF KEYS

If you know the common name of a plant covered in this book, a quick check in the index can direct you to the page number for the species. Another method would be to thumb through the book and look for an illustration of a plant similar to the one you are trying to identify. But if you cannot match the plant precisely to any illustration, it is time to use the keys.

Taxonomic keys provide a convenient shortcut method of identifying plants by outlining and grouping related types. The keys consist of a series of couplets, with a choice of contrasting statements. The first choice may sound like the right description, but read both categories to make sure. The second category, by contrast, may actually help to explain the first one. After a choice is made, a number at the end of the category directs you to either the page for the plant description or to the next couplet.

The keys and species descriptions were written in a way to avoid botanical terms as much as possible. When terms are used, they are immediately defined in parenthesis. This methods saves time and eliminates the need for a glossary or having to memorize such terms as obovate, cuneate, etc. Often, more than one character is used to identify plants in the key. Leaves, flowers, and fruit commonly are described, but winter characters such as leaf scars and buds are usually not. For those interested in keying out winter twigs, refer to a publication that is available from the Missouri Department of Conservation titled *A Key to Missouri Trees in Winter*, by Jerry Cliburn and Ginny Klomps.

NOTES ON SPECIES DESCRIPTIONS

The trees are arranged by scientific name in alphabetical order. When a scientific name has changed, the older name or less commonly used name is mentioned in the "Remarks" section under species descriptions. All names mentioned, both common and scientific, are listed in the index.

As an aid to identifying the tree in question, key characters for the tree are highlighted in **bold type**.

The state maps, showing counties in which the particular species has been found and verified with a herbarium collection, are provided by George Yatskievych, Missouri Conservation Department, who has updated county records in preparation for his revision of Julian A. Steyermark's *Flora of Missouri*.

MISSOURI'S CHAMPION TREES

In Missouri, there is a Champion Tree Program that recognizes the largest known specimen of every tree species in the state. Called the Champion Tree Program, trees are scored on a point system with points determined by the size of the trunk, height of the tree, and spread of the tree's crown. For example, the largest tree on record in Missouri is a bald cypress tree in New Madrid County with 456 points. The smallest tree is Carolina buckthorn in Stoddard County with 27 points. All 50 states have a champion tree program with the largest trees listed in a National Register of Big Trees, which is maintained by American Forests, a private forest conservation organization (www.americanforests.org/resources/bigtrees/register.php). Missouri currently has 6 national champion tree species.

A list of Missouri champion trees is maintained by the Missouri Department of Conservation. The list is available at Conservation Department offices or can be printed from their website at www.conservation.state.mo.us/forest/IandE. Once there, click on the Champion Trees link for a seven-page list that also includes a link on how to measure a tree for champion status, a form to record it on, and where to send the information. A Conservation Department forester will need to verify the tree species and measurement for the official record.

Anyone can nominate a champion tree. If you think that you might have a champion tree, review the list, measure the tree, and send in the information to the Conservation Department. If your tree does qualify, you will receive a certificate mounted on a walnut plaque and listed as the owner of a state champion tree.

Landscaping With Native Trees

Maybe it is a part of human nature, or maybe we have been conditioned, to always want to look for something new and different; this desire is nowhere more apparent than with the pursuit of new plants. Seed and plant catalogs and garden nurseries strive to offer the "improved" variety that displays a different flower shape or color or some other characteristic that sets it apart from past examples.

Unfortunately, along with the desire for something bigger and better or new and improved, comes the feeling that the plant has to be exotic; that is, from another country. We have been so conditioned this way that we often are surprised when we see something "native" that catches our eye, and wonder where it has been all the while.

Native plants have been ignored too long because of the attention that has been focused on the use of exotics, but the natives slowly are gaining the attention of people that are concerned about the threat exotics pose to our diminishing natural communities. Even exotics planted in backyards can spread into nearby habitats. They often out-compete native trees, shrubs, and wildflowers, and as a result, reduce the diversity of plants that wildlife depend upon for food and cover. This vigor for invading into new areas is attributed to the plant's lack of predators such as insects and fungi that have evolved with the plant in its native homeland but did not make the journey with them to the new world.

A drive through the residential areas of St. Louis County in April underscores the severity of this problem. The understory along the highways' wooded corridors is solid with the green foliage of bush honeysuckle. This aggressive shrub is early to leaf out in the spring and one of the last to drop its leaves in autumn, thereby robbing seedling trees, shrubs, and showy wildflowers of the necessary sunlight to grow. This is one example among many where exotic plants have been highly promoted. Once established, many have proved to be hard or almost impossible to eradicate.

Native trees contain many fine attributes worthy of ornamental use. They are very economical, since they are long-lived and seldom need replacing. They have adapted throughout thousands of years to the local climate and soils, so they are more likely to survive the extremes of heat, cold, and drought. They are easy to grow, and do not require constant attention once they are established. There is a variety of heights and shapes, foliage patterns, and colors and shapes of flowers and fruits from which to choose.

(Note: for interesting shrubs and woody vines for landscape purposes, refer to Missouri Department of Conservation's book *Shrubs and Woody Vines of Missouri*.)

The following list of selected trees are grouped by habitat desirability or by features of interest for landscaping purposes.

Trees for Moist Sites or Along Stream Banks

Acer saccharinum, silver maple
Acer saccharum ssp. *saccharum*, sugar maple
Aesculus glabra, Ohio buckeye
Aesculus pavia, red buckeye
Asimina triloba, pawpaw
Betula nigra, river birch
Carpinus caroliniana, hornbeam
Carya illinoinensis, pecan
Carya laciniosa, shellbark hickory
Carya ovata, shagbark hickory
Celtis laevigata, sugarberry
Cladrastis kentukea, yellowwood
Cornus amomum ssp. *obliqua*, swamp dogwood
Cornus foemina, stiff dogwood
Crataegus viridis, green haw
Euonymus atropurpureus, wahoo
Fagus grandifolia, American beech
Fraxinus pennsylvanica, green ash
Gymnocladus dioica, Kentucky coffee tree
Hamamelis vernalis, Ozark witch hazel
Hamamelis virginiana, Eastern witch hazel
Ilex decidua, possum haw
Ilex opaca, American holly
Juglans nigra, black walnut
Liquidambar styraciflua, sweet gum
Liriodendron tulipifera, tulip tree
Magnolia acuminata, cucumber tree
Platanus occidentalis, sycamore
Populus deltoides, cottonwood
Quercus alba, white oak
Quercus macrocarpa, bur oak
Quercus palustris, pin oak
Quercus rubra, Northern red oak

Salix species, willows
Sambucus racemosa, red-berried elder
Staphylea trifolia, bladdernut
Taxodium distichum, bald cypress
Tilia americana, American basswood

Understory Trees for Shady Areas

Aesculus pavia, red buckeye
Amelanchier arborea, service berry
Asimina triloba, pawpaw
Carpinus caroliniana, musclewood
Cercis canadensis, Eastern redbud
Cornus florida, flowering dogwood
Euonymus atropurpureus, wahoo
Hamamelis virginiana, Eastern witch hazel
Ostrya virginiana, hop hornbeam
Rhamnus caroliniana, Carolina buckthorn
Staphylea trifolia, bladdernut
Viburnum prunifolium, black haw
Viburnum rufidulum, Southern black haw

Trees With Interesting Fruit

Aesculus glabra, Ohio buckeye ✷ leathery capsule, shiny brown seed
Aesculus pavia, red buckeye ✷ leathery capsule, shiny brown seed
Amelanchier arborea, service berry ✷ red, edible
Asimina triloba, pawpaw ✷ bananalike, edible
Aralia spinosa, devil's walking stick ✷ large black clusters
Carya species, hickories ✷ several are edible
Castanea species, chestnuts ✷ edible
Cornus alternifolia, alternate-leaved dogwood ✷ blue-black
Cornus florida, flowering dogwood ✷ bright red
Cornus foemina, stiff dogwood ✷ bright blue

Cornus amomum ssp. *obliqua*, swamp dogwood ✷ pale blue
Cotinus obovatus, smoke tree ✷ smoky appearance when in fruit
Crataegus species, hawthorns ✷ red
Diospyros virginiana, persimmon ✷ edible
Euonymous atropurpureus, wahoo ✷ red capsule, scarlet seeds
Gymnocladus dioica, Kentucky coffee tree ✷ large pod, huge seeds
Ilex decidua, possum haw ✷ red, persists into winter
Ilex opaca, American holly ✷ red, persists into winter
Juglans nigra, black walnut ✷ edible
Liquidambar styraciflua, sweet gum ✷ ornamental fruit
Malus species, crab apples ✷ edible
Morus rubra, red mulberry ✷ edible
Pinus species, pine trees ✷ ornamental pine cones
Prunus species, wild plums, wild cherries ✷ black, red, dark red, reddish-yellow, edible
Ptelea trifoliata, hop tree ✷ large waferlike wings
Quercus species, oaks ✷ acorns, some edible
Rhamnus caroliniana, Carolina buckthorn ✷ shiny black
Rhus copallina, winged sumac ✷ red clusters, persist into winter
Rhus glabra, smooth sumac ✷ red clusters, persist into winter
Sambucus racemosa, red-berried elder ✷ red clusters
Sassafras albidum, sassafras ✷ red stalk, shiny blue fruit
Staphylea trifolia, bladdernut ✷ large inflated capsules
Vaccinium arboreum, farkleberry ✷ bluish-black, edible
Viburnum prunifolium, black haw ✷ bluish-black, persist into winter
Viburnum rufidulum, Southern black haw ✷ bluish-black, persist into winter

Trees With Showy Flowers

Acer rubrum, red maple ✷ red
Aesculus glabra, Ohio buckeye ✷ yellow
Aesculus pavia, red buckeye ✷ red
Amelanchier arborea, service berry ✷ white
Aralia spinosa, devil's walking stick ✷ yellow
Asimina triloba, pawpaw ✷ dark reddish-purple

Castanea species, chestnuts ✹ white
Catalpa species, catalpa ✹ white
Cercis canadenis, Eastern redbud ✹ red
Chionanthus virginicus, fringe tree ✹ white
Cladrastis kentukea, yellowwood ✹ white
Cornus species, dogwoods ✹ white
Crataegus species, hawthorns ✹ white
Hamamelis vernalis, Ozark witch hazel ✹ yellow to
    dark red
Hamamelis virginiana, Eastern witch hazel ✹
    yellow
Liriodendron tulipifera, tulip tree ✹ yellow, orange,
    and green
Magnolia acuminata, cucumber tree ✹ white
Malus species, crab apples ✹ white or pink
Prunus species, wild plums, wild cherries ✹ white
Robinia pseudo-acacia, black locust ✹ white
Salix discolor, pussy willow ✹ yellow
Sambucus racemosa, red-berried elder ✹ white
Sapindus drummondii, soapberry ✹ yellow
Sassafras albidum, sassafras ✹ yellow
Staphylea trifolia, bladdernut ✹ white
Viburnum species, arrow woods ✹ white

Trees For Showy Fall Color

Acer rubrum, red maple ✹ scarlet or red
Acer saccharum, sugar maple ✹ bright yellow,
    orange, or red
Amelanchier arborea, service berry ✹ pale orange
    or gold
Carya species, hickories ✹ yellow
Cercis canadensis, redbud ✹ yellow
Cladrastis kentukea, yellowwood ✹ yellow to
    orange-gold
Cornus florida, flowering dogwood ✹ reddish-purple
Cotinus obovatus, smoke tree ✹ reddish-orange
Crataegus crus-galli, cockspur thorn ✹ orange to red
Crataegus mollis, downy hawthorn ✹ red
Crataegus phaenopyrum, Washington thorn ✹ red
Crataegus viridis, green haw ✹ purplish-red
Hamamelis vernalis, Ozark witch hazel ✹ yellow
Hamamelis virginiana, Eastern witch hazel ✹
    yellow
Liquidambar styraciflua, sweet gum ✹ gold, red,
    pink, or purple
Liriodendron tulipifera, tulip tree ✹ yellow
Nyssa sylvatica, black gum ✹ scarlet, orange,
    purple or yellow
Populus grandidentata, bigtooth aspen ✹ yellow to
    orange

Populus tremuloides, quaking aspen ✹ bright yellow
    to golden
Quercus species, oaks ✹ yellow, red, scarlet red, or
    purple
Rhus species, sumacs ✹ bright red
Sapindus drummondii, soapberry ✹ yellow-gold
Sassafras albidum, sassafras ✹ yellow, orange, red,
    or scarlet
Taxodium distichum, bald cypress ✹ golden to
    reddish-brown
Tilia species, basswoods ✹ yellow

Trees for Planting in a Landscape Setting

Large Trees (70 feet plus)
Carya illinoinensis, pecan
Carya laciniosa, shellbark hickory
Carya ovata, shagbark hickory
Celtis laevigata, sugarberry
Celtis occidentalis, hackberry
Fagus grandifolia, American beech
Fraxinus americana, white ash
Fraxinus pennsylvanica, green ash
Liquidambar styraciflua, sweet gum
Liriodendron tulipifera, tulip tree
Nyssa sylvatica, black gum
Pinus echinata, short-leaf pine
Platanus occidentalis, sycamore
Quercus alba, white oak
Quercus bicolor, swamp white oak
Quercus falcata, Southern red oak
Quercus imbricaria, shingle oak
Quercus macrocarpa, bur oak
Quercus pagoda, cherrybark oak
Quercus palustris, pin oak
Quercus phellos, willow oak
Quercus rubra, Northern red oak
Quercus shumardii, Shumard's oak
Taxodium distichum, bald cypress

Medium Trees (30 to 70 feet)
Acer rubrum, red maple
Acer saccharum, sugar maple
Betula nigra, river birch
Carya cordiformis, Bitternut hickory
Catalpa speciosa, Northern catalpa
Cladrastis kentukea, yellowwood
Gymnocladus dioica, Kentucky coffee tree
Magnolia acuminata, cucumber magnolia
Populus tremuloides, quaking aspen

Quercus bicolor, swamp white oak
Quercus falcata, Southern red oak
Quercus imbricaria, shingle oak
Quercus velutina, black oak
Sapindus drummondii, soapberry
Tilia americana, American basswood

Small Trees (13 to 30 feet)
Aesculus glabra Ohio buckeye
Aesculus pavia, red buckeye
Amelanchier arborea, service berry
Aralia spinosa, devil's walking stick
Asimina triloba, pawpaw
Carpinus caroliniana, musclewood
Cercis canadensis, Eastern redbud
Chionanthus virginicus, fringe tree
Cornus species, dogwoods
Cotinus obovatus, smoketree
Crataegus species, hawthorns
Euonymus atropurpureus, wahoo
Hamamelis vernalis, Ozark witch hazel
Hamamelis virginiana, Eastern witch hazel
Ilex decidua, possum haw
Ilex opaca, American holly
Ilex verticillata, winterberry
Juniperus virginiana, red cedar
Malus species, crab apples
Prunus species, wild plums
Rhamnus caroliniana, Carolina buckthorn
Sambucus racemosa, red-berried elder
Staphylea trifolia, bladdernut
Viburnum species, arrow woods

This list is by no means inclusive. These are plants, however, that may be more readily available from plant nurseries or plant catalogs. You do have the option of broadening your selection by collecting and propagating seeds, which is discussed later. Digging plants from the wild is not recommended. Most plants do not survive from the shock of transplanting, and the practice is not desirable from a conservation standpoint.

Landscaping to Help Bring Wildlife to Your Backyard

Some of our fondest childhood memories involve wildlife discoveries made in our own backyards. Remember the thrill of watching a colorful butterfly flutter and alight on a flower, or a squirrel scamper up a tree? How about the delight of dis-

covering your first robin's eggs in a mud-lined nest? All these experiences can help nurture a lifelong interest in nature.

Wildlife will not be drawn to urban backyards, however, unless you can provide a habitat composed of three basic ingredients: food, water, and shelter. Food comes from plants that produce fruits, berries, grains, seeds, acorns, nuts, or nectar. The plants can be herbaceous annuals, biennials, and perennials, or trees, shrubs, and woody vines.

Mixtures of all these types provide a variety of foods that are available throughout the year for butterflies and other insects, birds, and mammals. In addition, insects—many of which feed on plant parts—provide protein for other insects, reptiles, amphibians, birds, and mammals.

Shelter or cover is also important for attracting wildlife to your property. Birds, especially, need places where they can hide from predators and escape from severe weather. Densely branching trees and large shrubs also provide good nesting places for birds and excellent cover for their fledglings.

Trees That Provide Beneficial Food and Cover for Wildlife

Acer species, red and sugar maple
Aesculus species, Ohio and red buckeye
Amelanchier arborea, service berry
Aralia spinosa, devil's walking stick
Asimina triloba, pawpaw
Betula nigra, river birch
Carya species, hickories, including pecan
Celtis species, hackberry and sugarberry
Cercis canadensis, Eastern redbud
Cornus species, dogwoods
Crataegus species, hawthorns
Diospyros virginiana, persimmon
Fraxinus species, ashes
Hamamelis species, witch hazels
Ilex species, hollies
Juniperus virginiana, red cedar
Liquidambar styraciflua, sweet gum
Liriodendron tulipifera, tulip tree
Malus species, crab apples
Morus rubra, red mulberry
Nyssa sylvatica, black gum
Pinus echinata, short-leaf pine
Prunus species, wild plums, wild cherries

Quercus species, oaks
Rhamnus caroliniana, Carolina buckthorn
Rhus species, sumacs
Salix species, willows
Sambucus racemosa, red-berried elder
Sassafras albidum, sassafras
Tilia species, basswoods
Viburnum species, arrow woods

*These are trees with fruits that can be messy around vehicles, walkways, driveways, patios, and lawns. They may be best planted along edges of properties or in low maintenance areas.

Water is the last ingredient. A source of water will more than double the numbers and variety of wildlife that will be attracted to your backyard habitat. A birdbath, water garden, or frog pond will provide a local source for water and eliminate the time wildlife would spend searching for it elsewhere.

For information on shrubs and woody vines that provide food and cover for wildlife, refer to the Missouri Department of Conservation's book *Shrubs and Woody Vines of Missouri.* Also, their recent publication, *Native Landscaping for Wildlife and People,* by Dave Tylka, is a very good reference book on how to use native vegetation to beautify your property and benefit wildlife. Additional worthwhile references are listed under Selected References.

Planting and Maintenance

Whether buying nursery stock or growing plants yourself, the same common-sense gardening techniques used for growing and caring for traditional garden plants can be applied to native trees. There are many excellent publications on the subject, many of which are free. Be sure to contact the University of Missouri Extension Center (located in most counties) or the Missouri Department of Conservation's Forestry Division or an MDC regional office for publications on the planting and maintenance of trees. One publication in particular called *Missouri Conservation Trees and Shrubs* offers detailed planting and care information along with information on 56 trees and shrubs. You can also access the MDC website at www.conservation.state.mo.us and locate the Search link in the upper right hand corner. Type

in "Tree Planting" and view one of the several publications that can be downloaded and printed.

Control Recommendations: It is sometimes necessary to control undesirable trees, especially if they are not native. The simplest method to eradicate trees is to cut the plant off at the base and treat with a herbicide. Roundup™ herbicide (a formulation of glyphosate) or an equivalent brand is available at most garden and farm supply stores. Buy the liquid herbicide in concentrated form and dilute to about 25 percent with water; apply within minutes to the freshly cut stump. A brush or sponge applicator is very effective and minimizes waste. Plastic bottles with mist sprayers also may be used.

The cut-stump treatment is most effective July to September when the sap is traveling down into the roots, carrying the herbicide with it. Treatment in winter has been somewhat effective but is not as reliable. Avoid applications when the plant is actively growing; sap is moving up into the branches, keeping the herbicide from entering the roots.

Since Roundup is a nonselective herbicide, it is not recommended as a foliar spray because the drift would contact, and possibly kill, nontarget species. Follow the same recommendations for treating unwanted shrubs, such as shrub honeysuckle and woody vines like Japanese honeysuckle, both exotic species. A foliar spray of 2 to 3 percent can be applied to the leaves if desirable species can be avoided. This is often the case with Japanese honeysuckle where rampant growth smothers other vegetation. Since this exotic is semi-evergreen, the leaves can be sprayed in November after a hard frost. By then, most native plants have gone dormant and will not be harmed by the herbicide.

Propagation

Growing woody plants from seeds, cuttings or by layering is an enjoyable and inexpensive way of adding diversity to your backyard. Unfortunately, several of the trees described in this book are not available from nurseries or plant catalogs. But with a little background knowledge on plant propagation, an afternoon's walk can yield a variety of interesting plants whose seeds can be collected and grown with little cost and effort. Time and patience, and a little attention, are the main requirements for successful plant propagation.

The collecting of seeds or the digging of plants on public land is usually not permitted. In 1993, Missouri passed a plant digging law (Revised Statute of Missouri Law No. 229.475) that makes it illegal to dig plants from roadsides of county, state, or interstate highways unless a person is granted special permission from the agency responsible for administering the roadside. The collection of above-ground plant parts is allowed, as long as the collection is not for commercial purposes. Digging and transplanting plants from the wild also is not recommended because of the low rate of recovery from loss and damage to the plant's root system.

Where available, nursery-grown stock is the easiest to work with; potted shrubs and trees already have a few years growth, which enables them to flower and fruit sooner. This is particularly advantageous if the flowers and fruits are the most interesting features. Most nurseries are limited in their supply of native plants, but ask if they can order what you want. Listed on pages 389–390 are mail-order nurseries that sell native woody plants. For larger planting operations, bare root seedlings are more economical but take longer to establish. A wide selection is available at the George 0. White State Nursery. (See Nursery Sources for Native Trees for the telephone number and address.)

Seeds: Growing trees from seeds is a cheap and easy alternative to nursery-grown plants, although it may take 10 to 20 years before the trees are old enough to flower and bear fruit. When collecting seeds be sure that the fruit appears ripe or mature. Fleshy fruit often changes color and softens, which indicates the seeds are ready. The seeds must be separated from the pulp and allowed to dry.

Other plants produce capsules that turn brown and split open when the seeds are ready. Seeds should be collected in a paper bag or envelope. Avoid putting any seeds in plastic bags or glass jars. These airproof containers can cause the seed to rot from excess moisture. Store seeds away from excessive heat and the sun's rays until you are ready to plant them.

Few seeds are capable of germinating right away. Many require certain conditions, such as a rest or dormant period.

Other seeds with thick coats, such as legumes, need scarification—a process whereby the seed's outer layer is worn down or cracks from cycles of heat or cold. Once the seed coat is damaged, water enters the seed to start the growing process. It may take a few years for this to occur in nature, but by nicking the seed coat with a file the swelling can occur overnight. Be sure to cut on the opposite side of where the seed was attached, and use a triangular file to make a notch deep enough so that you see a change in color.

Some seeds are not fully mature when they leave their parent plant. The embryo needs additional time to fully mature. This can happen during a process called stratification, where the seeds are exposed to warm and/or cold temperatures for several weeks or months.

In both cases the seeds need moisture. Fringe tree seeds, for example, exhibit what is called a double dormancy. The seeds are produced during the growing season, overwinter, and receive warm stratification the following summer; after winter's cold treatment, the seeds germinate the following spring. Fortunately, this two-year process happens in only a few other shrubs and trees, such as witch hazel, spice bush, hop hornbeam, elderberry, and viburnums.

Most seeds simply need cold stratification. This is easily accomplished by placing the seeds in a plastic bag mixed with equal parts of coarse sand, sphagnum moss or peat moss that is moist, but not excessively wet. (If sand is used, be sure to boil it first to destroy insect eggs and any fungus that might be present.) Then place the bag in the refrigerator for a couple of months at around 40 degrees Fahrenheit.

This is best done in February or March for planting in April, either in the ground or in pots for later transplanting. Seed treatment requirements for many of the plants described in this book may be found in "Seeds of Woody Plants in the United States" (USDA Forest Service, Agriculture Handbook No. 450, 1974). Ask your local library or garden center for a copy to review. Also, several of the books under Selected

References offer information on seed germination requirements for trees.

The easiest way to propagate plants from seeds is simply to plant the seed directly in soil, usually at a depth of twice its diameter. If the seed is collected from plants and sown within their normal range, chances are they will successfully germinate. Attention also must be given to planting them in soil conditions similar to that of the parent plant's. Seeds planted out of the natural range of the parent plants often will not germinate. Flowering dogwood is a good example. The range for this plant is in the southern half of Missouri. Apparently, the seeds are sensitive to the colder winter temperatures of northern latitudes.

On the other hand, more northern ranging plants such as red-berried elder and pussy willow may find winters either not cold enough or the summers too hot and dry for seed germination, or maybe a combination of both. Stratifying seeds and planting them in pots under controlled conditions, such as in your house, greenhouse, or in a cold frame, is a sure way to start plants.

Cuttings: Growing plants from cuttings takes a little more effort and attention, but it allows you to start plants faster. With a cutting, the growth rate is often one to three years ahead of the seedling. Also, the desirable characteristics of the parent plant will be duplicated in the cutting, because it is just an extension of the same genes.

With seeds, the new plants may or may not look exactly like the parent plant because the genetic makeup of each seed is not exactly the same. If you find a flowering dogwood with pink flowers, for example, you will produce offspring with that same characteristic by growing new plants from cuttings. Seeds typically will revert to the flowering dogwood's normal color of white.

The best time to take cuttings is at the plant's softwood stage. This is usually after the twig has finished producing new leaves, which is around late June through July. The twig is just beginning to harden or become firm, and the bark is still partly green. Early in the morning is the best time to take cuttings—before wind and sun begin drawing moisture out of the twigs and leaves. With a sharp knife, cut 6- to 8-inch sections off the tips of branches and place them in either a moist plastic bag or in water until they are ready to be planted.

Next, strip the lower leaves, leaving 2 to 3 inches of the twig bare. With a sharp knife, cut a shallow slice along one side of the bare part of the twig, removing only the thin bark. At this stage, dusting the wound with rooting hormone will stimulate the roots to grow faster. Rooting hormone is available at most nursery supply stores, with certain types specifically formulated for use on woody plants.

Place the cuttings in a medium composed of moistened sphagnum moss, or a combination of peat or perlite—also available at stores selling plants. Sterilized sand also may be used, but it must be coarse to allow air spaces for the roots. The container should be covered with a plastic bag or plastic wrap, which provides humidity and keeps the soil from drying out. A six-pack Styrofoam cooler works very well; be sure to punch drainage holes in the bottom. Place the container in a shaded location with an air temperature of between 70 and 80 degrees Fahrenheit.

The cutting should root in about three weeks and begin new top growth in six weeks. Gently tug at the cutting, and if it resists, the roots have developed. Gradually remove the covering to allow the plants to "harden off"; this refers to the plants' need to adapt to the conditions of wind and lower humidity. The rooted cuttings may be either planted or left in the container to overwinter for spring planting. In the latter case, the container should overwinter on the north side of a building, and be mulched to protect the new plants from severe cold temperatures.

Layering: This requires the least amount of attention and is directed towards shrubs and small trees. The practice is not as reliable in producing new plants. A young limb of a shrub or small tree is wounded by scraping away a small section of bark on the underside of the twig. Bury the section in a shallow trench, anchor it, and cover with soil; be sure to leave about 1 to 3 feet of the tip above ground. After 1 to 2 years, the newly rooted branch can be separated and replanted. Fast-growing, cane-forming, or sprawling species root better with layering than slower growing trees or shrubs. Sometimes this form of propagation happens naturally and a spade or trowel is all that is needed to retrieve a rooted section of stem for transplanting.

Keys to the Trees

1. Leaves needlelike, scalelike or awl-like (short, narrowly triangular, and sharply pointed like an awl) . . . . Key A, p. 16
1. Leaves not needlelike, scalelike or awl-like 2

2. Leaves opposite or in whorls . .Key B, p. 16
2. Leaves not opposite or in whorls 3

3. Leaves alternate and compound (consisting of multiple leaflets) . . . . Key C, p. 20
3. Leaves alternate and simple (consisting of a single leaf) . . . . .Key D, p. 22

Key A. Leaves needlelike, scalelike or awl-like

1. Leaves evergreen 2
1. Leaves not evergreen 10

2. Leaves needlelike 3
2. Leaves scalelike or awl-like 9

3. Needles in bundles of 2 or 3 4
3. Needles in bundles of 5 . . . . . .White pine, *Pinus strobus*, p. 226

4. Needles in bundles of 3 5
4. Needles in bundles of 2 6

5. Needles 3 to 5 inches long...Short-leaf pine, *Pinus echinata*, p. 224
5. Needles 5 to 9 inches long...Loblolly pine, *Pinus taeda*, p. 228

6. Needles 3/4 to 1 1/2 inches long...Jack pine, *Pinus banksiana*, p. 387
6. Needles 1 1/2 to 7 inches long 7

7. Needles 1 1/2 to 3 inches long...Scrub pine, *Pinus virginiana*, p. 230
7. Needles 3 to 7 inches long 8

8. Twigs brown to reddish-brown, usually covered with a whitish coating; needles flexible; cones brown, the scales not shiny...Short-leaf pine, *Pinus echinata*, p. 224
8. Twigs light brown, not covered with a whitish coating; needles stiff; cones yellowish-brown, the scales somewhat shiny...Austrian pine, *Pinus nigra*, p. 387

9. Margin of the scale-like leaves finely toothed under magnification; trunk branched emerging at the base; bark with conspicuous white blotches on the trunk and branches...Ashe' juniper, *Juniperus ashei*, p. 188
9. Margin of the scale-like leaves entire; trunk solitary; bark lacking white blotches on the trunk and branches...Red cedar, *Juniperus virginiana*, p. 190

10. Leaves needlelike, 1/2 to 3/4 inch long, in two rows on opposite sides of the small twigs...Bald cypress, *Taxodium distichum*, p. 350
10. Leaves scale-like, up to 1/8 inch long, alternate along the twigs...Saltcedar, *Tamarix ramosissima*, p. 348

Key B. Leaves opposite or in whorls

1. Tip of twig or shoots tapering into a spine...Common buckthorn, *Rhamnus cathartica*, p. 316
1. Tip of twig or shoots not tapering into a spine 2

2. Each leaf divided into 2 or more separate leaflets 3
2. Each leaf single, not divided into 2 or more separate leaflets 14

3. Leaflets 3 4
3. Leaflets 5 to 11 5

4. Leaflets finely toothed; flowers white, showy; fruit 3-lobed, inflated...bladdernut, *Staphylea trifolia*, p. 346

4. Leaflets coarsely toothed; flowers greenish, not showy; fruit winged...Box elder, *Acer negundo*, p. 42

5. Leaves with 5 to 7 leaflets palm-shaped . . .6
5. Leaves with leaflets arranged feather-like .7

6. Small to medium-sized tree, petals more or less equal, greenish-yellow; stamens long, extending beyond the petals; fruit prickly; leaflets 5 to 7, bluish-green or grass-green on upper surface...Ohio buckeye, *Aesculus glabra*, p. 52
6. Shrub to small tree; petals unequal in length, width, and shape, red or rarely yellow; stamens shorter than or only slightly longer than the upper petals; fruit smooth; leaflets mainly 5, dark green on upper surface...Red buckeye, *Aesculus pavia*, p. 54

7. Leaflets with close and crowded teeth, 4 to 14 per 1/2 inch; flowers white; fruit fleshy and berrylike, or bladdery and 3-lobed, but not winged 8
7. Leaflets with mainly 1 to 4 teeth per 1/2 inch; flowers greenish, greenish-yellow, or purplish; fruit with 1 or 2 wings 9

8. Leaflets usually 5 to 7; flowers numerous (greater than 10), in upright clusters; fruit fleshy, berry-like, red...Red-berried elder, *Sambucus racemosa*, p. 340
8. Leaflets usually 3 (rarely 5), flowers few (less than 10), in drooping clusters, fruit bladderlike, 3-lobed, green turning brown...bladdernut, *Staphylea trifolia*, p. 346

9. Leaflets usually 3 to 5 (rarely 7), with coarse teeth of usually 1–2 per 1/2 inch; fruit winged...Box elder, *Acer negundo*, p. 42
9. Leaflets usually 5 to 11, either smooth-edged (entire) or with shallow teeth of 1 to 6 per 1/2 inch; fruit with 1 wing 10

10. Some part of the twig 4-sided...Blue ash, *Fraxinus quadrangulata*, p. 164
10. Twig round, not 4-sided 11

11. Leaflets, leaf stalks, and twigs smooth (without hairs)...White ash, *Fraxinus americana*, p. 158

11. Leaflets, leaf stalks, and twigs light to densely hairy 12

12. Leaflet stalks, at least the lower ones, narrowly winged, short usually 1/4 inch or less...Green ash, *Fraxinus pennsylvanica*, p. 160
12. Leaflet stalks lacking wings, 1/8 to 3/4 inches long 13

13. Lower surface of leaflets noticeably whitened or gray-green; main body of fruit (containing seed) winged no more than 1/3 of its length; fully grown fruit 1 to 2 inches long; trees of upland slopes...Biltmore ash, *Fraxinus biltmoreana*, p. 387
13. Lower surface of leaflets yellowish-brown or brownish-green; main body of fruit (containing seed) winged to about 1/2 its length; fully grown fruit 1 1/2 to 3 inches long; trees of swamps and bottomland forests... Pumpkin ash, *Fraxinus profunda*, p. 162

14. Margins of leaves toothed or lobed 15
14. Margins of leaves entire (without teeth) .30

15. Leaves very large, 6 to 16 inches long and broad, broadest just below the middle, heart-shaped, only slightly lobed or angled 16
15. Leaves smaller, or if large, displaying conspicuous lobes, teeth, or angles 19

16. Flower pale violet to purple; stamens 4; leaves opposite, in 2's; fruit egg-shaped, 1 1/2 to 2 1/2 inches long...Empress tree, *Paulownia tomentosa*, p. 222
16. Flower white, marked with yellow and purple; stamens 2; leaves usually in whorls (circles) of 3; fruit a long cylindrical, narrow, pencil-like capsule, 6 to 20 inches long . .17

17. Leaves smooth (without hairs), or the lower surface becoming smooth with age, often sharply lobed or angled; flowers up to 3/4 inch across, yellow with orange and spotted violet; capsules up to 3/8 inch in diameter; small shrubs or trees, sometimes flowering when only 2 1/2 feet tall...Chinese catalpa, *Catalpa ovata*, p. 102
17. Leaves persistently soft-hairy on lower surface, mostly without lobes or angles; flowers

3/4 to 1 1/2 inches across, white, with yellow and purple spots; capsules 3/8 to 1 1/8 inch across; large trees 18

18. Odor of bruised leaves strong scented, unpleasant; bark of older trees thin and scaly; throat of flower with conspicuous purple lines and yellow and purple spots...Southern catalpa, *Catalpa bignonioides*, p. 100

18. Odor of bruised leaves mildly scented, not unpleasant; bark of older trees grooved with short ridges, not scaly; throat of flower slightly spotted with yellow blotches and dark lines...Northern catalpa, *Catalpa speciosa*, p. 102

19. Margins of leaves lobed, the lobes smooth-edged (entire) or toothed 20
19. Margins of leaves toothed but not lobed . .27

20. Base of lobes (sinuses) of the leaf rounded, U-shaped or trough-shaped (sometimes V-shaped for *Acer ginnala*); flowers appearing with or after the leaves develop; fruit ripening in summer and fall (July–September); winter buds usually sharply pointed at the tip 21
20. Base of lobes (sinuses) of the leaf more or less sharply angled or V-shaped; flowers appearing before the leaves expand; fruit ripening in spring (May–June); winter buds blunt or rounded 25

21. Lower surface of leaves green or yellowish-green; leaf margins somewhat turned under along the edges; leaves not deeply lobed with base of lobes greater than 90°; leaf stalks abruptly enlarged at the base...Black maple, *Acer saccharum* ssp. *nigrum*, p. 48
21. Lower surface of leaves gray- or silvery- or blue-green but not yellow-green; leaf margins usually with a flat surface; leaves more deeply lobed with base of lobes less than 90°; leaf stalks only gradually enlarged at the base 22

22. Leaves with center lobe the longest, leaf margins densely toothed...Amur maple, *Acer ginnala*, p. 40

22. Leaves with center lobe about equal in length to the other lobes, leaf margins smooth (entire) or irregularly toothed . . .23

23. Rare type in Missouri; mature leaves small, 1 1/4 to 3 1/2 inches long, 1 1/4 to 4 inches broad; lobes of leaves short, blunt; leaves often drooping or turned in along the margins...Southern sugar maple, *Acer saccharum* spp. *floridanum*, p. 50
23. More commonly found in Missouri; mature leaves mainly 3 to 6 inches long and 3 to 6 inches broad; lobes of leaves long and prominently pointed; leaves mainly with a flat margin . . . . .24.

24. Veins of lower surface of leaves densely hairy; leaf stalks hairy or smooth...Hairy sugar maple, *Acer saccharum* ssp. *schneckii*, p. 50
24. Veins of lower surface of leaves smooth, not hairy except for tufts of hairs in the axils of the main veins; leaf stalks usually smooth...Sugar maple, *Acer saccharum* spp. *saccharum*, p. 50

25. Leaves cut deep, 1/2 to 2/3 of the distance to the central vein, the middle lobe taking up much more than 1/2 the length of the complete leaf; middle lobe conspicuously narrowed at the base...Silver maple, *Acer saccharinum*, p. 46
25. Leaves usually cut less than 1/2 of the distance to the central vein, the middle lobe taking up 1/2 or less than the length of the complete leaf; middle lobe broadest at the base 26

26. Lower surface of leaves densely hairy, at least on the main veins; found in swamps and bottomland forests in southeastern Missouri and along margins of sinkhole ponds in the Ozarks...Drummond's red maple, *Acer rubrum* var. *drummondii*, p. 44
26. Lower surface of leaves without hairs or with few hairs; more common type found in rocky woods, ravines, upper slopes and ridges; rarely in low, wet woods...Red maple, *Acer rubrum* var. *rubrum*, p. 44

27. Twigs green and somewhat 4-sided or with 4 prominent lines...Wahoo, *Euonymous atropurpureus*, p. 152

27. Twigs neither green or 4-sided . . . . .28.

28. Leaf bases narrowly wedge-shaped; flowers and fruits in clusters on stem of previous year...Swamp privet, *Forestiera acuminata*, p. 156

28. Leaf bases usually rounded to heart-shaped; flowers and fruits in clusters on stem of current year 29

29. Rust-colored hairs and/or numerous dots on lower surface of leaves, especially along the central vein, also on leaf stalks; leaves leathery, glossy on upper surface...Southern black haw, *Viburnum rufidulum*, p. 372

29. Few or no rust-colored hairs or numerous dots on lower surface of leaves, or along central vein or leaf stalk; leaves rather thin, not leathery, dull on upper surface...Black haw, *Viburnum prunifolium*, p. 370

30. Leaves very large, 6 to 16 inches long and broad, broadest just below the middle, heart-shaped 31

30. Leaves smaller, less than 6 inches long . .34

31. Flower pale violet to purple; stamens 4; leaves opposite, in 2's; fruit egg-shaped, 1 1/2 to 2 1/2 inches long...Princess tree, *Paulownia tomentosa*, p. 222

31. Flower white, marked with yellow and purple; stamens 2; leaves usually in whorls (circles) of 3; fruit a long cylindrical, narrow, pencil-like capsule, 6 to 20 inches long . .32

32. Leaves smooth (without hairs), or the lower surface becoming smooth with age, often sharply lobed or angled; flowers up to 3/4 inch across, yellow with orange and spotted violet; capsules up to 3/8 inch in diameter; small shrubs or trees, sometimes flowering when only 2 1/2 feet tall...Chinese catalpa, *Catalpa ovata*, p. 102

32. Leaves persistently soft-hairy on lower surface, mostly without lobes or angles; flowers 3/4 to 1 1/2 inches across, white, with yellow and purple spots; capsules 3/8 to 1/2 inch across; large trees 33

33. Odor of bruised leaves strong scented, unpleasant; bark of older trees thin and scaly; throat of flower with conspicuous purple lines and yellow and purple spots...Southern catalpa, *Catalpa bignonioides*, p. 100

33. Odor of bruised leaves mildly scented, not unpleasant; bark of older trees grooved with short ridges, not scaly; throat of flower with slightly spotted with yellow blotches and dark lines...Northern catalpa, *Catalpa speciosa*, p. 102

34. Leaves 4 to 8 inches long; flowers in clusters along the twig at the leaf axils...Fringe tree, *Chionanthus virginicus*, p. 112

34. Leaves up to 4 inches long (rarely 5 inches); flowers in clusters at the end of twigs . . .35

35. Leaves alternate, but often crowded at ends of twigs and appearing whorled; most of the leaf stalks 3/4 to 2 1/4 inches long...Alternate-leaved dogwood, *Cornus alternifolia*, p. 116

35. Leaves opposite; most of the leaf stalks 1/4 to 3/4 inches long 36

36. Flowers greenish-yellow in a dense headlike cluster surrounded by 4 large white or pink petal-like bracts; fruit bright red; small trees up to 40 feet...Flowering dogwood, *Cornus florida*, p. 122

36. Flowers white or creamy-white in an open broad cluster, not surrounded by bracts; fruit blue or white; shrubs to small trees from 3 to 20 feet tall .37

37. Lower surface of leaves woolly with loose curled or curving hairs; upper surface of leaves rather rough-hairy (rarely smooth)...Rough-leaved dogwood, *Cornus drummondii*, p. 120

37. Lower surface of leaves either lacking hairs or slightly hairy with minute hairs lying close against the surface; upper surface of leaves smooth .38

38. Lower surface of leaves green and without any hairs; pith of the twigs of the present year and up to 2 years old white and less

than 1/3 the diameter of the twig...Stiff dogwood, Cornus foemina, p. 124

38. Lower surface of leaves whitish, grayish, or
gray to silver green with minute colorless
hairs lying close against the surface; pith
of the twigs of the present year and up to
2 years old pale brown or tan; or, if white,
the pith at least half the diameter of the
twig .39

39. Youngest twigs densely hairy; older branches
reddish-brown; fruit bluish; flower cluster
flat or indented at the summit, broader than
tall; stalks of the flowers yellow
brown...Swamp dogwood, Cornus amomum
ssp. obliqua, p. 118

39. Youngest twigs lacking hairs; older branches
gray; fruit white on red stalks; flower cluster
dome- or globe-shaped; stalks of the flowers
red...Gray dogwood, Cornus racemosa, p. 126

Key C. Leaves alternate and compound (consisting of multiple leaflets)

1. All of the leaflets 3...Hop tree, Ptelea trifoliata, p. 268

1. Some or all of the leaflets 5 or more to a
leaf 2

2. Prickles (sharp outgrowth from the bark)
present on at least the stems, branches, or
twigs of the plant 3

2. Prickles absent on all parts of the plant . . .7

3. Leaves more than simply divided once, with
the lateral stalks or leaf-divisions further
divided into additional leaflets 4

3. Leaves simply divided once, with the lateral
stalks attached directly to the main stalk
and not further divided into additional
leaflets 5

4. Leaflets large, 2 to 6 inches long, the margins with short-pointed, outwardly projecting
teeth; upper surface with tiny, soft prickles;
lower surface silvery or gray-
green...Hercules club, Aralia spinosa, p. 64

4. Leaflets small, 3/4 to 2 inches long, the margins with wavy or sometimes with very

small, rounded teeth; upper surface lacking
tiny, soft prickles; lower surface dull green...
Honey locust, Gleditsia triacanthos, p. 168

5. Leaflets without teeth (entire); stipels (tiny
bracts or appendages at base of leaflets) present, but stipules (small bracts at base of
main leaf stalk) absent; flowers pea-shaped,
the petals of a flower of different sizes and
shapes...Black locust, Robinia pseudo-acacia,
p. 322

5. Leaflets with wavy or sometimes with very
small, rounded teeth; stipels absent at base
of the leaflets, but stipules may or may not
be present at base of main leaf stalk, either
united to it or free at the base; flowers not
pea-shaped, the petals similar in size and
shape 6

6. Fruit usually with only one seed (rarely with
2 or 3 seeds), fruit somewhat oval, 1 to 3 1/2
inches long; trees found only in the swamps,
bottomland forests, and edges of sloughs in
southeastern Missouri up to St. Charles
County...Water locust, Gleditsia aquatica,
p. 166

6. Fruit with many seeds, long, narrow, flattened, 6 to 18 inches long; trees found in
bottomlands along streams and their valleys,
also upland slopes and open or wooded pastures throughout the state...Honey locust,
Gleditsia triacanthos, p. 168

7. Fruit a pod (dry fruit, splitting down the
sides), 3 to 10 inches long 8

7. Fruit not a pod, but berrylike, bladderlike, or
winged 10

8. Leaflets about 1/2 inch long; flowers pink,
crowded in tassel-like globe-shaped
heads...Mimosa, Albizia julibrissin, p. 58

8. Leaflets 3/4 to 4 inches long; flowers
greenish-white or white, not crowded in
tassel-like heads 9

9. Compound leaves with an even number of
leaflets, or with a pair of leaflets at the tip;
pods large, 4 to 10 inches long; seeds 3/4
inch long; flowers greenish-white, petals
similar in size and shape...Kentucky coffee
tree, Gymnocladus dioica, p. 170

9. Compound leaves with an odd number of leaflets, or with 1 leaflet at the tip; pods small, 3 to 4 inches long; seeds about 3/8 inch long; flowers white, pea-shaped... Yellowwood, *Cladrastis kentukea*, p. 114

10. Leaves and twigs, when bruised, with a spicy odor; lower surface of leaflets dotted with glands; petals absent; male flowers arranged in drooping, slender cylindrical catkins 11
10. Bruised twigs or leaves possibly ill scented but not with spicy odor or fragrance; lower surface of leaflets not dotted with glands; petals present; none of the flower clusters arranged in cylindrical catkins 21

11. Pith of twigs, when cut lengthwise, separates into chambers or stepladderlike tiers; leaves usually with 11 to 19 (sometimes only 7) leaflets, the middle leaflets larger than those at the tip; husk of fruit not splitting open, the shell grooved 12
11. Pith of twigs continuous and solid brown; leaves usually with 5 to 11 (sometimes 17) leaflets, the topmost leaflets generally the largest; husk of fruit splitting open, the shell smooth or slightly net-veined 13

12. Pith of twigs light brown; bark dark brown or black with rough edges; fruit somewhat globe-shaped and as about broad as long, the husk not sticky...Black walnut, *Juglans nigra*, p. 186
12. Pith of twigs dark brown; bark gray with smooth ridges; fruit longer than broad, husk sticky...Butternut, *Juglans cinerea*, p. 184

13. Bud on end of twig yellow or orange-yellow, rather flattened, appearing naked (lacking scales); fruit husk winged along the lines where it splits .14
13. Bud on end of twig brown or gray, rounded, not flattened, consisting of 6 or more scales; fruit husk not winged 16

14. Bud on end of twig bright yellow; bark interlacing with thin ridges and shallow grooves...Bitternut hickory, *Carya cordiformis*, p. 80

14. Bud on end of twig yellow-brown; bark loose 15

15. Teeth of leaflet usually prominent, side veins of leaflet branching near the tip; nut cylindrical...Pecan, *Carya illinoinensis*, p. 84
15. Teeth of leaflet usually rather inconspicuous, side veins rarely branching near the tip; nut flattened...Water hickory, *Carya aquatica*, p. 78

16. Bark loose, shaggy, breaking into long, broad strips; outer bud scales loose but persistent 17
16. Bark tight, not shaggy, not breaking into long, broad strips; outer bud scales flattened or often breaking away 18

17. Leaflets usually 5 (rarely 7); margin of leaflet with tufts of short hairs along the outer edge of teeth; twigs hairy...Shagbark hickory, *Carya ovata*, p. 88
17. Leaflets usually 5 to 9 (usually 7); margin of leaflet lacking tufts of short hairs along the teeth...Shellbark hickory, *Carya laciniosa*, p. 86

18. Leaf stalk densely hairy; lower surface of leaflet with light orange to brown hairs, dense; bud at tip of twig 1/2 inch or greater...Mockernut hickory, *Carya tomentosa*, p. 94
18. Leaf stalk smooth to somewhat hairy but not densely hairy; lower surface of leaflet smooth, or with silver scales, or with rusty hairs, not dense; bud at tip of twig less than 1/2 inch 19

19. Buds, twigs, leaf stalks, and lower surface of leaflets smooth (lacking hairs and minute scales)...Pignut hickory, *Carya glabra*, p. 82
19. Buds, twigs, leaf stalks, and lower surface of leaflets with hairs and minute scales 20

20. Buds, twigs, leaf stalks, and lower surface of leaflets with rusty hairs and minute scales...Black hickory, *Carya texana*, p. 92
20. Buds, twigs, leaf stalks, and lower surface of leaflets with silvery hairs and minute scales...Sand hickory, *Carya pallida*, p. 90

21. Broken leaves and twigs with white sticky sap; fruit red, hairy, each about 1/8 across; plants more commonly shrublike than forming small trees 22

21. Broken leaves and twigs lacking white sticky sap; fruit yellow or brown, smooth, each about 1/2 inch or larger; plants growing from small to medium-sized trees 24

22. Branches and leaf stalks densely velvety-hairy with spreading and obvious hairs; leaves finely dissected; introduced from cultivation...Staghorn sumac, *Rhus typhina*, p. 388

22. Branches and leaf stalks smooth (without hairs) or with a minute hairiness; leaves not finely dissected; native shrubs or trees . .23

23. Branches and leaf stalks smooth; leaflets coarsely toothed; main stalk where leaflets are attached not winged in the spaces between the leaflets...Smooth sumac, *Rhus glabra*, p. 320

23. Branches and leaf stalks covered with a minute hairiness; leaflets smooth, teeth minute or absent; main stalk where leaflets are attached winged in the spaces between the leaflets...Smooth sumac, *Rhus copallina*, p. 318

24. Leaflets with 2 to 4 glandular teeth at the base; fruit winged, flat, twisted towards the tip...Tree of heaven, *Ailanthus altissima*, p. 56

24. Leaflets lacking glandular teeth at the base; fruit not winged, either berrylike or an inflated capsule 25

25. Leaflet shape curved with unequal sides; leaflet margin smooth (teeth absent); fruit berrylike, about 1/2 inch in diameter... Soapberry, *Sapindus drummondii*, p. 342

25. Leaflet shape not curved, sides equal; leaflet margin coarsely toothed; fruit an inflated capsule, 1 to 2 inches long...Goldenrain tree, *Koelreuteria paniculata,* p. 192

Key D. Leaves alternate and simple (consisting of a single leaf)

1. Plants rare, confined to roadside ditches, swamps, and other low areas in the southeastern Missouri Bootheel; flowers lacking petals and produced in male and female catkins on separate plants before the leaves emerge; single-stemmed shrubs or small trees often producing colonies from root sprouts...Corkwood, *Leitneria floridana*, p. 194

1. Plants without the above combination of characters 2

2. Leaves smooth-edged (entire) without teeth or lobes 3

2. Leaves with either teeth or lobes or both 26

3. At least part of the stem, branches, or twigs bearing prickles or spines 4

3. No prickles or spines present on stems, branches, or twigs 6

4. Leaves long tapering to a pointed tip, leaves broadest below the middle; flower lacking petals; fruit green, the size of an orange or small grapefruit...Osage orange, *Maclura pomifera*, p. 200

4. Leaves rounded, blunt or short-pointed at the tip, broadest above the middle; flowers with white petals; fruit black, only 1/3 to 1 inch long 5

5. Lower surface of leaves densely hairy; twigs more or less hairy...Woolly buckthorn, *Bumelia lanuginosa*, p. 72

5. Lower surface of leaves smooth or nearly so; twigs smooth or nearly so...Southern buckthorn, *Bumelia lycioides*, p. 74

6. Leaves heart-shaped, broadly rounded, as broad as or broader than long...Eastern redbud, *Cercis canadensis*, p. 110

6. Leaves not heart-shaped or broader than long 7

7. Young twigs and at least the lower surface of leaves covered with a dense silvery or whitish hairiness . . . . .8.

7. Young twigs and leaves not covered with a dense silvery or whitish hairiness 9

8. Leaves densely silvery-scaly on at least the lower surface and often on both sides; outside of flowers silvery-scaly; flowers not in catkins...Russian olive, *Elaeagnus angustifolia*, p. 150

8. Leaves silvery- or whitish-hairy but not silvery-scaly; outside of flowers not silvery-scaly; flowers in catkins...Pussy willow, *Salix discolor*, p. 330

9. Leaves with 3 main veins arising from the same place at the very base of the leaf blade at the junction of the leaf stalk 10

9. Leaves with 1 main vein down the middle of the leaf with side veins originating at different points along the main vein 11

10. Shrub or small tree, up to 24 feet tall; growing in dry, rocky, exposed situations and dolomite glades; appearance is often somewhat scraggly; upper surface of leaf often leathery, rough, dark green...Dwarf hackberry, *Celtis tenuifolia*, p. 108

10. Medium to large tree, up to 80 feet tall; growing in low, wet bottomland along streams and in valleys, but also as small trees on glades and bluffs; with stout spreading branches, not scraggly; upper surface of leaf not leathery, smooth, light green...Sugarberry, *Celtis laevigata*, p. 104

11. Most of the leaves (blades) 6 to 12 inches long 12

11. Most of the leaves (blades) less than 6 inches long 13

12. Leaves broadest near the base or the middle; flowers at the tip of the twig, greenish-yellow, the petals 2 to 3 inches long; twig does not emit a disagreeable odor when broken...Cucumber magnolia, *Magnolia acuminata*, p. 202

12. Leaves broadest above the middle; flowers along the sides of the twigs, dark reddish-purple, about 1 inch long and wide; twig

emits a disagreeable odor when broken...Pawpaw, *Asimina triloba*, p. 66

13. Some or all of the flowers in crowded slender catkins (narrow, slender flower clusters); fruit either a small capsule, less than 3/8 inch long, crowded in an elongated cluster or an acorn 14

13. Flowers not arranged in catkins; fruit either with capsules 3/8 inch or longer, not crowded into a dense spike or elongated cluster; or a fleshy, one to many-seeded fruit 16

14. Buds covered by 1 scale having two layers; twigs long and slender, with few if any side branches; leaves not tipped by a bristle; male and female catkins on separate plants; fruit splitting open into two sides; seeds with tufts of hairs...Pussy willow, *Salix discolor*, p. 330.

14. Buds covered by several scales; twigs rather stout and short, with many side branches; leaves tipped with a bristle; male and female catkins on same plant; fruit an acorn; seeds not bearing hairy tufts 15

15. Lower surface of leaves hairy; leaves 1 to 2 inches wide; tip of leaf lacking bristlelike projection; leaf stalk usually hairy; tree common, in most counties of Missouri...Shingle oak, *Quercus imbricaria*, p. 282

15. Lower surface of leaves smooth (not hairy) or with some hairs along the main vein or in the axils of the veins; leaves 1/3 to 1 inch wide; tip of leaf with bristlelike projection; leaf stalk smooth (not hairy); trees rare, occurring in swamps and low ground of southeast Missouri...Willow oak, *Quercus phellos*, p. 300

16. Bruised leaves and bark with a spicy or pleasant smell or spicy taste; some leaves on tree with 2 or 3 lobes; flowers yellow, fruit fleshy, with 1 seed...Sassafras, *Sassafras albidum*, p. 344

16. Bruised leaves and bark not producing a pleasant smell or spicy taste (leaves somewhat fragrant in Smoke tree, *Cotinus obovatus*); leaves mostly simple, not lobed; flowers

white, creamy, pale yellow, pink, rose, or greenish; fruit fleshy, 1 to many-seeded or a many-seeded capsule 17

17. Buds naked (not covered by scales except for Common buckthorn, *Rhamnus cathartica*, which has bud scales but no bud at tip of twig), densely hairy, slender, elongated; stipules (leafy appendages) sometimes present at base of leaf stalks; leaf margins mostly entire but sometimes minute teeth present; stamens opposite the petals 18

17. Buds covered by scales, short and broadest at the base; stipules absent; leaf margins toothed; stamens alternate with the petals 19

18. Leaves with mostly 3 to 4 veins on each side of the central vein; some leaves appearing alternate, but most opposite; leaves abruptly pointed at the tip; twigs often ending up at a spiny tip...Common buckthorn, *Rhamnus cathartica*, p. 316

18. Leaves usually with 4 to 10 veins on each side of the central vein; leaves mainly alternate; leaves gradually pointed at the tip; none of the twigs ending in a spiny tip...Carolina buckthorn, *Rhamnus caroliniana*, p. 314

19. Larger leaves 3/8 to 2 inches across 20

19. Larger leaves mainly 2 to 3 inches across 22

20. Broken leaf stalks and twigs not producing milky sap; flowers about 1/4 long in slender drooping clusters; fruit with 10 to many seeds...Farkleberry, *Vaccinium arboreum*, p. 368

20. Broken leaf stalks and twigs producing milky sap; flowers small, about 1/4 inch long in dense, tight clusters; fruit 1-seeded 21

21. Lower surface of leaves densely hairy; twigs more or less hairy...Woolly buckthorn, *Bumelia lanuginosa*, p. 72

21. Lower surface of leaves smooth or nearly so; twigs smooth or nearly so...Southern buckthorn, *Bumelia lycioides*, p. 74

22. Flowers about 1/4 to 1/2 inch long, urn-shaped with recurved petals; fruit about 3/4 to 1 1/2 inches long and wide, orange to orange-purple, sweet, edible when ripe... Persimmon, *Diospyros virginiana*, p. 148

22. Flowers minute, less than 1/4 inch long, not urn-shaped; fruit less than 1/2 inch long, black or blue-black, sour or bitter when ripe, not edible 23

23. Leaves rounded or blunt at the tip, upper surface bluish-green; leaf stalk and lower surface of fully grown leaf blade smooth (without hairs); bruised leaves somewhat fragrant; some of the flower stalks with a feathery hairiness...Smoke tree, *Cotinus obovatus*, p.128

23. Leaves short- to long-pointed at the tip, upper surface dark green; either the leaf stalk and/or the lower surface of leaf blade somewhat hairy; flower stalks without a feathery hairiness or smooth (without hairs) 24

24. Main side veins 5 to 6 on each side of the central vein; petals 4; stamens 4; flowers perfect (both male and female parts in same flower); fruit rounded, about 1/3 inch long...Alternate-leaved dogwood, *Cornus alternifolia*, p. 116

24. Main side veins 6 to 15 on each side of the central vein; petals 5 or absent; flowers with male and female parts on separate plants; fruit egg-shaped or elongated, 1/2 to 1 inch long 25

25. Leave usually with 1 or more teeth on the margins, sometimes entire (without teeth); leaf stalks 1 to 3 inches long; leaf abruptly pointed at the tip; flowers solitary; fruit about 1 inch long; trees of swamps in the southeastern Missouri Bootheel and upland sinkhole ponds of Oregon and Ripley counties...Water tupelo, *Nyssa aquatica*, p. 216

25. Leaves usually without teeth (entire) on margins, rarely with few teeth; leaf stalks less than 1 inch long; leaf tip blunt or tapering to a point but not abruptly pointed; flowers usually 5 or more in clusters; fruit about 1/2 inch long; trees of the southern and east-central Ozarks and in bottomland

forests of the southeastern Missouri Bootheel...Black gum, *Nyssa sylvatica*, p. 218

26. Leaves lobed, the lobes toothed or toothless 27
26. Leaves toothed only, the teeth wavy, rounded, or pointed 67

27. Lobes of leaves without teeth 28
27. Lobes of leaves with teeth 35

28. Fruit not an acorn; none of the flowers in catkins 29
28. Fruit an acorn; male flowers in drooping, long and slender catkins (narrow, cylindrical clusters of flowers) 30

29. Bruised leaves and bark producing a pleasant smell or spicy taste; tip of leaf pointed or rounded; flowers small, several in a cluster, about 1/2 inch across, yellow throughout... Sassafras, *Sassafras albidum*, p. 344
29. Bruised leaves and bark not producing a pleasant smell or spicy taste; tip of leaf more or less broadly V-shaped or flat-topped with a shallow or deep notch or depression at the center; flowers large, single, showy, 3 to 4 inches across, yellow with an orange center...Tulip tree, *Liriodendron tulipifera*, p. 198

30. Lower surface of fully grown leaves without hairs (rarely some hairs along main veins or in their axils) 31
30. Lower surface of fully grown leaves with hairs more or less covering the surface . .32

31. Lower surface of fully grown leaves whitened; leaves usually with 6 to 10 lobes; acorn 3/4 to 1 inch long; acorn cup with warty or corky scales; common tree throughout Missouri...White oak, *Quercus alba*, p. 274
31. Lower surface of fully grown leaves dull or slightly pale green, not whitened; leaves with usually with 3 lobes at the tip; acorn about 1/2 inch long; cup with flat, thin scales; tree of lowlands of the southeastern Missouri Bootheel...Water oak, *Quercus nigra*, p. 294

32. Leaves with bristle-like points projecting from the ends of the lobes...Black jack oak, *Quercus marilandica*, p. 288
32. Leaves without bristle-like points projecting from the ends of the lobes 33

33. Twigs and small branches rather densely hairy throughout the season; leaf blades usually with 3 to 5 main lobes; hairs on lower surface of leaves erect and with only few branches (use magnifying lens); lower scales of cup of acorn flat or somewhat indented; mature nut usually less than 1/2 inch in diameter...Post oak, *Quercus stellata*, p. 308
33. Twigs and small branches mainly smooth (without hairs) at maturity; leaf blades usually with 5 to 9 main lobes; hairs on lower surface of leaves horizontally spreading and with many branches (use magnifying lens); lower scales of cup of acorn with some thickening or enlargement in the upper part; mature nut more than 1/2 inch in diameter 34

34. Base of the two largest lobes extending almost to the central vein; tips of all the lobes somewhat rounded and similar in appearance; scales along the edge of the acorn cup producing a fringed or ragged border, giving a mossy appearance...Bur oak, *Quercus macrocarpa*, p. 286
34. Bases of all the lobes about the same distance to the central vein; tips of the middle lobes often somewhat squarrish; scales along the edge of the acorn cup short-pointed or blunt sometimes forming a small fringe but not ragged or mossy in appearance... Overcup oak, *Quercus lyrata*, p.284

35. Bark on limbs of older trees flaking off and exposing large white patches; buds covered by the enlarged base of the leaf stalk; flowers in tight, rounded heads; fruit in dense, rounded heads...Sycamore, *Platanus occidentalis*, p. 234
35. Bark on limbs not flaking off exposing white patches; buds exposed, not covered by base of the leaf stalk; flowers not in tight, rounded heads; fruit not in dense, rounded heads 36

36. Leaves with the side (lateral) veins arising at different locations along the main vein and not from the base of the leaf where the leaf stalk attaches 37

36. Leaves with the main veins all arising from the same place at the base of the leaf where the leaf stalk attaches 62

37. Fruit an acorn; leaves large, mainly 3 to 10 inches or more long; petals absent, some of the flowers clustered in long, drooping, slender catkins 38

37. Fruit fleshy or dry, but not an acorn; leaves smaller, mainly 1 to 4 inches long; petals present, showy; flowers not in catkins . . .52

38. Teeth of mature leaves lacking bristlelike points 39

38. Teeth of mature leaves with bristlelike points 42

39. Some of the side veins of the lower surface of leaves not ending in the teeth, especially near the base and tip of the leaf; stalks of fruits 3/4 to 2 1/2 inches long, longer than the leaf stalks...Swamp white oak, *Quercus bicolor*, p. 276

39. All of the side veins of the lower surface of leaves ending in the teeth; stalks of fruits absent or shorter than the leaf stalks 40

40. Trees occurring in bottomland forests of the southeastern Missouri lowlands; acorn large, 3/4 to 1 1/2 inches long; leaves mostly with rounded teeth; lower surface of leaves velvety to the touch...Swamp chestnut oak, *Quercus michauxii*, p. 290

40. Trees in other parts of Missouri; acorn smaller, 1/2 to 3/4 inches long; leaves with blunt or pointed teeth; lower surface of leaves hairy but not velvety to the touch 41

41. Shrub to small tree, up to 15 feet tall; teeth along the margin of the leaf mostly 4 to 8 on each side, typically blunt but also pointed; leaves mainly 1 1/2 to 4 inches long; leaf stalk 1/4 to 3/4 inch long...Dwarf chinquapin oak, *Quercus prinoides*, p. 302

41. Usually a medium to large tree, up to 70 feet tall, but sometimes shrubby and only 7 feet tall; teeth along the margin of the leaf mostly 8 to 13 on each side, typically sharp, pointed, and prominent; leaves mainly 4 to 8 inches long; leaf stalks 3/4 to 1 1/4 inches long...Chinkapin oak, *Quercus muehlenbergii*, p. 292

42. Lower surface of mature leaves more or less hairy on some part of the surface or over the whole surface .43

42. Lower surface of mature leaves without hairs, except for small tufts in the main axils where the side veins join the central vein 46

43. Lower surface of mature leaves with a yellowish, grayish, or whitish hairiness; leaves conspicuously drooping or hanging from the branches; scales of the acorn cup with a reddish-brown dark border; nut enclosed by cup about 1/3 of its length; trees of extreme southern and southwestern Missouri 44

43. Lower surface of mature leaves with a rusty or brownish hairiness; leaves mostly stiffly erect, ascending or spreading from the branches, not drooping; scales of the acorn cup without a dark border; nut enclosed by cup about 1/2 its length; trees mostly throughout Missouri 45

44. Leaves broadest near the base; first pair of lobes typically the largest and longest; lobes 3 to 5 (rarely 7), often curved or sickle-shaped and usually cut more than halfway to the central vein...Southern red oak, *Quercus falcata*, p. 280

44. Leaves broadest at or above the middle; lobes fairly evenly spaced and uniform in size; lobes 5 to 11, mostly at right angles to the central vein, not curved and cut less than halfway to the central vein...Cherry bark oak, *Quercus pagoda*, p. 296

45. Leaves mostly fan-shaped or more broadened at the top, usually with 3 broad lobes, other lobes none or poorly developed; fully grown twigs with scattered scurfy hairs; buds covered with rusty-colored hairs; leaf stalks mostly 1/2 to 3/4 inch long...Black jack oak, *Quercus marilandica*, p. 288

45. Leaves narrower at the top, broadest around the middle, with 5 to 9 long and narrow or short and broad lobes separated by prominent spaces; fully grown twigs mostly without hairs; buds covered with gray hairs; leaf stalks mostly 1 to 3 inches long...Black oak, *Quercus velutina*, p. 312

46. Leaves fan-shaped or broadened toward the summit with a generally 3-lobed upper half 47
46. Leaves not fan-shaped or broadened toward the summit but narrower at the summit and broadest at the middle or toward the base with 5 to 11 long an narrow or short and broad lobes separated by spaces, the longest lobes near the middle of the leaf 48

47. Leaves only slightly, if at all, longer than broad, sometimes as wide as long, usually rounded at the base, rarely straight or tapering; lower surface of leaf yellow-brown or yellow-green; leaf stalks 1/2 to 3/4 inch long; acorn cup turban-shaped...Black jack oak, *Quercus marilandica*, p. 288
47. Leaves usually 1 1/2 to 2 times longer than broad, tapering to a narrowed base; lower surface of leaf pale green; leaf stalks less than 1/4 inch long; acorn cup saucer-shaped...Water oak, *Quercus nigra*, p. 294

48. Lobes along the leaf not even in size and length with lobes along upper half of leaf short and broad; acorn 1 to 1 1/4 inches long...Northern Red oak, *Quercus rubra*, p. 304
48. Lobes along the leaf fairly evenly sized in length and width; acorn less than 1 inch in length 49

49. Acorn cup shallow, less than 1/4 inch long, 3/8 to 5/8 inch across; nut 3/8 to 1/2 inch long; mature buds very small, less than 1/4 inch long...Pin oak, *Quercus palustris*, p. 298
49. Acorn cup over 1/4 inch long, over 5/8 inch across; nut 1/2 to 1 inch long; mature buds 1/4 to 3/8 inch long 50

50. Scales of cup without hairs, shiny, brown or chestnut-colored; tip of nut often with concentric rings; base between middle lobes typically C-shaped; trees of the southeastern Ozarks, west to Shannon and Douglas counties...Scarlet oak, *Quercus coccinea*, p. 278
50. Scales of cup with silky or flattened hairs, dull, ashy-gray; tip of nut smooth and lacking concentric rings; base between middle lobes typically U-shaped; trees of central and southern, or southeastern lowlands of Missouri 51

51. Mature leaves 6 to 8 inches long; leaf stalks 1 1/2 to 2 1/2 inches long; cup of acorn saucer-shaped to top-shaped, rounded or flattened at base with a shallow rim, usually enclosing 1/4 to 1/3 of the nut, 3/4 to 1 1/4 inches across; fully mature buds completely smooth (without hair); known from central and southern Missouri...Shumard's oak, *Quercus shumardii*, p. 306
51. Mature leaves 3 to 6 inches long; leaf stalks 3/4 to 2 inches long; cup of acorn top-shaped to deep cup-shaped, sloping or stalked at the base, usually enclosing 1/3 to 5/8 of the nut, 1/3 to 3/4 inch across; fully mature buds noticeably hairy or at least slightly hairy on margins of upper scales; known only from the southeastern Missouri lowlands...Nuttall oak, *Quercus texana*, p. 310

52. Spine-tipped spur shoots (short, compact stems resembling spines) on twigs or stems 53
52. Spine-tipped spur shoots on twigs or stems absent but conspicuous spines present . .54

53. Lower surface of leaf with densely matted hairs; green cup-shaped receptacle at the base of the petals densely hairy on the outside...Prairie crab apple, *Malus ioensis*, p. 208
53. Lower surface of leaf slightly hairy when young, smooth with age; green cup-shaped receptacle at the base of the petals smooth...Sweet crab apple, *Malus coronaria*, p. 206

54. Veins of the leaves running to both the tips of the lobes and teeth and the base in between the lobes; flowers about 1/2 inch across 55

54. Veins of the leaves running only to the tips of the leaves and teeth; flowers often exceeding 1 inch across 57

55. Leaves deeply lobed, the base of some of the lobes almost reaching the central vein; twigs stout; occurring in swampy woods and low

    ground of the southeastern Missouri lowlands ...Parsley haw, *Crataegus marshallii*, p. 146

55. Leaves more shallowly lobed, the base of the lobes less than half the distance to the central vein; twigs slender; occurring in upland woods in southern Missouri but not in the southeastern lowlands 56

56. Leaves sharply pointed at the tip, broadly-rounded to nearly flattened at the base; leaves of the flowering branches typically 3-lobed...Washington thorn, *Crataegus phaenopyrum*, p. 136

56. Leaves rounded to slightly pointed at the tip and gradually tapering to a narrow base; leaves of the flowering branches sometimes lobed but not symmetrically 3-lobed...Littlehip hawthorn, *Crataegus spathulata*, p. 140

57. Leaves typically broadest above the middle; more than half of the total leaf surface above the middle of the central vein...Urn-tree hawthorn, *Crataegus calpodendron*, p. 130

57. Leaves typically broadest at or below the middle; more than half of the total leaf surface below the middle of the central vein 58

58. Glands (a minute structure that secretes sticky or oily substances) on leaf stalks, leaves and flowering parts; flowers in simple to slightly branched 4 to 7 flowered clusters...Thicket hawthorn, *Crataegus intricata*, p. 146

58. Glands absent; flowers usually in many flowered, branched clusters 59

59. Under surface of leaves very hairy, often woolly; young twigs hairy...Downy hawthorn, *Crataegus mollis*, p. 134

59. Under surface of leaves smooth (without hairs) or with tufts of hairs in the axils of veins 60

60. Sepals (flower structure below petals) broad, toothed; flowers about 1 inch across; leaves broad at the base, nearly heart-shaped or flattened...Kansas hawthorn, *Crataegus coccinioides*, p. 146

60. Sepals narrow, entire, not toothed; flowers less than 3/4 inch across; leaves rounded to flattened or tapering at the base 61

61. Leaves narrowing to the base; plants of low, wet ground...Green haw, *Crataegus viridis*, p. 144

61. Leaves rounded or broadly flattened at the base; plants of rocky upland woods...Frosty hawthorn, *Crataegus pruinosa*, p. 138

62. Leaves star-shaped with 5 (sometimes 7) lobes, the lobes long-pointed; bruised leaves fragrant; some of the 2-year old twigs with corky ridges; fruit round with spiny projections...Sweet gum, *Liquidambar styraciflua*, p. 196

62. Leaves not star-shaped, nor long-pointed; bruised leaves not fragrant; twigs not corky; fruit not round with spiny projections . . .63

63. Young twigs covered with a white cottony mat of hairs; lower surface of leaves densely white-hairy...Silver poplar, *Populus alba*, p. 236

63. Young twigs and lower surface of leaves not densely hairy 64

64. No milky sap produced by broken leaf stalks or twigs; petals present in flowering plants, showy; both male and female parts present in each flower...Rose of Sharon, *Hibiscus syriacus*, p. 176

64. Broken leaf stalks and twigs producing a milky sap; petals absent; male and female flowers in catkins on separate plants or on the same plant .65

65. Central vein of the upper leaf surface with noticeably longer hairs as compared with other hairs; lower surface of leaf soft-hairy with dense long hairs; leaf stalks 1 to 4

inches long, hairy; twigs hairy; female flowers and fruit ball-shaped; bark smooth...Paper mulberry, *Broussonetia papyrifera*, p. 70

65. Central vein of upper leaf surface without noticeably longer hairs as compared with other hairs; lower surface of leaf smooth or with short hairs; leaf stalks 1/2 to 1 inch long; leaf stalks and twigs smooth or with short, flattened hairs; female flowers in catkins and fruit short cylinder-shaped . .66

66. Lower leaf surface of leaf hairy between the 3 large veins...Red mulberry, *Morus rubra*, p. 214

66. Lower surface of leaf without hairs, or, if hairs are present, they are along the 3 large veins as small tufts in the axils of the veins...White mulberry, *Morus alba*, p. 212

67. Thorns, prickles, spines, or spine-tipped spur shoots (short, compact stems resembling spines) on twigs or stems 68

67. No thorns, prickles, spines, or spine-tipped spur shoots on twigs or stems 78

68. Stems with prominent spines and a bud producing a leaf or a twig at the base of each spine 69

68. Stems with spine-tipped spur shoots (short, compact stems resembling spines), not with prominent spines or a bud at the base . . .74

69. Leaves averaging broader than long...Round-leaved hawthorn, *Crataegus margaretta*, p. 146

69. Leaves averaging longer than broad 70

70. Leaves small, averaging less than 1 inch long; leaf stalk stout, hairy, less than 1/4 inch long; flowers solitary or rarely 2 to 3...One-flower hawthorn, *Crataegus uniflora*, p. 142

70. Leaves larger, usually averaging more than 1 1/4 inch long; leaf stalks hairy or smooth, often more than 1/4 inch long; flowers usually more than 4 in clusters 71

71. Under surface of leaves smooth (without hairs) or essentially so; leaf stalks smooth 72

71. Under surface of leaves moderately to densely hairy, or with persistent tufts of hairs in the vein axils; leaf stalks smooth or hairy 73

72. Leaves broadest at the middle, up to 1 1/2 times as long as wide; margin both coarsely and finely toothed above the middle...Red haw, *Crataegus succulenta*, p. 146

72. Leaves broadest above the middle, over 1 1/2 times as long as wide; margin finely toothed but never coarsely toothed...Cockspur thorn, *Crataegus crus-galli*, p. 132

73. Upper surface of leaves shiny, veins not noticeable; margin finely toothed; twigs flexible; leaf stalks usually less than 1/4 as long as the leaf blade...Barberry-leaved hawthorn, *Crataegus engelmannii*, p. 146

73. Upper surface of leaves dull, veins noticeably indented; margin both finely and coarsely toothed; leaf stalks more than 1/4 as long as the leaf blade...Dotted hawthorn, *Crataegus collina*, p. 146

74. Fruit pear-shaped; petals white; flower clusters with a central stalk where side flower stalks emerge; winter buds mostly smooth...Pear, *Pyrus communis*, p. 270

74. Fruit round or globe-shaped, apple-like; flower clusters usually rosy or pink, fading to white; flower clusters simple, without a central stalk; winter buds hairy 75

75. Fruit 1 to 4 inches in diameter; leaves with rounded teeth; leaves similar in shape and toothing on both vegetative and flowering branches; cultivated tree...Apple, *Malus pumila*, p. 210

75. Fruit 1/2 to 1 1/4 inches in diameter; leaves more or less sharply toothed, those on the vegetative branches more coarsely cut or toothed than those of fruiting branches; trees native 76

76. Leaves narrow, broadest in the middle and tapering at both ends to lance-shaped; tree endangered, found only in the southeastern Missouri Bootheel...Narrow-leaved crab apple, *Malus angustifolia*, p. 204

76. Leaves not narrow, often broadest below the middle to sometimes triangular-shaped; tree more commonly found in the state 77

77. Lower surface of leaf with densely matted hairs; green cup-shaped receptacle at the base of the petals densely hairy on the out-side...Prairie crab apple, *Malus ioensis*, p. 208

77. Lower surface of leaf slightly hairy when young, smooth with age; green cup-shaped receptacle at the base of the petals smooth...Sweet crab apple, *Malus coronaria*, p. 206

78. At least two of the lowest side veins conspic-uous and arising at the very base of the leaf blade, there joining the base of the central vein 79

78. Lowest side veins joining the central vein above the very base of the leaf blade 97

79. Leaf blade more or less lop-sided (asymmet-rical) with one half longer or broader than the other half, most noticeable at the base 80

79. Leaf blade not lop-sided, each half the same length and width as the other half 86

80. Leaf margin wavy or with rounded teeth with 1 to 2 per 1/2 inch 81

80. Leaf margin toothed with 4 to 6 teeth per 1/2 inch 82

81. Flowering from October to the end of December; flowers yellow; twigs smooth or slightly hairy...Eastern witch hazel, *Hamamelis virginiana*, p. 174

81. Flowering from January to April; some part of the flower usually tinged with orange, reddish, or salmon; twigs densely hairy or woolly...Ozark witch hazel, *Hamamelis ver-nalis*, p. 172

82. Leaves 1/2 to 2 inches wide; teeth not gland tipped; fruit berrylike, fleshy 83

82. Leaves 3 to 5 inches wide; teeth gland tipped; fruit nutlike, dry 85

83. Leaves of both fruiting branches and leafy shoots with 10 to 40 teeth all around the margins except at the very base; leaf tip usu-ally abruptly long-pointed; fruit 1/4 to 1/2 inch in diameter; fruiting stalks usually much longer than the leaf stalks... Hackberry, *Celtis occidentalis*, p. 106

83. Leaves of fruiting branches without teeth or with few teeth on one or both margins; leaves of vegetative (leafy) branches similar or with teeth nearly all around the margins; leaf gradually tapering to a pointed tip; fruit about 1/4 inch in diameter; fruiting stalks either shorter or slightly longer than the leaf stalks 84

84. Shrub or small tree, up to 24 feet tall; grow-ing in dry, rocky, exposed situations and dolomite glades; appearance is often some-what scraggly; upper surface of leaf often leathery, rough, dark green...Dwarf hack-berry, *Celtis tenuifolia*, p. 108

84. Medium to large tree, up to 80 feet tall; growing in low, wet bottomland along streams and in valleys, but also as small trees on glades and bluffs; with stout spread-ing branches, not scraggly; upper surface of leaf not leathery, smooth, light green... Sugarberry, *Celtis laevigata*, p. 104

85. Lower leaf surface green, smooth (without hairs) except for tufts of hairs in the axils of the main lateral (side) veins; flower stalk, flower cluster stalk and strap-shaped bract smooth...American Basswood, *Tilia ameri-cana*, p. 352

85. Lower leaf surface whitened with sparse to dense hairs; flower stalk, flower cluster stalk, and strap-shaped bract hairy...White basswood, *Tilia heterophylla*, p. 354

86. Buds naked, not covered by scales; some star-shaped hairs present (use magnifying lens) on young twigs, veins on lower leaf surface, and lower leaf surface, flowers with 4 ribbonlike yellow, orange, or red petals; mature fruit bearing 2 shiny black seeds 87

86. Buds covered by scales; hairs when present on twigs or leaves not star-shaped; flower and fruit otherwise, not as above 88

87. Flowering from October to the end of December; flowers yellow; twigs smooth or

slightly hairy...Eastern witch hazel, *Hamamelis virginiana*, p. 174

87. Flowering from January to April; some part of the flower usually tinged with orange, reddish, or salmon; twigs densely hairy or woolly...Ozark witch hazel, *Hamamelis vernalis*, p. 172

88. Broken leaf stalks and twigs producing a milky sap; buds not resinous (not sticky); seeds lacking hairy tufts 89
88. Broken leaf stalks and twigs not producing a milky sap; buds usually resinous (sticky); seeds bearing silky tufts of hair 91

89. Central vein of the upper leaf surface with noticeably longer hairs as compared with other hairs; lower surface of leaf soft-hairy with dense long hairs; leaf stalks 1 to 4 inches long, hairy; twigs hairy; female flowers and fruit ball-shaped; bark smooth...Paper mulberry, *Broussonetia papyrifera*, p. 70
89. Central vein of upper leaf surface without noticeably longer hairs as compared with other hairs; lower surface of leaf smooth or with short hairs; leaf stalks 1/2 to 1 inch long; leaf stalks and twigs smooth or with short, flattened hairs; female flowers in catkins and fruit short cylinder-shaped; bark scaly or furrowed 90

90. Lower leaf surface of leaf hairy between the 3 large veins...Red mulberry, *Morus rubra*, p. 214
90. Lower surface of leaf without hairs, or, if hairs are present, they are along the 3 large veins as small tufts in the axils of the veins...White mulberry, *Morus alba*, p. 212

91. Lower surface of fully grown leaves covered with a white felt of hairs; at least the leaves at end branches maplelike with 3 to 5 lobes...Silver poplar, *Populus alba*, p. 236
91. Fully grown leaves not covered with a white felt of hairs, not 3 to 5 lobed 92

92. Leaves coarsely toothed with large or broad teeth, these usually than 15 on each edge 93

92. Leaves with closely spaced teeth, these usually 15 to 50 or more on each edge 94

93. Teeth of leaves somewhat triangular and short-pointed; mature leaves mainly 2 1/2 to 5 inches long, 1 1/2 to 3 1/2 inches wide; under surface of leaves smooth (without hairs) or with few hairs; at least the topmost bud hairy...Large-toothed aspen, *Populus grandidentata*, p. 240
93. Teeth of leaves mostly blunt or rounded at their tips: mature leaves averaging smaller, mainly 3/4 to 2 1/2 inches long, 3/4 to 1 1/2 inches wide; under surface of leaves densely hairy to nearly smooth; buds not hairy... European aspen, *Populus tremula*, p. 246

94. Pith of stems orange; tip of leaf usually blunt or round (rarely short-pointed); base of leaf usually heart-shaped or prominently rounded; leaf stalks round in cross section; trees of the swamps of southeastern Missouri...Swamp cottonwood, *Populus heterophylla*, p. 242
94. Pith of stems white; tip of leaf short- to long-pointed; base of leaf tapering or narrowed or rather straight-edged; leaf stalks flattened or compressed toward the tip; trees of other habitats or in other parts of Missouri 95

95. Teeth along edge (margin) of leaves rather blunt or rounded at tip; leaves usually broadest near the middle, nearly round; margin of leaves without a thinner translucent border (not permitting light to pass through); trees of northern Missouri only...Quaking aspen, *Populus tremuloides*, p. 246
95. Teeth along edge of leaves ending in a more prominent or narrowed or curved point; leaves usually broadest at the very base; margin of leaves with a thin translucent border (permitting light to pass through); trees found in all parts of Missouri 96

96. Tree with a narrow, erect, slender, columnar shape, the branches all conspicuously ascending or erect; no glands at base of leaf blade; no tiny hairs on edges of leaf blade... Lombardy poplar, *Populus nigra*, p. 244
96. Tree with more widely spreading branches and a more open crown, not narrow and

slender-looking; glands (small projections) usually present at base of leaf blade; tiny hairs present on edges of leaf blade...Cottonwood, *Populus deltoides*, p. 238

97. Leaves evergreen, thick and leathery, with spiny edges...American holly, *Ilex opaca*, p. 180

97. Without the above combination of characters 98

98. Teeth of leaf blades rounded, blunt, or somewhat pointed, all with unequal sides 99

98. Teeth of leaf blades either sawlike, or short- or long-pointed with equal sides 107

99. Buds slightly to conspicuously sticky (resinous); leaf stalks mostly 1/2 as long as to nearly as long as the length of the leaf blade, 1 1/2 to 3 1/2 inches long; all the flowers in drooping or arching catkins (slender cylindrical flower clusters); male and female flowers on separate trees 100

99. Buds not sticky; leaf stalks much less than 1/2 the length of the leaf blade, less than 1 1/4 inch long; flowers not in catkins . . .106

100. Lower surface of fully grown leaves covered with a white felt of hairs; at least the leaves at end branches maplelike with 3 to 5 lobes...Silver poplar, *Populus alba*, p. 236

100. Fully grown leaves not covered with a white felt of hairs, not 3 to 5 lobed 101

101. Leaves coarsely toothed with large or broad teeth, these usually than 15 on each edge 102

101. Leaves with closely spaced teeth, these usually 15 to 50 or more on each edge 103

102. Teeth of leaves somewhat triangular and short-pointed; mature leaves mainly 2 1/2 to 5 inches long, 1 1/2 to 3 1/2 inches wide; under surface of leaves smooth (without hairs) or with few hairs; at least the topmost bud hairy...Large-toothed aspen, *Populus grandidentata*, p. 240

102. Teeth of leaves mostly blunt or rounded at their tips: mature leaves averaging smaller, mainly 3/4 to 2 1/2 inches long, 3/4 to 1 1/2 inches wide; under surface of leaves densely

hairy to nearly smooth; buds not hairy... European aspen, *Populus tremula*, p. 246

103. Pith of stems orange; tip of leaf usually blunt or round (rarely short-pointed); base of leaf usually heart-shaped or prominently rounded; leaf stalks round in cross section; trees of the swamps of southeastern Missouri...Swamp cottonwood, *Populus heterophylla*, p. 242

103. Pith of stems white; tip of leaf short- to long-pointed; base of leaf tapering or narrowed or rather straight-edged; leaf stalks flattened or compressed toward the tip; trees of other habitats or in other parts of Missouri . . .104

104. Teeth along edge (margin) of leaves rather blunt or rounded at tip; leaves usually broadest near the middle, nearly round; margin of leaves without a thinner translucent border (not permitting light to pass through); trees of northern Missouri only...Quaking aspen, *Populus tremuloides*, p. 246

104. Teeth along edge of leaves ending in a more prominent or narrowed or curved point; leaves usually broadest at the very base; margin of leaves with a thin translucent border (permitting light to pass through); trees found in all parts of Missouri 105

105. Tree with a narrow, erect, slender, columnar shape, the branches all conspicuously ascending or erect; no glands at base of leaf blade; no tiny hairs on edges of leaf blade... Lombardy poplar, *Populus nigra*, p. 244

105. Tree with more widely spreading branches and a more open crown, not narrow and slender-looking; glands (small projections) usually present at base of leaf blade; tiny hairs present on edges of leaf blade... Cottonwood, *Populus deltoides*, p. 238

106. Leaf blades with the tip more or less rounded; upper surface glossy; petals united into a tube; fruit purplish, many-seeded... Farkleberry, *Vaccinium arboreum*, p. 368

106. Leaf blades with the tip more or less blunt to somewhat pointed; upper surface dull; petals separate to their base; fruit red...Possum haw, *Ilex decidua*, p. 178

107. Fruit an acorn (nut surrounded at base by a cup)...Sawtooth oak, *Quercus acutissima*, p 272.
107. Fruit not an acorn 108

108. Buds covered by 1 scale; all the flowers in catkins (slender cylindrical flower clusters), all the catkins erect or ascending, male and female flowers on separate plants; seeds with a tuft of silky hairs 109
108. Buds with 2 or more scales; flowers either not in catkins or if in catkins, the male and female catkins found on the same plant; seeds without any hairy tuft 123

109. Leaves green on both sides (those at tips of shoots sometimes covered with silvery-silky hairs) 110
109. Leaves silvery, gray-white, pale bluish-green, or covered with a whitish coating on under surface 113

110. Buds sticky; leaf stalks with glands just below the base of the leaf blade; introduced tree...Crack willow, *Salix fragilis*, p. 326
110. Buds not sticky, leaf stalks without glands; mostly native trees and shrubs 111

111. Teeth on margins of leaves randomly and unequally spaced, only 3 to 12 to an inch; leaves with very short stalks or nearly stalk-less...Sandbar willow, *Salix exigua*, p. 334
111. Teeth on margins of leaves closely and equally spaced, mostly 13 to 25 to an inch; leaves with leaf stalks 1/4 to 1/2 inch long 112

112. Leaves narrowly lance-shaped with a long tapering tip, 5 to 10 times as long as broad; twigs brittle at the base; catkins appearing with the leaves...Black willow, *Salix nigra*, p. 336
112. Leaves broader, broadest in the middle and tapering at both ends, 3 to 4 times as long as broad; twigs not brittle at the base; catkins appearing before or with the leaves... Missouri willow, *Salix eriocephala*, p. 332

113. Lower side (surface or veins or both) of some or all of the leaves more or less hairy 114

113. Lower side of leaves smooth (without hairs) or mainly so 118
114. Youngest twigs or topmost part of twigs or small branches hairy 115
114. Youngest twigs or topmost part of twigs smooth (without hairs) or nearly so 116

115. Leaves up to 7 inches long, narrowly lance-shaped; shrubs to small trees of rocky stream beds and gravel bars and rocky banks of the Ozark region of southern and central Missouri...Carolina willow, *Salix caroliniana*, p. 328
115. Leaves up to 3 inches long, broadest in the middle and tapering at both ends; small to medium-sized trees of floodplains along the Missouri and Mississippi Rivers and their larger tributaries; also as shrubs in wet ground along streams, spring branches and in fens...Missouri willow, *Salix eriocephala*, p. 332

116. Stipules (leafy appendages found at the base of the leaf stalk) conspicuous up to 3/4 inch across, toothed, mostly persistent on the young or new leafy shoots...Carolina willow, *Salix caroliniana*, p. 328
116. Stipules either none or minute or narrow, small and inconspicuous, or not persisting and soon falling off 117

117. Medium-sized tree up to 80 feet tall; planted tree, spreading from cultivation...White willow, *Salix alba*, p. 326
117. Shrub to small tree; native, occurs in fens, swampy ground around springs, and spring branches in the eastern part of the Ozarks... Silky willow, *Salix sericea*, p. 338

118. Youngest twigs or upper end of twigs or small branches hairy...Carolina willow, *Salix caroliniana* p. 328
118. Youngest twigs or upper end of twigs or small branches smooth (not hairy) 119

119. Leaves and shoots emerging in spring with conspicuous stipules (leafy appendages found at the base of the leaf stalk) that nearly encircle the twig...Missouri willow, *Salix eriocephala*, p. 332

119. Leaves and shoots emerging in spring with no stipules or stipules minute and quickly disappearing 120

120. Tiny glands are not present at the upper part of the leaf stalk; leaf stalk is twisted; native tree found along the Missouri, Mississippi, and large streams of eastern, central, and northern Missouri...Peach-leaved willow, *Salix amygdaloides*, p. 324

120. Tiny glands occur at the upper part of the leaf stalk; leaf stalk not twisted; planted tree, spreading from cultivation 121

121. Small branches of previous year's growth drooping or hanging down...Weeping willow, *Salix babylonica*, p. 326

121. Small branches not drooping or hanging down 122

122. Small branches hard to break, tough; leaf stalk of young leaves sticky; teeth averaging 8 to 12 per 1/2 inch of leaf margin...White willow, *Salix alba*, p. 326

122. Small branches easily broken, brittle; leaf stalk of young leaves sticky toward the tip; teeth averaging 4 to 8 per 1/2 inch of leaf margin...Crack willow, *Salix fragilis*, p. 326

123. Leaf stalks, when fully grown, mostly 1 1/2 to 2 1/2 inches long; leaf blades with 0 to 4 (rarely 6) teeth on each side; male and female flowers on separate plants...Swamp tupelo, *Nyssa aquatica*, p. 216

123. Leaf stalks nearly absent, very short, or up to 1 1/4 inches long; leaf blades with usually many teeth closely crowded along the margins; flowers with male and female parts in same flower or in separate flowers on the same plant or on separate plants 124

124. Flowers without petals or sepals or both 125

124. Flowers with both petals and sepals 140

125. Leaves with 1 to 3 teeth per 1/2 inch along the leaf margin; most or all of the teeth simple and more or less equal, without smaller teeth between the main teeth 126

125. Leaves with 4 to 11 teeth per 1/2 inch along the leaf margin; most or all of the teeth

unequal in size with smaller teeth between the larger ones .130

126. Bark light- to steel-gray, smooth; buds longer, slender, and pointed, at least 4 times as long as broad; leaves as very thin as tracing paper; male flowers in rounded head-like clusters; nuts sharply triangular...American beech, *Fagus grandifolia*, p. 154

126. Bark dark brown, with shallow, irregular grooves separating the broad flat ridges; buds less than 4 times as long as broad, not long, slender, and pointed; leaves thicker and firmer; flowers in long, narrow catkins; nuts rounded or flattened on one side, not sharply triangular 127

127. Trees escaped from cultivation; fruit (husk) splitting into 4 sections; nuts typically 3 128

127. Trees native, not escaped from cultivation; fruit splitting into 2 sections; nuts typically 1 129

128. Leaves and spines of fruit smooth (without hairs)...American chestnut, *Castanea dentata*, p. 96

128. Leaves (lower surface) and spines of fruit hairy...Chinese chestnut, *Castanea mollissima*, p. 96

129. Leaves 6 to 10 inches long; teeth about 3/8 inch long; fruit about 1 1/2 inches in diameter (including the spines)...Ozark chinquapin, *Castanea pumila* var. *ozarkensis*, p. 98

129. Leaves relatively small, 4 to 6 inches long; teeth shallow or sometimes barely visible, up to 1/8 inch long; fruit less than 1 inch in diameter (including the spines)...Allegheny chinquapin, *Castanea pumila* var. *pumila*, p. 98

130. Leaf blades often more or less lopsided (asymmetrical) with one half longer or broader than the other, most noticeable at the base; some or all of the flowers with both male and female parts 131

130. Leaf blades usually not lopsided, each half the same length and width as the other half; with male and female flowers, both on the same tree 137

131. Margins of leaves with most of the teeth simply-toothed (without any break or cut on each tooth); bark thin and scaly; trunk forking usually near the base; fruit a wingless bur-like nut...Water elm, *Planera aquatica*, p. 232

131. Margins of leaves with most of the teeth double-toothed (each tooth cut into or broken); bark rough or ridged; trunk single; fruit flat with a broad wing 132

132. Upper surface of leaves rough, like sandpaper, to the touch, with erect stiff hairs; bud scales conspicuously covered with a dense orange-brown or rusty-colored hairs... Slippery elm, *Ulmus rubra*, p. 364

132. Upper surface of leaves more or less smooth to the touch, without hairs or these not stiff or erect; buds scales either without hairs or the hairs either inconspicuous or not orange-brown or rusty-colored 133

133. Cultivated tree, sometimes escaped from cultivation; leaves nearly equal-sided at the base; margins of leaves simply toothed (without any break or cut on each tooth); lower surface of leaves smooth (without hairs); flowers nearly without stalks, not drooping; margins of fruits without hairs projecting...Siberian elm, *Ulmus pumila*, p. 362

133. Native trees; leaves mostly unequal-sided at the base, one side longer or wider or more curved than the other; margins of leaves usually double-sided (each tooth slightly cut into or broken on one side); lower surface of leaves hairy or sometimes smooth (without hairs); flowers with long stalks, soon drooping; margins of fruits with dense hairs projecting 134

134. None of the branches developing corky wings or woody outgrowths; flowers occurring in clusters or groups, their stalks originating from the same point; lower surface of leaves hairy or becoming smooth...American elm, *Ulmus americana*, p. 358

134. Some of the young or old branches, or both, developing corky wings or woody outgrowths; flowers in clusters becoming longer than broad; lower surface of leaves generally remaining hairy 135

135. Trees flowering in the fall; base of trunk often swollen and fluted; trees rare, restricted to the southeast Missouri lowlands...Cedar elm, *Ulmus crassifolia*, p. 360

135. Trees flowering in the spring; base of trunk not swollen or fluted; trees uncommon or common but not rare, not restricted to the southeast Missouri lowlands 136

136. Common in the Ozark region, often in dry and rocky sites but also in lowlands or along streams; leaf stalks usually about 1/8 inch long; base of leaf stalk hairy; buds smooth (without hairs) or nearly so; young branchlets often developing corky wings; fully grown leaves mostly 1 1/2 to 3 inches long, 3/8 to 1 1/4 inches wide; fruits less than 1/4 inch across...Winged elm, *Ulmus alata*, p. 356

136. Uncommon, and chiefly mainly outside of the Ozark area in northern, central, and extreme southeastern Missouri, along streams and wet woods; leaf stalks 1/8 to 3/8 inch long; base of leaf stalks smooth; buds rather hairy; corky growth only on older branches; fully grown leaves mostly 3 to 6 inches long, 1 1/4 to 3 1/2 inches wide; fruits 3/8 to 5/8 inch across...Rock elm, *Ulmus thomasii*, p. 366

137. Lower surface of leaves whitish- or grayish-white; bark peeling off in reddish-brown papery strips, exposing a pale smooth layer...River birch, *Betula nigra* p. 68

137. Lower surface of leaves green or pale green, not white or grayish-white; bark smooth or rough, not peeling 138

138. Leaf blades with a blunt or rounded tip and rounded teeth...Alder, *Alnus serrulata*, p. 60

138. Leaf blades with a pointed tip or pointed teeth, or both .139

139. Bark smooth, twisty, bluish-gray; lower surface of fully grown leaves smooth (without hairs), except for some hairy tufts in the axils of the veins none of the large side veins forked...Hornbeam, *Carpinus caroliniana*, p. 76

139. Bark scaly, light brown or brownish-gray; lower surface of fully grown leaves mostly hairy; some of the side veins forked near the tips...Hop hornbeam, *Ostrya virginiana*, p. 220

140. Petals united into a short bell-shaped to cylindrical tube so that the attempt to remove one portion disturbs the neighboring section of the flower; stamens 10... Farkleberry, *Vaccinium arboreum* p. 368
140. Petals free from each other, separated all the way down to their base so that one petal can be removed without tearing or disturbing the other petals; stamens 4, 5 to 8, or 10 to 50 141

141. Male and female flowers on separate trees 142
141. Flowers complete with both male and female parts .143

142. Teeth of leaves round or blunt; tip of leaf rounded or blunt...Possum haw, *Ilex decidua*, p. 178
142. Teeth of leaves sharp-pointed; tip of leaf tapering to a point...Winterberry, *Ilex verticillata*, p. 182

143. Flowers small, greenish-yellow; stamens 5 144
143. Flowers showy, white, pink, or rose-colored; stamens 10 to 50 145

144. Leaves with mostly 3 to 4 veins on each side of the central vein; some leaves appearing alternate, but most opposite; leaves abruptly pointed at the tip; twigs often ending up at a spiny tip...Common buckthorn, *Rhamnus cathartica*, p. 316
144. Leaves usually with 4 to 10 veins on each side of the central vein; leaves mainly alternate; leaves gradually pointed at the tip; none of the twigs ending in a spiny tip... Carolina buckthorn, *Rhamnus caroliniana*, p. 314

145. Bark light gray and smooth when young, becoming dark gray with shallow furrows and long ridges when older; among the first woody plants to bloom in early spring . .146

145. Bark dark red to reddish- or grayish-brown, breaking into thin, scaly plates; not one of the first woody plants to bloom in early spring 147

146. Large shrub to small to medium-sized tree, not suckering from the roots; petals 3/8 to 5/8 inch long; teeth of leaves fine, 6 to 12 per 1/2 inch; flower clusters nodding or drooping; native trees...Service berry, *Amelanchier arborea*, p. 62
146. Dwarf shrub to small tree, suckering from the roots to form colonies; petals 1/4 to 3/8 inch long; teeth 3 to 7 per 1/2 inch; flower clusters upright; cultivated shrub, sometimes escaping along roadsides...Low service berry, *Amelanchier humilis*, p. 387

147. Leaves broadest below the middle to rather round, not much, if any longer than broad, the base heart-shaped to broadly rounded...Perfumed cherry, *Prunus mahaleb*, p. 256
147. Leaves lance-shaped, narrowly broadest below the middle but obviously longer than broad, the base not heart-shaped or broadly rounded 148

148. A colored, usually brownish-red or brownish (sometimes pale) gland at the tip or side of the teeth along the leaf margin 149
148. No gland arising from the teeth of leaves 152

149. Mature leaf blades mainly 3/4 to 2 inches long, 1/4 to 3/4 inch wide...Chickasaw plum, *Prunus angustifolia*, p. 250
149. Mature leaf blades mainly 2 to 4 inches long, 1 to 2 1/4 inches wide 150

150. Teeth of leaves relatively coarse and prominent; leaf stalk without any hairs, with poorly developed glands; leaflike bracts conspicuous at the base of the fruit stalks or flower clusters; stone of fruit round...Sour cherry, *Prunus cerasus*, p. 252
150. Teeth of leaves relatively fine or minute; leaf stalk with 1, 2, or more conspicuous glands near the tip just below the leaf blade; leaflike bracts not developed at base of fruit- or flower clusters 151

151. Gland arising from the very tip of each tooth of the leaf; teeth of leaves pointed, conspicuous, spreading away from the margin; fully grown leaves flat with each half spread out, not folded...Hortulan plum, *Prunus hortulana*, p. 254

151. Gland arising from that end of each tooth facing the indented lower side of the margin; teeth of leaves low or not pointed, not conspicuous or spreading; fully grown leaves more or less folded lengthwise, troughlike...Wild goose plum, *Prunus munsoniana*, p.260

152. Leaf blades blunt or nearly so at the tip, mainly 3/4 to 13/4 inches long, less than 3/4 inch wide; spiny or thorny shrub or tree 10 to 15 feet tall; fruit 3/8 to 5/8 inch in diameter, blue turning black...Blackthorn, *Prunus spinosa*, p. 387

152. Leaf blades short- to long-pointed at the tip, mainly 1 1/2 to 6 inches long, 3/4 to 2 1/2 inches wide; nonspiny or thorny shrubs or trees 10 to 100 feet tall; fruit either small, 1/4 to 3/8 inch in diameter and dark red to black or if large then 3/4 to1 1/4 inches or more in diameter; then red, gray-blue or purple, or yellow-green with orange or red 153

153. Buds strongly hairy; fruit velvety hairy; stone deeply pitted and sculptured; leaves troughlike, the halves more or less folded lengthwise, conspicuously drooping...Peach, *Prunus persica*, p. 262

153. Buds smooth (without hairs) or with a few hairs; fruit smooth; stone not sculptured; leaves not folded, not conspicuously drooping 154

154. Flowers and fruits in elongated clusters longer than broad, with 15 to 30 fruits; clusters appearing on stems of the new year's growth; mature fruits approximately 3/8 to 1/2 inch across 155

154. Flowers and fruits with 1 or 2 to 5 in a cluster; clusters appearing on stems of preceding year; mature fruits about 1 inch across 156

155. Teeth of leaf margin sharp or conspicuously pointed, spreading upward, but not curved inward; leaf blades rather thin, dull green, abrupt and short pointed at the tip, broadest below the middle to above the middle; low shrub or small tree...Choke cherry, *Prunus virginiana*, p. 266

155. Teeth of leaf margin blunt, short, and curved-in along the margin; leaf blades thick, firm, dark green, shiny, gradually tapering to the longer tip, broadly lance-shaped to broadly egg-shaped; tree becoming 100 feet or more tall...Black cherry, *Prunus serotina*, p. 264

156. Leaf stalks hairy all around; twigs more or less hairy; lower surface of mature leaf blades hairy; fruit eventually turning grayish-blue or grayish-lavender...Big tree plum, *Prunus mexicana*, p. 258

156. Leaf stalks smooth (without hairs); twigs smooth; lower surface of mature leaf blades smooth or sparsely hairy on the main veins; fruit eventually turning red or sometimes yellow, conspicuously marked with pale dots...Wild plum, *Prunus americana*, p. 248

Trees
of
Missouri

Amur maple

Acer ginnala Maxim.

Maple family (Aceraceae)

Appearance: Large multi-stemmed shrub to small tree; up to 20 feet tall with spreading branches.

Flowers: April–June, fragrant, yellow to cream-colored, borne in clusters at the tips of branches and appearing with the leaves; individual flowers on short stalks with four or five small petals, both male and female flowers present.

Fruit: August–September, **persisting into the fall season**, long after the leaves are mature, the samaras (winged fruit) are in pairs, 3/4 to 1 inch long, brown to red.

Leaves: Simple, opposite, **margins densely toothed**, leaves 1 1/2 to 3 inches long, 3/4 to 1 1/2 inches wide, **with three lobes with the center lobe the longest, lobes tapering to sharp pointed tips**; upper surface green to bluish-green, the lower surface a lighter green, smooth or hairy along the veins; leaves turn bright red in the fall.

Twigs: Slender, smooth, yellowish-brown to brown, pores along the stem are lighter colored; buds opposite, broadly rounded at the base, pointed at the tip.

Trunk: Bark grayish-brown, thin, smooth with darker striations or furrows becoming separated into long thin plates on older trees.

Habitat: Capable of escaping from cultivation into fields and forests.

Range: Introduced from Asia and widely planted across the United States as an ornamental.

Wildlife Uses: The twigs are browsed by white-tailed deer and cottontail rabbit. The seeds are eaten by squirrels. The trees are considered a fair cover for songbirds.

Remarks: Amur maple was introduced as an ornamental into the United States about 1860. There are at least five cultivated varieties that have been developed. The first record of its escape in Missouri was at the Plant Material Center of the Natural Resources Conservation Service, Elsberry. There is an extensive population in the nearby fields and forests. With Amur maple's potential to be invasive, planting it is not recommended. A better substitute would be the native red maple.

Amur (pronounced ämoor´) maple is named for a basin where the Amur River flows generally southeast for 1,000 miles, forming the boundary between Russia and China. It is the largest river in Siberia with a total length of 2,700 miles.

The name maple is from Middle English *mapil*, which is from the Anglo-Saxon *mapel*.

Acer is from the Celt and means "hard," in reference to the wood; *ginnala* possibly is from the Greek *ginnos* (a small mule), referring to the size and hardiness of the tree.

Acer ginnala ❧ a. Growth form with fruit, b. Flower cluster, c. Flower, d. Twig

Box elder

Acer negundo L.

Maple family (Aceraceae)

Also called ash-leaved maple, Manitoba maple

Appearance: Medium-sized tree, 40 to 70 feet tall with a broad, uneven crown.

Flowers: April–May, appearing before or with the leaves; male and female flowers on separate trees, small, greenish, drooping, on slender stalks; petals absent.

Fruit: August–October, borne in early summer, **often remaining on the tree over winter**, in drooping clusters 6 to 8 inches long; the samaras (winged fruit) are in pairs, 1 to 2 inches long, seeds at base of wings, reddish-brown, about 1/2 inch long.

Leaves: Opposite, **compound, with 3 to 5 leaflets**; each leaflet 2 to 4 inches long, 1 1/2 to 3 inches wide, egg-shaped, **margins coarsely toothed, sometimes with short lobes**, tip pointed; light green above, light grayish-green beneath; leaves turn greenish-yellow to brown in the fall.

Twigs: Slender, smooth, shiny or with whitish coating that rubs off easily, **green to olive green**, sometimes becoming purple or brownish.

Trunk: Young bark smooth, green, later pale gray to brown, separating into long thin ridges with shallow grooves; wood whitish, soft, weak, close-grained.

Habitat: Occurs in bottomlands, margins of swamps, moist ground along streams, bottom of ravines, base of bluffs, edges of woods, and disturbed sites.

Range: Arizona, New Mexico, Texas, Oklahoma, and Missouri; eastward to Florida, northward to New Brunswick, and west to Manitoba, Minnesota, and Nebraska.

Wildlife Uses: Seeds are an important winter food source for many species of birds, also squirrels, chipmunks, and other small mammals. The leaves are fed on by box elder bugs, which can be pests around homes.

Medicinal Uses: Native Americans used tea made from the inner-bark as an emetic (induces vomiting).

Remarks: Two varieties occur in Missouri: *Acer negundo* var. *negundo,* with twigs smooth or covered with a whitish coating, found commonly throughout the state; and *Acer negundo* var. *texanum,* with twigs with densely short hairs; it is scattered in the western half of the state and Lincoln County. Box elder is the only maple that lacks petals and has compound leaves. Unlike other maples that are insect pollinated, box elder is wind pollinated which can cause hay fever in the spring. Box elder is a fast growing tree but rarely lives beyond 80 years. It is particularly susceptible to wind or storm damage and easily sheds limbs. The wood is used for paper pulp, crates, woodenware, and cheap furniture. Box elder's sugary sap is considered inferior to that of sugar maple.

Box elder takes its name from its elder-like leaflets. Elder or poison elder is another name for poison ivy. Its wood is like that of the European box tree.

Acer is from the Celtic and means "hard," in reference to the wood; *negundo* is from *negundi*, the Sanskrit name of the chaste tree of India.

Acer negundo ❧ a. Growth form, b. Flower cluster, c. Seed cluster, d. Twig, e. Leaf scar with bud

Red maple

Acer rubrum L.

Maple family (Aceraceae)

Appearance: Small to medium tree, up to 60 feet tall, with a long, clear trunk supporting a narrow, irregular crown.

Flowers: March–April, male and female flowers borne on the same tree or on separate trees in tassel-like clusters; **flowers red**, appearing in early spring before the leaves; petals 4 or 5, small.

Fruit: May–June, borne on slender, drooping stalks, 2 to 4 inches long; **winged-fruit (samaras) are in pairs**, wings 3/4 to 1 1/4 inches long, **red**.

Leaves: Simple, opposite, egg-shaped to oval 2 to 5 inches long with 3 to 5 lobes; lobes with pointed tips, **middle lobe taking up 1/2 or less than the length of the complete leaf, broadest at the base; base of lobes (sinuses) angled or V-shaped**, margins irregularly toothed; upper leaf surface green to dark green, lower surface whitish; leaves turn scarlet or red in autumn.

Twigs: Slender, smooth, reddish, shiny, pores pale; bud at tip is blunt.

Trunk: Bark light gray and smooth at first, becoming darker, furrowed and flaky on older trees; wood light reddish-brown, close-grained, hard, not strong.

Habitat: Bottomland forests, edges of streams, swamps and sinkhole ponds, mesic (moist) to dry upland forests, and along bluffs.

Range: Texas, Oklahoma, Arkansas, and Missouri; east to Florida, north to Newfoundland, and west to Ontario, Wisconsin, and Minnesota.

Wildlife Uses: Seeds are eaten by many species of birds, also squirrels, chipmunks, and other small mammals.

Medicinal Uses: Native Americans used inner bark in tea for coughs, diarrhea, diuretic, expectorant, and "blood purifier."

Remarks: Two varieties occur in Missouri: red maple, *Acer rubrum* var. *rubrum* has the leaf undersurface pale green, smooth to sparsely hairy; common in the Ozark uplands; and Drummond's red maple, *Acer rubrum* var. *drummondii* with the leaf lower surface densely hairy and whitish; found along edges of swamps, and bottomland forests of the Bootheel, and along edges of sinkhole ponds in the southeastern Ozarks.

The wood is used for furniture, veneer, interior finish, flooring, kitchenware, clothes hangers, clothespins, gunstocks, woodenware, and pulpwood. Red maple has been cultivated since 1656. It is often used in ornamental plantings because of its red twigs and fruits, and its brilliant fall colors.

The name maple is from Middle English *mapil* which is from the Anglo-Saxon *mapel*.

Acer is from the Celtic and means "hard," in reference to the wood; *rubrum* denotes the red color.

Acer rubrum* var. *rubrum ❧ a. Growth form, b. Fruit cluster, c. Single flower, d. Flower cluster, e. Twig

Silver maple

Acer saccharinum L.

Maple family (Aceraceae)

Also called soft maple

Appearance: Medium to large tree to 100 feet tall with a rounded crown and slender spreading branches.

Flowers: January–April, separate male and female flowers borne on the same tree and appearing before the leaves in clusters; yellow to red with 3 to 7 stamens, no petals; **earliest of the maple trees to flower in the spring**.

Fruit: April–June, borne on slender, drooping stalks, the reddish- to yellowish-brown samaras (winged-fruit) are in pairs, each wing 1 1/2 to 2 inches long.

Leaves: Simple, opposite, leaves 4 to 7 inches long, broadly triangular in shape with five lobes; **lobes deep, narrow, pointed at the tip, middle lobe taking up more than 1/2 the length of the complete leaf, conspicuously narrowed at the base**, margins toothed, **base of lobes (sinuses) V-shaped**, upper surface of leaf pale green, **undersurface silvery white**; leaves turning yellow in autumn.

Twigs: Slender, brittle, shiny, reddish-brown, producing a disagreeable odor when bruised or broken; bud at tip is blunt.

Trunk: Bark smooth and light gray on young trees, **later breaking into long thin plates and ridges**; wood pale brown, soft, somewhat brittle, moderately strong, easily worked, decaying rapidly on exposure.

Habitat: Bottomland forests, mesic (moist) forests in ravine bottoms, edges of streams and rivers, margins of ponds and lakes; planted around farmsteads and homes.

Range: Oklahoma, Missouri, Arkansas, and east Texas, east to Florida, north to New Brunswick, and west to Ontario, the Dakotas, Nebraska, and Kansas.

Wildlife Uses: Seeds are eaten by songbirds, squirrels, and small rodents; larger branches and trunk, hollowed by heart-rot, provide dens for squirrels or raccoons.

Remarks: Silver maple is the earliest of the maples to flower and has been cultivated since 1725. There are a number of horticultural varieties selected for cut leaves, pyramid or columnar tops, weeping branches, and yellow-bronze leaves. Silver maple is a popular urban tree in Missouri, planted along city streets and in yards. It grows rapidly and provides lots of shade with its spreading crown. The major disadvantage is that its branches have a tendency to break off in ice, snow, and wind storms, and its roots often clog drains and sewers. The samaras drop as "whirlybirds," which provide amusement for young children but rapidly germinate in gardens, alleys, vacant yards, and rain gutters.

The wood is made into furniture, veneer, pulpwood, woodenware, boxes, and crates.

Silver maple is named for the undersurface of the leaves, which easily flutter in the summer breezes due to their long, slender leaf stalks. The name maple is from Middle English *mapil* which is from the Anglo-Saxon *mapel*.

Acer is from the Celtic and means "hard," in reference to the wood; *saccharinum* refers to the sweet sap, which has been harvested to some extent for maple syrup production.

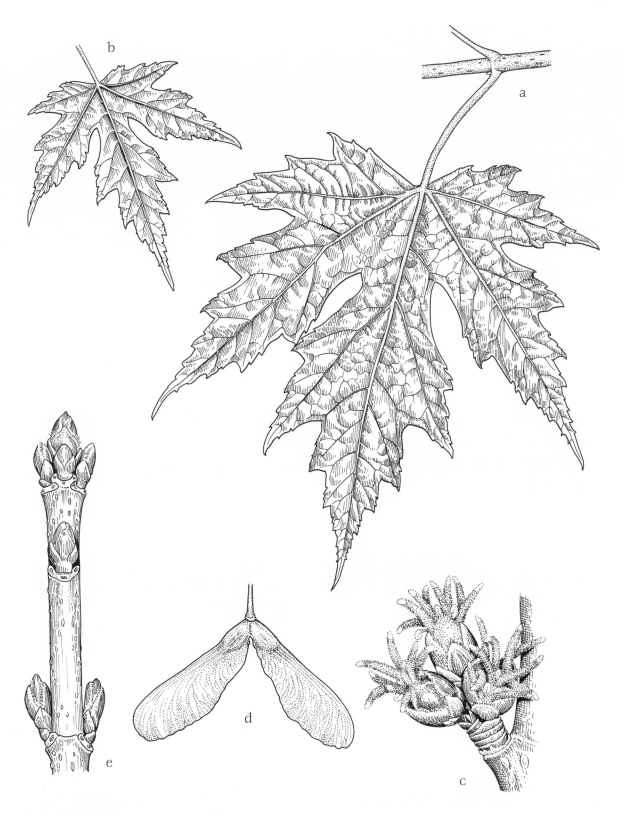

Acer saccharinum ❧ a. Leaf arrangement, b. Leaf, c. Flowers, d. Fruit, e. Twig

Black maple

Acer saccharum Marshall ssp. *nigrum* (Michaux f.) Desmarais

Maple family (Aceraceae)

Appearance: Medium to large tree to 80 feet tall with stout branches, forming a large broad crown.

Flowers: April–May, male and female flowers typically on the same tree, both often in the same leafy shoot, flowers appear when the leaves are half grown; flowers greenish-yellow, no petals, stamens 7 to 8.

Fruit: August–October, reddish-brown, samaras (winged-fruit) are in pairs, each wing 1/2 to 1 inch long.

Leaves: Simple, opposite, leaves 4 to 6 inches long or wide, usually 3-lobed, occasionally 5-lobed with the two additional lobes being small; lobes broad, pointed, **sinuses greater than 90 degrees; leaf margins lacking teeth, often slightly curled under**; upper leaf surface dark green, dull; lower surface yellowish-green to green and usually hairy; **leaf stalk abruptly enlarged at the base**; leaves turn yellow to brilliant red in autumn.

Twigs: Stout, thicker than sugar maple, shiny, green to orange or brown to gray; bud at tip is sharp-pointed.

Trunk: Bark becoming moderately thick, deeply furrowed into long, narrow, blackish ridges; wood hard, heavy, strong.

Habitat: Mesic (moist) to dry upland forests, ravines, valleys, and along streams.

Range: Missouri east to Tennessee, and North Carolina; north to Ontario, and west to Wisconsin, Minnesota, and Iowa.

Wildlife Uses: Seeds are eaten by songbirds, squirrels, and small rodents; white-tailed deer browse on the young growth.

Remarks: Black maple is also known as *Acer nigrum* Michaux f. Black maple is highly shade-tolerant, slow growing, and long lived. The leaves are variable and it is suggested that black maple often intergrades with sugar maple. Black maple has the outstanding ornamental characteristics of sugar maple, but is more tolerant of heat and drought. It is known as a source for maple sugar and syrup. The wood is similar to sugar maple for its uses.

The common name refers to the bark, which turns dark gray to black with age. The name maple is from Middle English *mapil* which is from the Anglo-Saxon *mapel*.

Acer is from the Celtic and means "hard," in reference to the wood; nigrum refers to the dark bark.

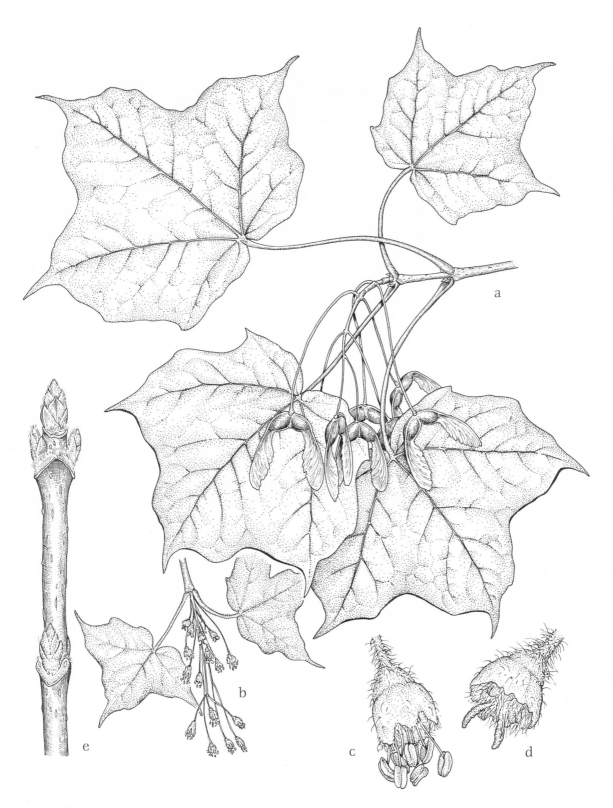

Acer saccharum* ssp. *nigrum ❀ a. Growth form with fruit, b. Flower cluster, c. Male flower, d. Female flower, e. Twig

Sugar maple

Acer saccharum Marshall ssp. *saccharum*

Maple family (Aceraceae)

Also called hard maple

Appearance: Medium to large tree to 100 feet tall with a large, round crown.

Flowers: April–May, male and female flowers commonly on the same tree but sometimes on separate trees, borne on long, hairy stalks that droop, appearing as the leaves are expanding; petals absent; stamens 5 to 8; yellow.

Fruit: August–October, reddish-brown, samaras (winged-fruit) are in pairs (rarely three), each wing 3/4 to 1 1/2 inches long.

Leaves: Simple, opposite, leaves 3 to 6 inches long, **broadly triangular in shape, sometimes wider than long**, usually 5-lobed but occasionally 3-lobed; lobes mostly entire or irregularly toothed, the tips pointed, **sinuses U-shaped**; upper surface dark green, **lower surface paler and whitish, smooth except for tufts of hairs at the vein axils**; leaf stalk smooth. Leaves turn various shades of yellow, orange, and red in the autumn.

Twigs: Slender, shiny, smooth, green at first, reddish-brown later; pores conspicuous, pale; bud at tip is sharp-pointed.

Trunk: Bark smooth and gray on young trees, later darker with grooves and irregular scaly plates; wood reddish-brown, close-grained, hard, strong, tough, durable.

Habitat: Mesic (moist) to dry upland forests, margins of glades, ledges, and bases of bluffs, and banks of streams.

Range: Oklahoma, Missouri, Arkansas, and east Texas; east to Florida, north to Newfoundland, and west to Manitoba, the Dakotas, Nebraska, and Kansas.

Wildlife Uses: Seeds are eaten by songbirds, squirrels, and small rodents; white-tailed deer feed on young twigs, buds, and leaves.

Medicinal Uses: Native Americans used the inner bark in tea for coughs, diarrhea, and as a diuretic, expectorant, and "blood purifier."

Remarks: In addition to ssp. *saccharum* in Missouri, there is also southern sugar maple, ssp. *floridanum* and Schneck's sugar maple, ssp. *schneckii*. The former differs by having smaller leaves, 1 1/4 to 4 inches long, lobes with blunt to rounded tips; rare, occurring in southern and central Missouri. The latter is similar to ssp. *saccharum* but with lower surface of leaves hairy along the veins and typically with three lobes; uncommon, occurring in eastern and southern Missouri.

Sugar maple is widely known as a source for maple sugar and syrup. The wood is made into furniture, interior finishing, cabinets, veneer, and flooring. Sugar maple is highly shade tolerant and attains its greatest size and density in the Mississippi and Missouri river hills where the soils are deep and less fire prone. It is a popular ornamental tree and has been in cultivation since 1753.

The name maple is from Middle English *mapil* which is from the Anglo-Saxon *mapel*.

Acer is from the Celtic and means "hard," in reference to the wood; *saccharum* refers to the sugar content of the sap.

Acer saccharum ssp. saccharum ❧ a. Growth form, b. Fruit cluster, c. Flower cluster,
d. Male flower, e. Female flower, f. Twig

Ohio buckeye

Aesculus glabra Willd.

Horse chestnut family (Hippocastanaceae)

Appearance: Variable from a shrub to medium-sized tree, up to 50 feet tall, depending upon site conditions; branches drooping with upcurved ends.

Flowers: April-May, clustered along an axis 4 to 8 inches long, 2 to 3 inches wide on the tips of twigs; **flowers greenish-yellow,** 1/2 to 3/4 inch long, in the shape of a tube; petals 4, two upright and two lateral, **equal in length**; stamens 8, **longer than the petals**.

Fruit: September-October, capsule leathery, 1 to 2 1/4 inches across, globe to inverted egg-shaped, light brown, **roughened by blunt spines**, splitting into three parts; seeds 3, sometimes flattened by pressure against each other, shiny, brown, 1 to 1 1/2 inches wide.

Leaves: Opposite, palm-shaped with **mainly 7 leaflets**, broadest in the middle and tapering at both ends to egg-shaped, tip pointed, base wedge-shaped, margin finely toothed, leaflet 4 to 6 inches long, 1 1/2 to 2 1/2 inches wide; upper surface bluish- or grass-green, smooth; lower surface paler, smooth, sometimes hairy on the veins; leaves turning yellow in early autumn, foul smelling when crushed; leaf stalks 4 to 6 inches long.

Twigs: Reddish-brown to gray, hairy at first, smooth later; pores orange; leaf scars large.

Trunk: Bark dark brown when young, smooth; older bark gray and broken into plates roughened by small numerous scales, foul smelling; wood whitish, fine-grained, soft, sapwood hardly distinguishable.

Habitat: Occurs in rich or rocky woods of valleys, ravines, gentle or steep slopes, base of bluffs, edge of low woods, thickets, and occasionally on edges of limestone glades. Throughout Missouri, except for the extreme southeastern region.

Range: Northeastern Texas, Oklahoma, Arkansas, Mississippi, and Alabama; north to Pennsylvania; and west to Ohio, Michigan, Iowa, northeastern Nebraska, and Kansas.

Wildlife Uses: The tubular greenish-yellow flowers are frequented by ruby-throated hummingbirds for their nectar.

Medicinal Uses: People have carried buckeyes in their pockets to prevent rheumatism. The bark or nuts have been used to cure skin sores and ulcers, the flowers to treat rheumatism, and the bark and fruit as a tonic and to treat fever.

Remarks: Ohio buckeye is sometimes planted for ornament in the Eastern United States and in Europe. It has been in cultivation since 1809. The leaves are the first to emerge in early spring before any other tree. It is a short-lived tree. The wood is easy to carve and resists splitting. It is used for fuel, paper pulp, artificial limbs, splints, woodenware, boxes, crates, toys, furniture, veneer for trunks, drawing boards and occasionally for lumber. The seeds are considered poisonous, but are rendered harmless after boiling or roasting; they were roasted and eaten by Native Americans as a starchy meal.

Aesculus is the ancient name for a European mast-bearing (seed-bearing) tree; *glabra* refers to the smooth leaves.

Aesculus glabra ❀ a. Growth form, b. Flower cluster, c. Fruit, d. Seed

Red buckeye

Aesculus pavia L.

Horse chestnut family (Hippocastanaceae)

Appearance: Shrub, or, more rarely, a small tree, up to 20 feet tall, with a somewhat dense crown, short branches, and drooping upcurved ends.

Flowers: April–June, clustered along an axis 4 to 8 inches long, flowers red, 3/4 to 1 1/2 inches long, in the shape of a tube 3/8 to 5/8 inch long ending in 2 upright and 2 lateral **petals unequal in length; stamens 8, shorter than or only slightly longer than the upper petals.**

Fruit: September–November, capsule 1 to 2 inches in diameter, leathery, somewhat globe- or egg-shaped, light brown, **smooth but finely pitted,** splitting into three parts; seeds 1 to 3, rounded or flattened by pressure against each other, shiny, light to dark brown, about 1 inch in diameter.

Leaves: Opposite, **palm-shaped with 5 leaflets,** lance-shaped with the broadest toward the tip or inverted egg-shaped, tip terminating in a sharp angle to abruptly pointed, base gradually narrowed, margin coarsely toothed, leaflet length 3 to 6 inches, width 1 to 1 1/2 inches; **upper surface shiny, dark green,** smooth with a few hairs on the veins, lower surface paler, smooth to matted hairs; leaf stalks nearly smooth or with varying degrees of hairiness, red, 3 to 7 inches long.

Twigs: Green to gray or brown, drooping with upcurved ends, stout, smooth; pores pale brown to orange; leaf scars large.

Trunk: Bark gray to brown, smooth on young branches, on old trunks roughened into short plates that flake off in small, thin scales; wood pale brown, light, soft, close-grained.

Habitat: Occurs in low rich woods in valleys, at the base of bluffs, low slopes and along streams. Also it persists in old pastures, clearings, and along utility rights-of-way. **Found wild only in southeastern Missouri.**

Range: Central Texas, Arkansas, Oklahoma, and Louisiana; north to Virginia, and west to Kentucky, southern Illinois, and southeastern Missouri.

Wildlife Uses: The tubular red flowers are frequented by ruby-throated hummingbirds for their nectar.

Medicinal Uses: It is reported that the powdered bark is used in domestic medicine for toothache and ulcers.

Remarks: This shrub, with its red flowers and palmately shaped foliage, is a popular ornamental that flowers in just a few years when grown from seed. The seeds and young foliage are poisonous to livestock. The powdered seeds have been used in ponds and slow-moving water to catch fish, which become groggy and float to the surface. The roots contain soap-foaming properties and have been used for washing clothes.

The name "buckeye" was given the big shiny brown seed, which, with the pale scar on one side, appeared like the detached eye of a deer.

Aesculus is the ancient name for an old mast-bearing (seed-bearing) tree; *pavia*, honors Peter Paaw (Petrus Pavius) (1564–1617), a Dutch botanist.

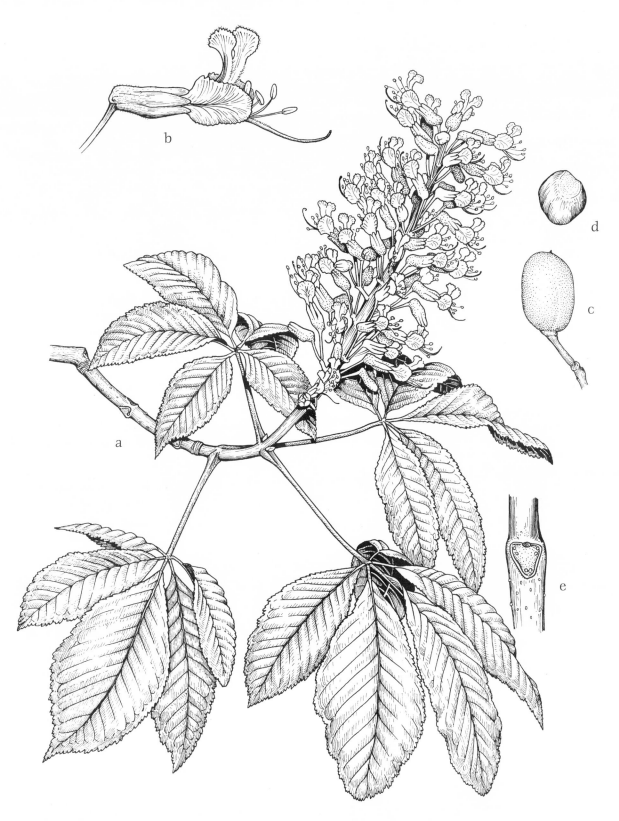

Aesculus pavia ✿ a. Growth form, b. Flower, c. Fruit, d. Seed, e. Leaf scar

Tree-of-heaven

Ailanthus altissima (Miller) Swingle

Quassia family (Simaroubaceae)

Appearance: Medium-sized tree, up to 60 feet tall, with stout branches spreading to form an open, very wide crown.

Flowers: May–June, male and female flowers on separate trees, borne in clusters, 6 to 12 inches long on new growth at the tips of branches; **flowers appear after leaves have expanded**; flowers small, about 1/3 inch across, with five, yellowish-green petals; **male flowers unpleasantly scented**.

Fruit: September–October, **in clusters of 1 to 5 samara (winged-fruit)**, each samara 1/2 to 1 1/2 inches long, **wing twisted toward the end**, light brown, with one seed; samaras persisting on the tree into winter.

Leaves: Alternate, pinnately compound (leaflets arranged on opposite sides of an axis), 8 inches to 2 1/2 feet long, rachis (main axis) and **leaves ill-scented when bruised**; leaflets 11 to 41, length 2 to 5 inches; egg-shaped to lance-shaped, pointed at the tip, **margin smooth except for 2 to 4 glandular teeth at the base**; upper surface dull dark green, lower surface paler and smooth; leaf stalk swollen at the base; leaves turning yellowish-green in autumn.

Twigs: Stout, tan to reddish with **prominent, raised pores**, leaf scars large and conspicuous; **ill-scented when broken**.

Trunk: Bark pale grayish-brown with shallow, light-colored grooves; wood light brown, medium hard, not durable, weak, open-grained, used for fuel, rough construction.

Habitat: Common in urban areas, escapes from cultivation and spreads from old homesites, slopes of bluffs, disturbed upland forests, edges of streams.

Range: Introduced from China; occurs in New Mexico, Texas, Oklahoma, Arkansas, Louisiana; east to Florida, north to Massachusetts and west to Ontario, Iowa, Missouri, and eastern Kansas.

Wildlife Uses: Not significant to wildlife species.

Medicinal Uses: In China the powdered bark has been used to treat tapeworm and is a remedy for dysentery.

Remarks: Tree-of-heaven was introduced into the United States by William Hamilton in 1784. Experimentally, it was grown to provide food for silkworms as it had in China. It is a rapid grower and spreads by suckers and by seed. The branches are very susceptible to breakage during storms. The leaves appear late in spring and the leaflets drop quickly at the first hard frost. The trees are typically short-lived (30 to 50 years), though some have survived for over 150 years.

Because tree-of-heaven is a prolific seed producer and grows rapidly, it is a threat to native vegetation and natural areas. Its usage should be discouraged.

Ailanthus is from a Chinese name, "Ailanto," meaning "tree-of-heaven," and refers to its height; *altissima* means "very tall."

Ailanthus altissima ❧ a. Growth form with fruit, b. Flower cluster, c. Male flower, d. Fruit, e. Twig

Mimosa

Albizia julibrissin Durazz

Mimosa family (Mimosaceae)

Also known as silktree

Appearance: Small tree to 40 feet tall, with widely spreading branches on a short trunk resulting in a broad, flat-topped crown.

Flowers: May–August, flowering after the leaves emerge, on the tips of branches, **pink, crowded in tassel-like round heads**, 1 1/2 to 2 inches across; heads contain 15 to 25 flowers with numerous stamen filaments; petals green, hairy; **fragrance is strong and sweet**.

Fruit: August–September, **pods are flat, linear**, straw-colored to yellowish-brown, 5 to 8 inches long, **forming large clusters**; seeds are flat, light brown, oval, about 1/2 inch long.

Leaves: Alternate, twice-pinnately compound (fern-like), 6 to 20 inches long, with 5 to 12 pairs of pinnae (first division of a compound leaf), pinnae 2 to 6 inches long; leaflets pale green, about 1/2 inch long, 8 to 30 pairs per pinnae, 2 to 4 times longer than broad, margin lacking teeth, hairs along the edges; glands (small swellings) near the base of the leaf stalk; **leaves emerge in late spring**.

Twigs: Moderately stout, green to brown or gray, somewhat fluted below nodes (where leaves attach), often zigzag, smooth; pores small, numerous.

Trunk: Bark smooth, tight, blotched gray, sometimes brownish on young trunks or limbs; pores large and conspicuous.

Habitat: Invades disturbed areas along roadsides, edges of woods, old fields, open vacant lots. Like many successful exotics, it is capable of growing in a wide range of soil conditions.

Range: Native to Asia, introduced into the United States in 1745. It has escaped as an ornamental planting from west Texas east to Florida, north to Rhode Island, and west to Kentucky, southern Illinois, southern Missouri, and Oklahoma. Sensitive to cold weather, it does not survive in northern states.

Wildlife Uses: Not significant to any native wildlife species.

Remarks: Planting mimosa should be discouraged. Mimosa was once thought not to escape from cultivation but in the past few decades it has acclimated to its environment and can be found as far north as central Missouri. Mimosa is susceptible to very cold temperatures and will suffer extensive limb damage and dieback.

As most legumes, Mimosa seeds are very durable. One study showed 90 percent viability after five years; another *Albizia* species had 33 percent germination of seeds after 50 years in open storage. The trees grow rapidly under good conditions but have weak, brittle wood. They are short-lived (10 to 20 years) due to disease (mimosa wilt) and insect problems. Mimosa resprouts quickly if cut or top-killed. The wood is used for cabinetmaking in Asia.

The common name and genus name mimosa was coined in 1731 from the Latin *mimus*, "mime," so-called because some species fold their leaves when touched, seeming to mimic animal behavior. However, this tree species does not fold its leaves.

Albizia is named after F. Degli Albizzi, an Italian nobleman and naturalist; *julibrissin* is a modification of the Persian name, presumably of the common name for the species.

Albizia julibrissin ❀ a. Growth form with flowers, b. Single flower, c. Fruit, d. Twig, e. Leaf scar with bud

Alder

Alnus serrulata (Ait.) Willd.

Birch family (Betulaceae)

Also called common alder, smooth alder, tag alder

Appearance: Irregularly shaped shrub or slender tree to 20 feet.

Flowers: March–April, borne in separate male and female catkins; male catkins in clusters of 2 to 5, 2 to 4 inches long, cylindric, drooping; stamens 3 to 6; female catkins in clusters of 2 to 3, about 1/4 inch long, green to purple.

Fruit: September–October, about 3/4 inch long, oval-shaped, a conelike cluster of woody bracts each below a nutlet; nutlet small, oval, flattened, sharp-angled, less than 1/8 inch long.

Leaves: Alternate, simple, deciduous, thick, 1 to 5 inches long, inverted egg-shaped to oval, **blunt or rounded at the tip**, terminating at a sharp angle or wedge-shaped at the base, **margin with teeth blunt or rounded**, rather dark green on both sides, and somewhat hairy or smooth beneath, veins prominent; leaf stalk smooth or hairy, 1/3 to 1/2 inch long; leaves turn dull yellow in autumn.

Twigs: Reddish-brown to brown, hairy at first, smooth later, slender, flexible.

Trunk: Bark reddish-brown to brown, with horizontal pores, with narrow grooves starting as a vertical row of dots and eventually opening to a narrow crack; wood lightweight, not strong, light brown.

Habitat: Occurs along stream banks, springs, spring branches and fens.

Range: East Texas, Oklahoma, Arkansas, and Louisiana; east to Florida, north to Maine and Nova Scotia; west to New Hampshire, New York, Ohio, Minnesota, Iowa, and Missouri.

Wildlife Uses: The fruit is eaten by several species of birds. Woodcock and ruffed grouse eat the buds, catkins and seeds. Alder provides cover for woodcocks from early spring through fall for nesting, feeding and resting. Beavers commonly use alders in dam construction.

Medicinal Uses: The dried, powdered bark steeped in water has been used for eye infections. Tea made from the bark has been used to treat diarrhea and as a blood purifier. Native Americans applied an extract of the inner bark to poison ivy rash.

Remarks: Alder, with its dense mass of roots, is sometimes planted to prevent erosion on stream banks. Alder roots also enrich the soil, for in association with certain bacteria, they absorb atmospheric nitrogen and make it available to neighboring plants. Alder easily spreads by vegetative growth, either by sprouting new shoots from the base of older plants or by sending up shoots from underground stems.

The woody, conelike female catkins are sometimes plated with gold or silver and used for jewelry.

Alder is from the Old English *alor*, a tree name originating over 5,000 years ago, with the "*d*" added in the 14th century.

Alnus is the classical name of the alder; *serrulata* refers to the finely toothed leaves.

Alnus serrulata ❊ a. Growth form, b. Winter twig, c. Male catkin, d. Female catkin, e. Fruit

Service berry

Amelanchier arborea (Michx. f.) Fern.

Rose family (Rosaceae)

Also called shadbush, sarvice berry, sarviss tree, June berry, shadblow, sugar plum, Indian cherry

Appearance: Tall shrub or small tree, rarely up to 30 feet tall, with a narrow, rounded crown.

Flowers: March–May, often appearing before the leaves; flower clusters 3 to 7 inches long, **rather dense, erect or nodding, silky-hairy**, fragrant, 6 to 12 flowered; petals 5, white, widest at the middle, rounded to flat-tipped, 1/2 to 1 inch long; stamens about 20.

Fruit: June–July, borne on long stalks, globe-shaped, 1/4 to 1/2 inch diameter, dry, **reddish-purple**, tasteless or sweetish; seeds small and numerous (4 to 10).

Leaves: Alternate, simple; blades 2 to 5 inches long, 1 to 2 inches wide; oval to longer than broad, tip pointed, base rounded or heart-shaped, sharply and finely toothed on the margin; smooth or nearly so above, young leaves paler and hairy beneath, usually smooth when mature; leaf stalk 1 1/2 to 2 inches long, slender, hairy at first but smooth later.

Twigs: Reddish-brown, slender, rather crooked, somewhat hairy when young but smooth later; pores numerous and pale.

Trunk: Bark light gray and smooth when young, becoming dark gray with shallow grooves and long ridges; wood dark brown, with a wide, white sapwood, sometimes used for making tool handles. It ranks with persimmon as the heaviest wood among North American trees, and as fifth in hardness.

Habitat: Open rocky woods, bluffs; usually on well-drained slopes.

Range: Northeast Texas, Oklahoma, Arkansas, and Louisiana; east to Florida, north to Newfoundland, and west to Quebec, Ontario, Michigan, and Minnesota; and south to Iowa, Missouri, and Kansas.

Wildlife Uses: Service berry is a valuable wildlife plant, with at least 35 species of birds eating the fruit and 11 species of mammals either eating the fruit or browsing the twigs and foliage.

Remarks: The showy white flowers are among the first woody plants to bloom in spring, appearing before the leaves open. It is occasionally used in landscaping for its showy white flowers and red fruit. The fall foliage is very colorful, turning a pale orange or gold blended with red and green. The fruit is edible and varies in sweetness. It can be eaten raw or cooked in pies, puddings or muffins. Native Americans used the fruit in breadmaking, first making a paste from it, then drying it and mixing it with cornmeal.

The word "service" is a derivation of *sarviss*, which is said to be a modified form of *sorbus*, the name applied to a fruit known to the Romans and resembling that of *Amelanchier*. Shadbush was so named by the European settlers along the Atlantic Coast for the timing of the blooms with the spawning runs of shad.

Amelanchier is from the name of a French province; *arborea* refers to its tree-like character.

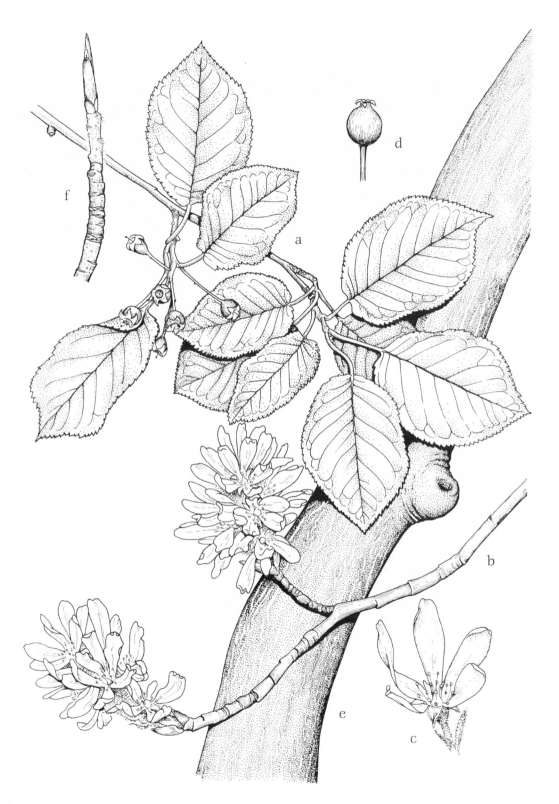

Amelanchier arborea ❀ a. Growth form with fruit cluster, b. Twig with flower clusters, c. Flower, d. Fruit, e. Stem with bark, f. Winter twig

Devil's walking stick

Aralia spinosa L.

Ginseng family (Araliaceae)

Also known as Hercules club, tear-blanket, angelica tree

Appearance: Spiny, few-branched shrub or slender, flat-topped small tree to 35 feet.

Flowers: July–September, the large, branched cluster of flowers is very conspicuous, stalks below the flowers are light yellow, flowers are white, 1/8 inch across, petals 5, white; stamens 5.

Fruit: September–October, in large clusters; fruit black, juice purple, diameter about 1/4 inch; seed solitary, longer than broad, rounded at ends, flattened, dry, brittle, brownish.

Leaves: Alternate, compound, **leaves more than simply once-compound, with the side leaf divisions further divided into additional leaflets; compound leaves generally borne at the top of the trunk; blades 3 to 4 feet long, 2 to 4 feet wide,** each stalk with 5 to 6 pairs of leaflets with a terminal leaflet; leaflets dark green above, paler beneath, 2 to 6 inches long; margin with short-pointed, outwardly projecting teeth, tiny prickles often on center vein of leaflet; lower surface silvery or gray-green, yellow in autumn; leaf stalk 18 to 20 inches long, clasping the base of the stem, prickly.

Trunk: Bark dark brown, grooves shallow, ridges irregular, **armed with stout, light brown to orange prickles**, inner bark yellow, **leaf scars abundant and conspicuous**; wood brown to yellow, weak, soft, light, close-grained.

Habitat: Low upland sandy woods, thickets, wooded slopes, bluffs and ravines.

Range: East Texas, Oklahoma, Arkansas, and Louisiana; east to Florida, north to New Jersey and New York; and west to Ohio, Indiana, Illinois, and Missouri.

Wildlife Uses: The seeds are eaten by many birds and the leaves browsed by white-tailed deer.

Medicinal Uses: Native Americans drank a watered extraction of the bark and root to purify the blood and to treat fever. The water that fresh roots were stored in has been used to treat irritated eyes. At one time the inner bark was used for curing toothaches.

Remarks: The author's first encounter comes from a painful appreciation for the stem's armor when reaching for a trunk to stabilize footing on an unstable slope. The shrub has high ornamental value and is often planted in Europe. It has been cultivated since 1688. A single devil's walking stick tree often forms a colony by sending up new shoots from underground runners. The wood was once used for small articles such as pen racks, button boxes, photograph frames, stools and rocking chair arms. The black fleshy fruits at one time were used for dyeing hair black.

Aralia is from the French-Canadian *Aralie*, the name appended to the original specimens sent to Tournefort, a French botanist, by the Quebec physician, Sarrasin; *spinosa* refers to the spiny trunk and branches.

Aralia spinosa 🌿 a. Growth form with flower clusters, b. Flower cluster, c. Flower, d. Fruit cluster, e. Stem with prickles

Pawpaw

Asimina triloba (L.) Dunal

Custard apple family (Annonaceae)

Appearance: Large shrub to small tree, up to 30 feet tall, with a slender trunk and broad crown; grows in small colonies.

Flowers: March–May, perfect (contains both male and female parts in same flower), **solitary, drooping, developing on previous year's growth along the side of the twig, about 1 inch across, appearing before the leaves; flowers dark reddish-purple**, petals 6, three outer petals much larger; numerous stamens; **flowers emit the odor of fermenting purple grapes**.

Fruit: September–October, **banana-shaped**, 2 to 4 times longer than broad, cylindrical, green at first but turning yellow when ripe, 3 to 5 inches long; pulp sweet, white or yellow, **aromatic, edible with a banana-like taste and custard-like texture**; seeds several, dark brown, large, flattened, about 1 inch long and 1/2 inch wide.

Leaves: Alternate, simple, 2 to 4 times longer than broad, broadest above the middle, 6 to 12 inches long, 3 to 5 inches wide; margins smooth, upper surface green, lower surface pale; **emits an odor when bruised**; leaf stalk short, stout.

Twigs: Slender, olive-brown, often blotched, smooth, becoming rougher when older, and often with a warty surface; **emits a disagreeable odor when crushed; terminal bud velvet brown, lacking scales; flower bud rounded, over winters on previous year's twig**.

Trunk: Bark light ash to dark brown, thin, smooth, later becoming warty with blotches; wood pale yellow, coarse-grained, soft, weak.

Habitat: Grows in dense shade on mesic (moist) lower slopes, ravines, valleys, along streams, and at the base of wooded bluffs.

Range: East Texas, Arkansas, and Louisiana; east to Florida, and north to New York, Ontario; west to Michigan, Illinois, Iowa, eastern Nebraska and eastern Kansas.

Wildlife Uses: The fruit is eaten by eastern kingbird, catbird, robin, veery, red-eyed vireo, bobwhite quail, wild turkey, squirrels, opossum, and raccoon.

Medicinal Uses: Leaves may cause rash; used as an insecticidal, diuretic (causes urination), applied to abscesses; seeds toxic, emetic (induces vomiting), powdered seeds once applied to the heads of children to control lice; fruit edible, also a laxative.

Remarks: Pawpaw produces suckers from the roots, forming groves or thickets. The leaves turn yellow in autumn and remain on the tree late into the season. The fruit is eaten raw or baked, used as a filling for pies, or is combined with eggs, cornstarch, and gelatin for a desert. Although the wood has no commercial use, the inner bark was woven into fiber cloth by Native Americans and pioneers used it for stringing fish. Pawpaw extract has been used experimentally in cancer therapy and has been rated 300 times as potent as taxol, the other, better known plant extract.

Pawpaw is the member of a tropical family and has no close relatives in Missouri. Pawpaw is derived from the Caribbean name for "tree."

Asimina is from the early French name *Asiminier*, which in turn was derived from the American Indian *Arsimin; triloba* refers to the petals, which are in sets of 3.

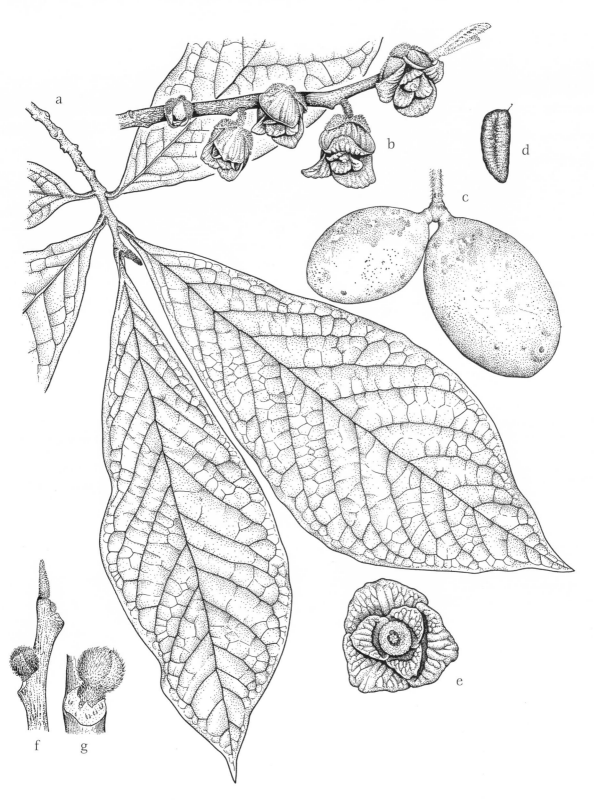

Asimina triloba ❧ a. Growth form, b. Flowers, c. Fruit, d. Seed, e. Flower, f. Twig, g. Leaf scar with flower bud

River birch

Betula nigra L.

Birch family (Betulaceae)

Appearance: Medium-sized tree, up to 80 feet tall, with an irregular, broad spreading crown.

Flowers: April–May, male catkins (a dense, elongated spike of flowers) formed the year before, becoming 1 to 3 1/2 inches long; stamens 4; female catkins formed from buds of the previous year, about 1/2 inch long, upright; flowering as the leaves appear; flowers are wind pollinated.

Fruit: May–June, barrel-shaped, hairy, 1 1/2 inches long, 1/2 inch wide; nutlet (a small, hard, dry nut) about 1/8 inch long.

Leaves: Alternate, simple, somewhat triangular to egg-shaped, 1 1/2 to 3 1/2 inches long, 1 to 2 inches wide; margins densely toothed; upper surface shiny dark green, **lower surface whitish, very hairy**; leaves turn a pale to rich yellow in autumn.

Twigs: New growth very hairy, gradually turning smooth; dark red, slender, shiny, dull reddish-brown in the second year.

Trunk: Bark reddish-brown or grayish, peeling into conspicuous papery strips exposing a light pinkish-tan or cinnamon-brown inner bark; pores dark, elongated; wood light brown, hard, strong, close-grained.

Habitat: Occurs in moist ground along streams and gravel bars; common throughout the state.

Range: From Texas, east to Florida, north to Massachusetts, and west to Minnesota and eastern Kansas.

Wildlife Uses: The seeds are eaten by songbirds and mice; the twigs are eaten by white-tailed deer.

Remarks: Native Americans and European settlers made birch beer by boiling the sap down or adding honey, then fermenting. The inner bark was used for dying fabric, especially wool, light brown or green with a copper mordant (a color fixer). The wood has been used for woodenware and furniture and, in the past, for ox yokes and wooden shoes. River birch has been grown as an ornamental since 1736. It is most striking when planted in groupings in yards and along streams and ponds.

River birch is the only spring seed-dispersing member of its family. It is considered a pioneer species, rapidly colonizing exposed, bare stream banks and gravel bars, stabilizing the soil and developing a forest for other trees to succeed. River birch is intolerant of competition. When shaded, it quickly stagnates and dies. River birch does not tolerate prolonged flooding and is not found on broad river bottoms, such as the Mississippi or the Missouri, that are subject to inundation.

Birch is from Old High German *birka*, for birches, and is related to the word bright, probably referring to the pale bark of some species.

Betula is the ancient classical Latin name of the birch, from *betu*, its Celtic name; *nigra* means "black" but its origin is obscure.

Betula nigra ❦ a. Growth form, b. Female catkin, c. Male catkin, d. Male flower, e. Female flower, f. Fruit, g. Twig with male catkins, h. Leaf scar with leaf bud

Paper mulberry

Broussonetia papyrifera (L.) Vent.

Mulberry family (Moraceae)

Appearance: Large shrub or medium-sized tree, up to 50 feet, with wide-spreading branches; root sprouts common.

Flowers: April–May, male catkins (a dense, elongated spike of flowers) and female flowers are both on the same tree; the yellow male catkins are 2 1/2 to 3 inches long and appear in groups; the female flowers are packed together in the shape of a globe, about 1/2 inch across, hanging.

Fruit: August–September, globe-shaped cluster of seeds with fleshy coatings similar to a raspberry fruit; 3/4 inch across, orange to red.

Leaves: Simple, alternate or opposite, 3 to 8 inches long, egg-shaped, entire to deeply 3- to 5-lobed, conspicuously veined; **3 principal veins arising from the base**; velvety hairy above and below; margin coarsely toothed; **milky sap exudes from the leaf stalks**; leaf stalk 1 to 4 inches long.

Twigs: Moderately stout, zigzag, round, gray-green, with large orange pores, hairy when young, **exuding milky sap when cut**.

Trunk: Bark smooth to somewhat grooved, yellowish-brown to gray-brown, thin; old trees become gnarly; wood light-colored, soft, not very durable.

Habitat: Escapes from cultivation onto open, disturbed sites, near homes, along roadways, and on farmlands.

Range: Native to Asia; introduced in the United States from New Mexico, Texas, Oklahoma, and Missouri to New York and southward.

Wildlife Uses: Not significant to any native wildlife species.

Remarks: Paper mulberry was introduced from Asia in about 1750. In Asian and Pacific countries, it has been known for almost 1,500 years as a plant whose bark can be used to make paper of various grades up to the highest quality for use in the production of flowers, umbrellas, lanterns, as well as lamps, dolls and toys, cloth, and others. The best quality materials are obtained from 6- to 12-month-old plants, with these being preferred by the factories. Most paper mulberry is currently being obtained from north and northeast Thailand together with Laos.

Paper mulberry is a rapid grower and sprouts freely from the roots. The pollen has been known to produce hay fever in some cases.

The common name, mulberry, is an ancient term for the closely related genus *Morus*.

Broussonetia is named in honor of Auguste Broussonet, a French naturalist; *papyrifera* refers to the use of the bark in papermaking.

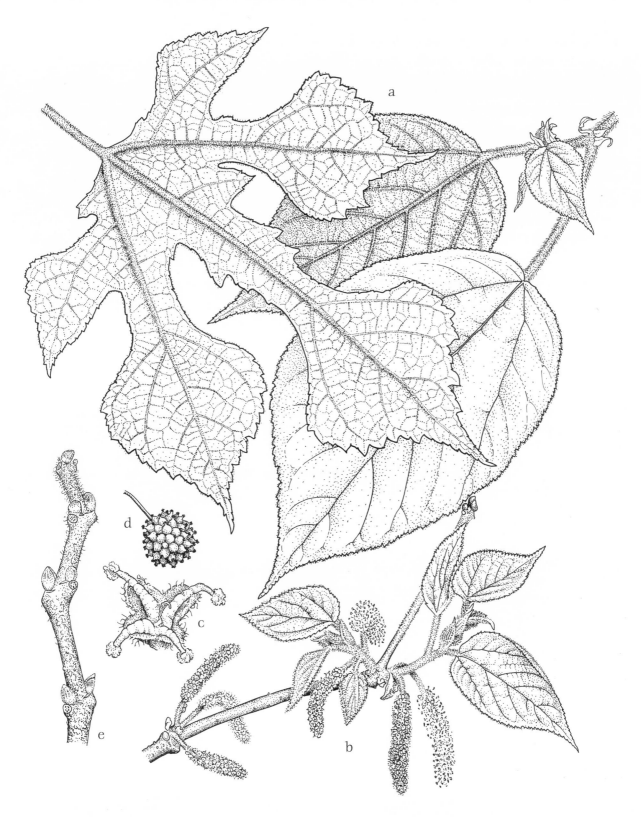

Broussonetia papyrifera ❧ a. Leaf shapes, b. Male catkins, c. Female flower, d. Fruit, e. Twig

Woolly buckthorn

Bumelia lanuginosa (Michaux) Pers.

Sapodilla family (Sapotaceae)

Also called chittim wood, false buckthorn, gum-elastic, gum bully

Appearance: Shrub or an irregularly shaped tree to 40 feet with thorns, short spur branches and milky sap.

Flowers: June–July, in dense clusters of 5 to 30 flowers at the leaf/stem axis, flowers white, about 1/8 inch long; petals 5, fused to form a tube; fragrant; stamens 5.

Fruit: September–October, borne on slender, drooping stalks, oval, about 1/2 inch long, shiny, black, fleshy, bittersweet, edible; seed solitary, large, brown, rounded, 1/4 to 1/2 inch long.

Leaves: Alternate or clustered, often on short lateral spurs, longer than broad, widest near the tip, tip rounded or blunt, base wedge-shaped, margin entire, blade length 1 to 3 inches, width to 1 inch, leathery, shiny green and smooth above, **lower surface varying from rusty to white or gray-woolly**; leaf stalk short, averaging about 1/2 inch long, densely hairy with matted wool; leaf stalks when broken producing a gummy or milky sap; leaves turn yellowish-green in autumn.

Twigs: Gray to reddish-brown, zigzag, slender, stiff, **with thorns; twigs hairy at first with gray, white or rusty matted hairs; twigs when broken, producing a gummy or milky sap.**

Trunk: Dark brown or grayish, with shallow grooves and forming a network of ridges with thickened scales; wood hard, heavy, yellow or brown, close-grained.

Habitat: Found in dry or open rocky woodlands, glades and bluff escarpments, crevices of bluffs, usually on upland ridges and slopes, rarely in valleys and ravine bottoms.

Range: East Texas, Oklahoma, Arkansas, and Louisiana; east to Florida, north to Virginia, and west to Illinois, Missouri, and Kansas; also in Mexico.

Wildlife Uses: Birds are very fond of the fruit, eating it as soon as it is barely ripe. White-tailed deer eat the fruit and the leaves, and cave-dwelling wood rats take leaves into their dens.

Remarks: Woolly buckthorn is also known as *Sideroxylon lanuginosum* Michx. This is the last of the native shrubs or small trees to come into flowering in Missouri. The foliage is long-persisting, and in late autumn turns a yellowish-green. The black fruit is edible, but not tasty, and has been reported to produce stomach disturbances and dizziness if eaten in quantity. The wood is used in small quantities for tool handles and cabinetmaking. A milky-colored gum is freely exuded from wounds on the trunk and branches. The tree has been in cultivation since 1806.

Bumelia is the ancient Greek name for the European Ash; *lanuginosa* refers to the woolly hairs of the leaf.

Bumelia lanuginosa ❧ a. Growth form, b. Twig with flower cluster, c. Fruit on short spur branch, d. Winter twig with short spur branches and thorns

Southern buckthorn

Bumelia lycioides (L.) Pers.

Sapodilla family (Sapotaceae)

Also called Carolina buckthorn, ironwood, smooth bumelia

Appearance: Large shrub or small tree to 25 feet with spreading branches, milky sap, spur branches, and stout thorns.

Flowers: June–July, in dense clusters of 10 to 50 flowers at the leaf/stem axis, flowers white, about 1/8 inch long, about 1/5 inch wide, petals 5, fused to form a tube; stamens 5.

Fruit: September–October, oval to egg-shaped, black 1/4 to 2/3 inch long, thin-skinned, pulpy, bittersweet, edible; seed solitary, large, smooth, egg-shaped, abruptly pointed at the tip.

Leaves: Solitary or clustered on short lateral spurs, except on vigorous growth, simple, alternate, blades 2 to 6 inches long, 1/2 to 2 inches wide, margin entire, tip pointed, rarely blunt, base gradually tapering; upper surface bright green and smooth, **lower surface smooth**, paler, veins netlike; leaf stalk slender, 1/3 to 1 inch long, hairy at first but smooth later, when broken, producing a gummy or milky sap.

Twigs: Rather stout, thick, with lateral spurlike branchlets, with or without stout thorns at the leaf base, **twigs smooth**, shiny, reddish-brown to gray, when broken, producing a gummy or milky sap.

Trunk: Smooth, thin, reddish-brown to gray, scales small and thin; wood brown to yellow, close-grained, heavy, hard, not strong.

Habitat: Found in low alluvial woods of floodplains and river bottom land, and thickets along streams. Known only from the Bootheel in southeastern Missouri.

Range: East Texas, Arkansas, and Louisiana; east to Florida, north to Virginia, and west to Kentucky, southern Indiana, southern Illinois, and southeast Missouri.

Wildlife Uses: The fruit is eaten by a number of species of birds. The leaves are browsed by white-tailed deer.

Remarks: Southern buckthorn is also known as *Sideroxylon lycioides* L. Missouri specimens of southern buckthorn frequently have thickened, spindle-shaped swellings of woody stems with small holes, apparently resulting from an insect laying its eggs in the plant tissue. This shrub is considered uncommon in southeastern Missouri due to loss of habitat. The Missouri Bootheel has experienced widespread clearing of once extensive bottomland forests and swamps for agricultural purposes. Recent surveys on Missouri Department of Conservation lands have located small populations of southern buckthorn.

Bumelia is the ancient Greek name for the European Ash; *lycioides* applies to the Lyciumlike fruit, which in turn is named for Lycia, an ancient country in Asia Minor.

Bumelia lycioides ❀ a. Growth form with flower cluster and thorns, b. Stem with fruit and thorn

Musclewood

Carpinus caroliniana Walter

Birch family (Betulaceae)

Also called blue beech, hornbeam

Appearance: Tall shrub or small tree to 35 feet, with a gray trunk and pendulous branches.

Flowers: April–May, flowers appearing before or as leaves emerge, male and female flowers separate but on the same tree; male flowers green, borne in long cylinder-shaped catkins (a hanging spike of flowers), 1 to 1 1/2 inches, scales of catkin triangular-shaped, tip pointed, green below, reddish above; stamens numerous; female catkins about 1/2 inch.

Fruit: August–October, nutlet or seed about 1/3 inch long, oval, borne at base of a 3-lobed bract (modified leaf), many together forming long hanging clusters 3 to 6 inches long. The middle lobe of the bract is lance-shaped and entire or toothed, and much longer than the lateral lobes.

Leaves: Simple, alternate, longer than broad, egg-shaped, tip pointed, base rounded, wedge-shaped, or heart-shaped, margin densely-toothed, dull bluish-green and smooth above, paler and hairy in axils of the veins below; leaf blade usually with 9 to 15 veins on each side of central vein; leaf stalk about 1/3 inch long, slender, hairy.

Twigs: Slender, zigzag, gray or red, smooth.

Trunk: Bark s**mooth, tight, thin, bluish-gray**, sometimes with darker or lighter blotches (some gray blotches may be due to crustose lichens), **trunk fluted into muscle-like ridges, hence the common name**; wood light brown, sapwood lighter, strong, hard, tough, heavy, close-grained.

Habitat: Found on north-facing bluffs, in rich woods at the base of bluffs, rocky slopes along streams, ravine bottoms, low wooded valleys, and moist woodland.

Range: East Texas, Oklahoma, Arkansas, and Louisiana; east to Florida, north to Nova Scotia, and west to Ontario, Michigan, Minnesota, Iowa, and Missouri.

Wildlife Uses: The seed is eaten by at least nine species of birds. Catkins and buds rank as one of the most important ruffed grouse foods by volume consumed during late autumn, winter and early spring. Quail occasionally eat the seeds, which are also considered a preferred winter food of turkeys. Small amounts of seeds, bark and wood are eaten by cottontail rabbits, beavers, and fox and gray squirrels. White-tailed deer will browse the twigs and foliage.

Remarks: The wood is used for golf clubs, handles, fuel, mallets, cogs, levers and wedges. It ranks as one of the hardest and strongest woods known in eastern North America—surpassing oak, hickory, locust and persimmon. Only flowering dogwood is harder. The tree has been cultivated as an ornamental since 1812.

The name hornbeam refers to the extreme hardness of the wood—"horn" for toughness, and "beam," an Old English word for tree.

Carpinus is the classical name for hornbeam; *caroliniana* refers to the states of Carolina, probably where it was first described.

Carpinus caroliniana ❀ a. Growth form with hanging fruit clusters in bracts, b. Pair of three-lobed bracts, c. Male (l) and female (r) flower clusters, d. Male flower, e. Female flower, f. Stem

Water hickory

Carya aquatica (Michaux f.) Nutt.

Walnut family (Juglandaceae)

Appearance: Medium to large tree, up to 100 feet tall, with a long, clear trunk, **buttressed (enlarged) base**, and a narrow, irregular crown.

Flowers: April–May, male and female flowers separate on the same tree, male catkins (a dense, elongated spike of flowers) hairy, 2 1/2 to 3 inches long, solitary or in threes, stamens usually 6; female flowers 2 to 6 per spike. For an illustration of the flower see p. 382

Fruit: September–October, pear to egg-shaped, often clustered, 1 to 1 1/2 inches long, about 1 inch wide; **noticeably flattened in comparison with other hickories, with a thin, 4-winged husk (with bright yellow scales)**, splitting at the base; nut flat, reddish, 4-angled or winged, with shallow furrows, shell thin; kernel dark reddish-brown, bitter, not edible.

Leaves: Alternate, feather-like arrangement, 9 to 15 inches long, composed of 7 to 15 leaflets; leaflets lance- to egg-shaped, curved, 2 to 5 inches long, tip tapering to a long point, **margins finely toothed to inconspicuous**; upper surface dark green, smooth, lower surface hairy, especially along the veins; leaf stalk hairy; leaves turn yellow in autumn.

Twigs: Slender, reddish-brown or gray, hairy; **end bud slightly flattened, covered with minute, yellow scales**; pores pale.

Trunk: Bark grayish-brown, sometimes tinged with red; **splitting freely into long, loose, plate-like shaggy scales**, brittle; wood dark brown, heavy, hard, brittle, close-grained.

Habitat: Found in the swamps and wet bottomland forests of southeastern Missouri's Bootheel.

Range: East Texas, Oklahoma, Arkansas, and Louisiana; east to Florida, north to Virginia, and east to southern Indiana, southern Illinois, and southeastern Missouri.

Wildlife Uses: The nuts are swallowed by wood ducks and mallards and eaten by squirrels and small mammals.

Remarks: The wood is hard to work, brittle, and considered inferior to that of other hickories. It is used in small amounts for fuel, posts, and props. Water hickory is a slow-growing tree that generally doesn't begin producing fruits until after age 20.

Water hickory readily hybridizes with pecan where the two species occur on the same site. Water hickory is found in swamps growing with bald cypress, water tupelo, swamp cottonwood, overcup oak, water locust, and Drummond's red maple.

The name hickory was first referenced in 1671 and is taken from the Algonquian (perhaps Powhatan) as a shortening of *pockerchicory* or a similar word for this genus in the walnut family.

Carya is the ancient Greek name for walnut; *aquatica* refers to the tree's wet habitat.

Carya aquatica ✿ a. Growth form, b. Fruit, c. Nut, d. Twig

Bitternut hickory

Carya cordiformis (Wangenh.) K. Koch

Walnut family (Junglandaceae)

Appearance: Medium-sized tree, up to 80 feet tall, with a long, clear trunk and broad spreading crown.

Flowers: April–May, male and female flowers separate on the same tree, male catkins in threes, slightly hairy, 3 to 4 inches long, stamens 4; female catkins mostly in ones or twos. For an illustration of the flower, see p. 382

Fruit: September–October, solitary or paired, pear- to globe-shaped, small, 1 to 1 1/4 inches long; *husk light yellow-green with yellow scales*, thin, splitting below the middle, partially winged along the lines where it splits; nut globe- to egg-shaped, slightly flattened, tip sharp-pointed, 3/4 to 1 inch long; kernel is bitter.

Leaves: Alternate, feather-like arrangement, 6 to 12 inches long, composed of *7 to 9 leaflets*; leaflets usually broadest above the center, 3 to 6 inches long, 1 to 2 inches wide, end leaflet with a short stalk; tip pointed, margin toothed; upper surface shiny, dark yellow-green, smooth; lower surface paler, hairy; leaves turn yellow in autumn.

Twigs: Stout, greenish-brown to reddish-brown, shiny, hairy at first and smooth later; pores numerous, small, pale; **buds bright yellow in winter**.

Trunk: Bark grayish-brown, with shallow narrow grooves and flat ridges, the smooth bark does not become scaly or shaggy; wood heavy, hard, strong, durable.

Habitat: Occurs in low woods along streams and river bottoms and at the base of mesic (moist) slopes and cliffs.

Range: East Texas, Oklahoma, Arkansas, Missouri, and Louisiana; east to Florida, and north to Maine, Ontario, Minnesota, eastern Nebraska, and eastern Kansas.

Wildlife Uses: The nuts are eaten by squirrels, mice, and white-tailed deer. Squirrels also eat the buds. Like other hickories, its leaves are fed on by large, showy moths, such as the luna moth, several colorful underwing moths, and the giant regal moth with its impressive 6-inch wingspan and its remarkable larvae called the hickory horned devil, the largest caterpillar in North America.

Remarks: Bitternut hickory was first cultivated in 1689. It makes a good park and lawn tree because it casts a relatively light and open shade which allows grass and other plantings to thrive under its canopy. For a hickory, it is the fastest grower but one of the shortest lived, up to 200 years. Fruit production begins at 25 to 30 years of age and then alternates between a year of heavy production and 2 or 3 years of light production. Early settlers pressed an oil from the nut to use as a remedy for rheumatism. They also burned the oil in their crude lamps. The bitter nuts are not edible. Like other hickories, its wood has shock resistant qualities and is used for striking tools such as hammers. It was formerly used for wooden wheels. The wood is reported to be the best fuel for giving meats the true "hickory smoked" flavor.

The name hickory was first referenced in 1671 and is taken from the Algonquian (perhaps Powhatan) as a shortening of *pockerchicory* or a similar word for this genus in the walnut family.

Carya is the ancient Greek name for walnut; *cordiformis* means "heart-shaped," in reference either to the fruit or the base of the leaflets.

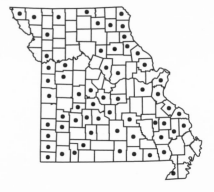

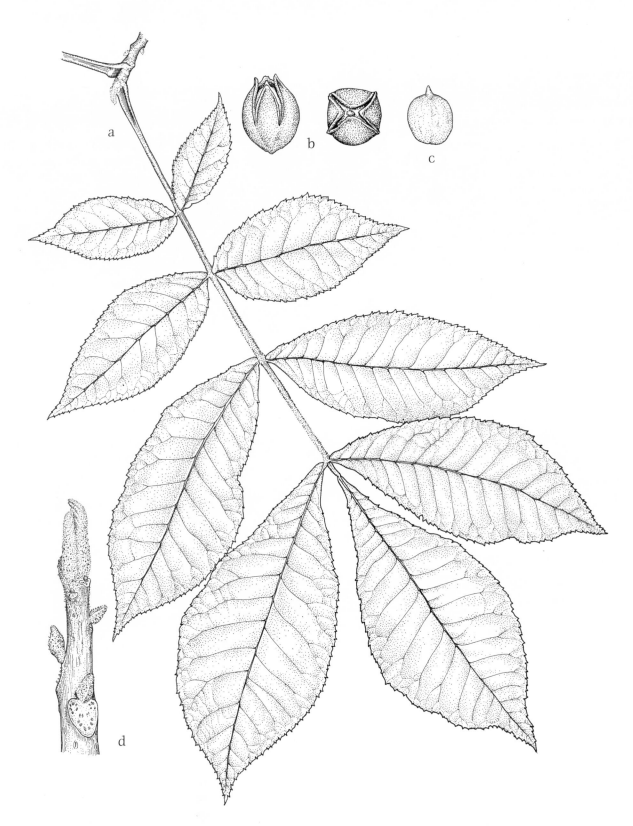

Carya cordiformis ❧ a. Leaf, b. Fruit, c. Nut, d. Twig

Pignut hickory

Carya glabra (Miller) Sweet

Walnut family (Juglandaceae)

Appearance: Medium-sized tree, up to 80 feet tall, with a rather narrow crown, 2 to 4 times longer than broad.

Flowers: April–May, male and female flowers separate on the same tree, male catkins 3-branched, 2 to 2 1/2 inches long, yellowish-green; stamens 4; female flowers few. For an illustration of the flower, see p. 382

Fruit: September–October, variable in size and shape, but usually pear- to egg-shaped, often with a neck-like base, somewhat flattened, about 1 1/4 inches long, 3/4 inch wide; husk dark brown, splitting open late along 2 to 4 lines or sometimes not at all; nut pear-shaped, with a short beak, somewhat flattened, brownish, thick-shelled; kernel sweet or somewhat bitter, hard to remove.

Leaves: Alternate, feather-like arrangement, 8 to 12 inches long **with 5 (rarely 7) leaflets**; leaflets lance-shaped but narrow at the base or near the middle; margin toothed, tip tapering to a point; upper surface yellowish-green and smooth, under surface paler and smooth or hairy along the veins; leaves turn bright yellow in autumn.

Twigs: Moderately slender, reddish-brown, smooth; pores pale colored.

Trunk: Bark gray, **thin, tight, rough from numerous shallow, criss-crossing cracks forming close, flattened scales**; wood brown, heavy, hard, strong, durable, elastic, close-grained.

Habitat: Occurs in dry upland woods, usually in acid soils derived from chert, sandstone, or igneous rock; also sandy or gravelly soils of dry upland wooded ridges in southeastern Missouri's Crowley Ridge.

Range: From east Texas, Arkansas, and Louisiana; east to Florida, north to Maine, and west to Ontario, Michigan, Illinois, Missouri, southeastern Nebraska, and eastern Kansas.

Wildlife Uses: The nuts are eaten by squirrels, mice, and white-tailed deer. Squirrels also eat the buds. Like other hickories, its leaves are eaten by large, showy moths, such as the luna moth, several colorful underwing moths, and the giant regal moth with its impressive 6-inch wingspan and its remarkable larvae called the hickory horned devil, the largest caterpillar in North America.

Remarks: Pignut hickory has been cultivated since 1750. It is a slow to moderately fast growing tree, depending upon soil conditions. Normally, 25 to 30 years are required before the trees begin to produce nuts and twice the age is needed to reach full production. The wood is used for fuel, tool handles, agricultural implements, and wagons.

Another hickory, called false shagbark or red hickory, *Carya ovalis*, has been reduced to a variety under *C. glabra* because its characteristics are so similar.

Apparently named pignut for the sometimes bitter nuts, which only were considered fit for pigs. The name hickory was first referenced in 1671 and is taken from the Algonquian (perhaps Powhatan) as a shortening of *pockerchicory* or a similar word for this genus in the walnut family.

Carya is the ancient Greek name for walnut; *glabra* refers to the smooth character of the leaves and leaf stalk.

Carya glabra ❧ a. Growth form, b. Fruit, c. Nut, d. Twig

Pecan

Carya illinoinensis (Wangenheim) K. Koch

Walnut family (Juglandaceae)

Appearance: Large tree, up to 150 feet tall, with a narrow, pyramid-shaped crown in the forest, broad and rounded in the open; largest of all the hickory trees.

Flowers: April–May, male and female flowers separate on the same tree; male catkins 3 to 6 inches long, usually 3-clustered; stamens 5 to 6, yellowish; female flowers fewer, hairy, yellow. For an illustration of the flower, see p. 382

Fruit: September–October, in clusters of 3 to 10, persistent; husk thin, aromatic, reddish-brown, winged, **splitting along 4 ridges at maturity to expose the nut**; nut thin, 1 to 3 inches long, 2 to 4 times longer than broad, **cylindrical**, pointed at the tip, light brown to reddish-brown, with irregular black markings on the shell; **kernel sweet and edible**.

Leaves: Alternate, feather-like arrangement, 9 to 20 inches long, **composed of 9 to 17 leaflets; leaflets curved**, 2 to 4 times longer than broad, lance-shaped, 4 to 8 inches long, pointed at the tip, margins toothed, **side veins branching near the tip**; upper surface dark green and smooth, lower surface paler, smooth to hairy; leaves aromatic when crushed; leaves turning yellow in autumn.

Twigs: Stout, reddish-brown, hairy, with numerous elongated orange-brown pores; **bud on end of twig yellow-brown**.

Trunk: Bark grayish-brown to light brown when young, becoming dark reddish-brown with age, ridges long, flat, loose; wood reddish-brown, heavy, hard, brittle, not strong, coarse-grained.

Habitat: Occurs in rich, moist bottomland soils.

Range: Texas, Oklahoma, Arkansas, and Louisiana; north to Tennessee, Kentucky, and Indiana; and west to Illinois, Missouri, and eastern Kansas.

Wildlife Uses: The nut is eaten by a variety of larger birds; squirrels, other small rodents, opossum, raccoon, white-tailed deer.

Remarks: Pecan has been cultivated since 1766. Since then, over 500 horticultural selections have been made for the size, taste, and ease of shelling of the nuts; and the hardiness and annual production of nuts by the trees. Pecan is one of the most important cultivated nuts of North America. The wood is not important commercially, but it is occasionally used for furniture, flooring, cabinets, and agricultural implements.

The word "pecan" first appeared in writing in 1712. It is from the Algonquin *paccan*, which means "hard-shelled nut."

Carya is the ancient Greek name for walnut; *illinoinensis* refers to the state of Illinois. The tree at one time was called "Illinois nuts," or "Mississippi nuts" by those in the East. Long before settlers crossed over the Allegheny Mountains into the fertile wilderness of the Mississippi Valley, traders and fur trappers brought the pecan nuts over the mountains with their beaver skins. One of the first to plant pecan trees was Thomas Jefferson at his Monticello estate. *Carya illinoinensis* is the correct spelling, despite the widespread use of *Carya illinoensis*.

Carya illinoinensis ❦ a. Leaf and fruit, b. Female flower, c. Female flower cluster,
d. Male catkins, e. Single male flowers, f. Fruit, g. Nut, h. Twig

Shellbark hickory

Carya laciniosa (Michaux f.) Loudon

Walnut family (Juglandaceae)

Also called kingnut hickory

Appearance: Large trees, up to 130 feet tall, with short, stout limbs, narrow crown, and shaggy bark.

Flowers: April–May, male and female flowers separate on the same tree, male catkins in threes, 5 to 8 inches long; stamens 3 to 10; female flowers 2 to 5. For an illustration of the flower, see p. 382

Fruit: September–October, solitary or in clusters of 2 to 3, egg-shaped to nearly globe-shaped, depressed at the tip, 1 to 3 inches long; husk light to dark brown, smooth to downy, hard, woody, 1/4 to 1/2 inch thick, **splitting easily along the 4 ribs at maturity**; nut yellowish-white, globe- to pear-shaped, flattened, pointed at the tip, hard, thick-shelled; kernel sweet; **largest of all the hickory nuts**.

Leaves: Alternate, feather-like arrangement, **largest of all the hickory species, 10 to 24 inches long with 5 to 9 leaflets, usually 7**; leaflets egg-shaped to lance-shaped and 2 to 4 times longer than broad, tip pointed, margin finely toothed; dark green, smooth and shiny above; pale green, hairy beneath; end leaflet with a stalk; **leaf stalk often persistent on the tree after the leaves have fallen**; leaves turn yellow in autumn.

Twigs: Stout, dark brown to reddish-orange; pores narrow and elongated.

Trunk: Bark gray, **separating into long, thin, shaggy plates hanging loosely, with ends curving away from the trunk**; wood dark brown, hard, strong, durable, heavy, very flexible, close-grained.

Habitat: Occurs in rich bottomland soils of valleys along streams and in river floodplains.

Range: Northeast Texas, Oklahoma, Arkansas, and Louisiana; east to Georgia; north to New York and west to Ontario, Minnesota, Iowa, and eastern Kansas.

Wildlife Uses: Important food source for gray squirrels.

Remarks: Shellbark hickory has been cultivated since 1800. The nuts are sweet and very rich in fats and oils and were an important food source for Native Americans. They, along with European settlers, used the inner bark for basketry and furniture (chair bottoms). The wood is used for snowshoe rims, barrel hoops, ladders, and tool handles.

Shellbark hickory is becoming rather scarce because it grows in rich, deep soils in river bottoms, many of which have been cleared to grow crops. It is a slow growing tree that makes an excellent shade tree in moist soil.

The "shell" from shellbark is from the Teutonic (Northern European) root word *skal*, which means to "peel off or separate." The name hickory was first referenced in 1671 and is taken from the Algonquian (perhaps Powhatan) as a shortening of *pockerchicory* or a similar word for this genus in the walnut family.

Carya is the ancient Greek name for walnut; *laciniosa* refers to the deep furrowing and splitting of the bark.

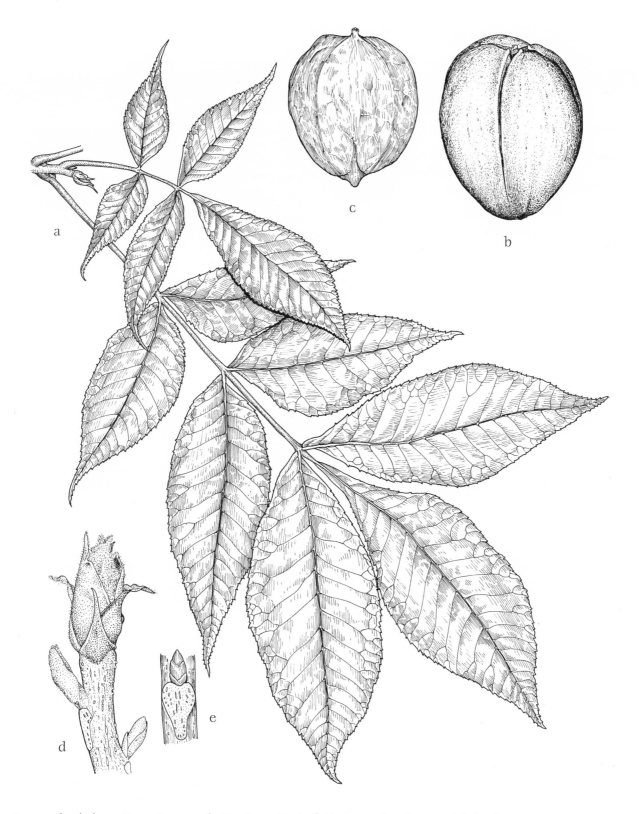

Carya laciniosa ❧ a. Leaves, b. Fruit, c. Nut, d. Twig, e. Leaf scar with bud

Shagbark hickory

Carya ovata (Miller) K. Koch

Walnut family (Juglandaceae)

Appearance: Medium-sized to large tree, up to 100 feet tall, with a crown 2 to 4 times longer than broad and shaggy bark.

Flowers: April–May, male and female flowers separate on the same tree, male catkins in threes after leaves appear, 4 to 5 inches long, slender, green, hairy; stamens 4; female flowers 2 to 5, cone-shaped. For an illustration of the flower, see p. 382

Fruit: September–October, solitary or in clusters up to 3, oval or round, 1 1/4 to 2 inches long; husk blackish- to reddish-brown, smooth or hairy, slightly depressed at the tip, 1/4 to 1/2 inch thick, **splitting to the base in four lines**; nut light brownish-white, oval, somewhat flattened, with 4 ridges, shell thin; kernel light brown, aromatic, sweet, edible.

Leaves: Alternate, feather-like arrangement, 8 to 17 inches long, composed of 3 to 5 (rarely 7) leaflets; leaflets lance- to pear- to egg-shaped, 4 to 7 inches long, with end leaflet stalked; upper 3 leaflets considerably larger than lower pair; pointed at the tip, **margins toothed with tufts of short hairs along the outer edge of the teeth**; upper surface yellowish-green, smooth, lower surface paler and smooth or hairy; leaves turn golden yellow in autumn.

Twigs: Stout, brown, and hairy when young, becoming gray and smooth; pores pale and elongated; outer bud scales loose but persistent.

Trunk: Bark gray, **separating into thick, long, shaggy strips, free at one end or both ends, and curved outward**; wood light brown, heavy, hard, strong, durable, flexible, close-grained.

Habitat: Occurs in bottomland forests in valleys along streams and in upland forests on slopes and ridges.

Range: East Texas, Oklahoma, Arkansas, Missouri, and Louisiana; east to Alabama, north to Maine and Quebec, and west to Minnesota, eastern Nebraska, and eastern Kansas.

Wildlife Uses: The nuts are eaten by squirrels, mice, and white-tailed deer. Squirrels also eat the buds. Like other hickories, its leaves are fed on by large, showy moths, such as the luna moth, several colorful underwing moths, and the giant regal moth with its impressive 6-inch wingspan and its remarkable larvae called the hickory horned devil, the largest caterpillar in North America. Shagbark and shellbark hickory, because of their loose bark, provide summer shelter for some bats, especially the endangered Indiana bat.

Remarks: Shagbark hickory has been cultivated since 1911. Over 75 horticultural varieties have been developed mostly for large, sweet, easy-to-crack nuts. The wood is aromatic and burns long with little or no smoke and is used to produce high-quality charcoal, also handles for axes and other tools, athletic goods, agricultural implements, baskets, wagons and, at one time, wagon wheels.

The name hickory was first referenced in 1671 and is taken from the Algonquian (perhaps Powhatan) as a shortening of *pockerchicory* or a similar word for this genus in the walnut family.

Carya is the ancient Greek name for walnut; *ovata* refers to the ovate (egg-shaped) leaves.

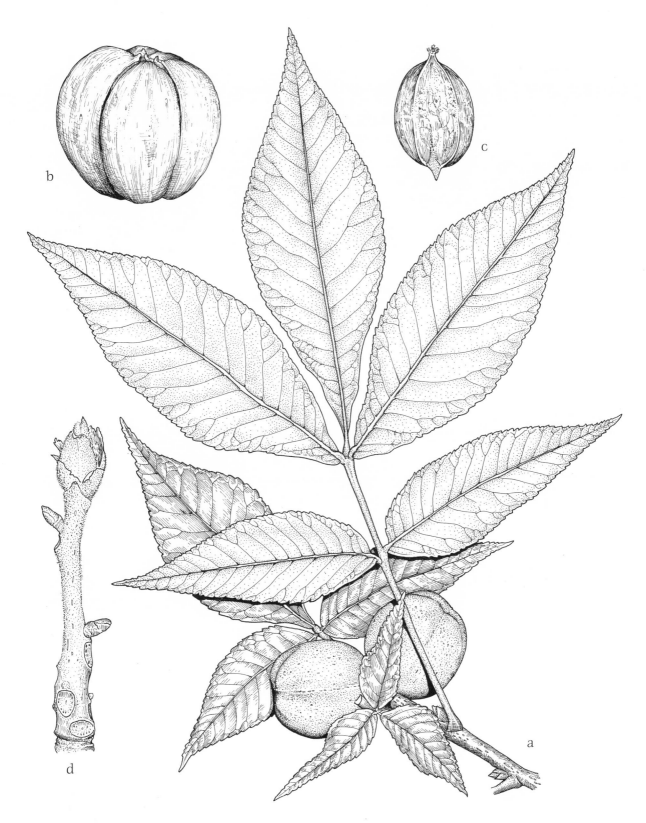

Carya ovata ❦ a. Leaves with fruit, b. Fruit, c. Nut, d. Twig

Sand hickory

Carya pallida (Ashe) Engelm. & Graebn.

Walnut family (Juglandaceae)

Appearance: Small to medium trees, up to 50 feet tall, but sometimes up to 100 feet on richer sites in the southeastern United States; forming a spreading crown with upper branches stout, erect; lower branches somewhat drooping.

Flowers: April–May, male and female flowers separate on the same tree, male catkins in threes, 2 to 2 1/2 inches long, yellowish-green; stamens 4; female flowers 2 to 6 on short spikes. For an illustration of the flower, see p. 382

Fruit: September–October, solitary or in clusters, pear- or globe-shaped, 1/2 to 1 1/2 inches long, dark brown, with fine hairs when young and **covered with minute reddish-brown scales**; husk thin, turning dark brown at maturity, late in splitting on 4 lines; nut small, sweet, edible but sometimes bitter.

Leaves: Alternate, feather-like arrangement, 6 to 15 inches long, with 5 to 7 (rarely 9) **leaflets; leaflets 4 to 6 times longer than broad**, lance- or pear-shaped, 4 to 6 inches long, end 3 leaflets the longest; pointed at the tip, margin toothed, upper surface yellowish-green, smooth; **lower surface paler, more or less hairy with silvery scales**; leaf stalk hairy with silvery scales; leaves turn yellow in autumn.

Twigs: Slender, reddish-brown when young and **covered with silvery hairs and minute scales**; older twigs gray to almost black, smooth; **buds covered with silvery hairs and minute scales**.

Trunk: Bark gray to black, **tight, not scaly**, ridges rough, forming a diamond shape, grooves deep; wood brown, moderately strong, hard, durable.

Habitat: In Missouri, found only in the Bootheel on dry sandy or gravelly soils in upland areas.

Range: Louisiana, east to northwestern Florida, north to New Jersey and Delaware, and west to Virginia, Kentucky, southern Illinois, Missouri, and Arkansas.

Wildlife Uses: Nuts are eaten by squirrels, smaller rodents, and larger birds.

Remarks: Like all hickories, trees are difficult to transplant because of the large taproots. The wood is used for tool handles and as fuel because, like other hickories, the dense wood has a high heating value.

The name hickory was first referenced in 1671 and is taken from the Algonquian (perhaps Powhatan) as a shortening of *pockerchicory* or a similar word for this genus in the walnut family. The common name refers to the type of soil where it grows.

Carya is the ancient Greek name for walnut; *pallida* refers to the pale lower surface of the leaves.

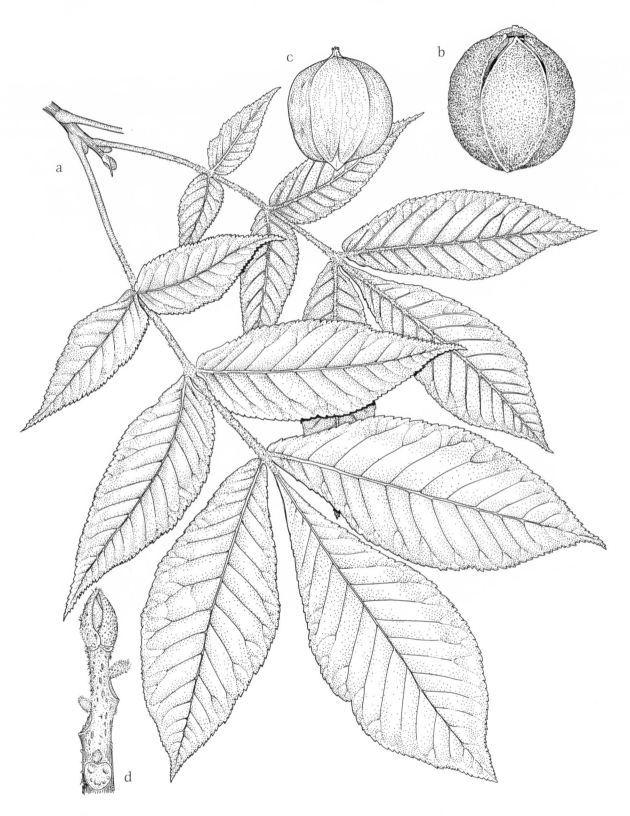

Carya pallida ❧ a. Leaves, b. Fruit, c. Nut, d. Twig

Black hickory

Carya texana Buckley

Walnut family (Juglandaceae)

Also called Ozark pignut hickory

Appearance: Small to medium trees, up to 80 feet tall, with short, crooked branches forming a narrow crown.

Flowers: April–May, male and female flowers separate on the same tree, male catkins in threes, 2 to 3 inches long; stamens 4 to 5; female flowers 1 to 2 with reddish hairs on all parts. For an illustration of the flower, see p. 382

Fruit: September–October, solitary or in small clusters, globe- to pear-shaped, 1 1/4 to 2 inches long; husk thin, dark brown, **covered with yellow scales**, splitting to the base along 4 lines; nut globe- or pear-shaped, somewhat flattened, reddish-brown; kernel small, rounded, sweet, edible.

Leaves: Alternate, feather-like arrangement, 8 to 12 inches long, with 5 to 7 leaflets; leaflets lance- to pear-shaped, 4 to 6 inches long, margin toothed, tip pointed; upper surface dark green, shiny, **lower surface yellow-green with rusty hairs; leaf stalks with rusty hairs and minute scales**; leaves turning yellow in autumn.

Twigs: Slender, often crooked, brown, with rusty hairs and scales when young, becoming grayish-brown and smooth later; with occasional elongated, raised pores.

Trunk: Bark dark gray to black, **tight, not scaly**, with irregular, blocky ridges, broken into deep grooves; wood brown, hard, brittle, durable, close-grained.

Habitat: Usually in acid soils derived from chert, sandstone, or igneous rock in rocky or dry upland woods.

Range: Louisiana and Texas, north to Oklahoma, southeastern Kansas, Arkansas, and Missouri; east to Illinois and Indiana.

Wildlife Uses: Nuts are eaten by squirrels and mice. Squirrels also eat the buds. Like other hickories, its leaves are fed on by large, showy moths, such as the luna moth, several colorful underwing moths, and the giant regal moth with its impressive 6-inch wingspan and its remarkable larvae called the hickory horned devil, the largest caterpillar in North America.

Remarks: The strong, hard wood is brittle and commonly used for fuel. The thick shell of the nut makes the kernel hard to extract but hogs sometimes crack them, hence the reference to the other common name of Ozark pignut hickory.

The name hickory was first referenced in 1671 and is taken from the Algonquian (perhaps Powhatan) as a shortening of *pockerchicory* or a similar word for this genus in the walnut family. The common name, black hickory, refers to the black bark.

Carya is the ancient Greek name for walnut; *texana* refers to the state of Texas.

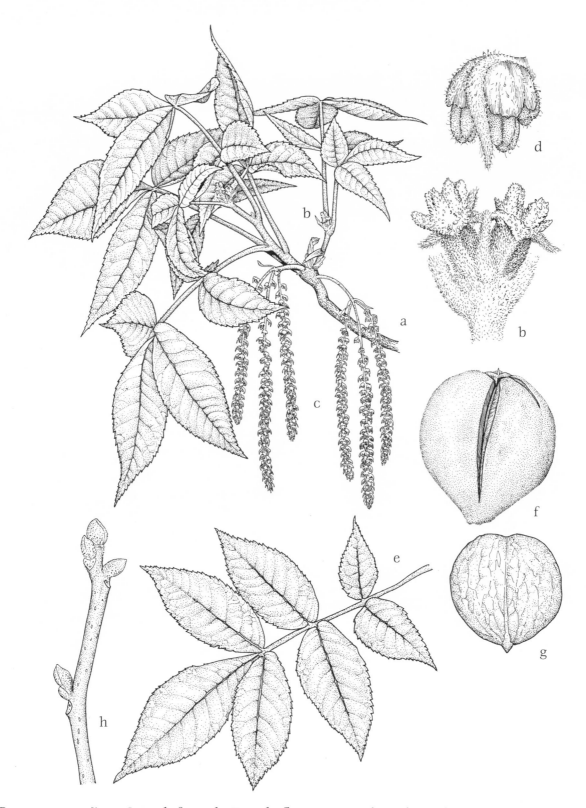

Carya texana ❧ a. Growth form, b. Female flowers, c. Male catkins, d. Male flower, e. Leaf, f. Fruit, g. Nut, h. Twig

Mockernut hickory

Carya tomentosa (Poiret) Nutt.

Walnut family (Juglandaceae)

Also called white hickory

Appearance: Large trees, up to 100 feet tall, with a narrow to broadly rounded crown, with stout, ascending branches.

Flowers: April–May, male and female flowers separate on the same tree, male catkins in threes, 4 to 5 inches long, hairy; stamens 4; female flowers 2 to 5 in hairy spikes. For an illustration of the flower, see p. 382

Fruit: September–October, solitary or in pairs, variable in size and shape, usually globe- to egg-shaped, 1 1/2 to 3 1/2 inches long, tip pointed; husk dark reddish-brown, woody, hairy or smooth, splitting along 4 lines to near the base; nut globe- or pear-shaped to longer than broad, somewhat flattened with 4 prominent ridges, brownish-white or reddish, shell thick, hard; kernel dark brown, small, sweet, edible.

Leaves: Alternate, feather-like arrangement, 8 to 15 inches long, with 5 to 9 (usually 7) leaflets; leaflets 3 to 7 inches long, lance-shaped to narrowly pear- or egg-shaped; margins toothed, pointed at the tip; upper surface shiny, yellowish-green, **lower surface paler, densely covered with light orange to brown hairs**; leaf aromatic when crushed; **leaf stalk with dense hairs**; leaves turn bright yellow in autumn.

Twigs: Stout, brown to dark gray, very hairy at first, smooth later; pores pale; **buds light tan, large, 1/2 inch or greater, hairy**.

Trunk: Bark gray, with shallow grooves, **plates flat, tight, never shaggy**; wood dark brown, heavy, hard, strong, durable, flexible, close-grained.

Habitat: Occurs in dry upland woods on upper slopes and ridges, commonly in acid soils over chert, sandstone, or igneous rock; occasionally in low woods along streams.

Range: Texas, Oklahoma, Arkansas, and Louisiana; east to Florida, north to New Hampshire, and west to Ohio, Indiana, Illinois, Iowa, Missouri, and southeastern Kansas.

Wildlife Uses: The nuts are eaten by squirrels, mice, and white-tailed deer. Squirrels also eat the buds. Like other hickories, its leaves are fed on by large, showy moths, such as the luna moth, several colorful underwing moths, and the giant regal moth with its impressive 6-inch wingspan and its remarkable larvae called the hickory horned devil, the largest caterpillar in North America.

Remarks: Mockernut hickory was first cultivated in 1766. A rapid grower in its early stages, this hickory begins producing nuts around age 20. Its optimum nut-bearing age is between 40 and 150 years. The wood is considered to be the hardest of all the hickories. It is used for tool handles, wood splints, and for the manufacture of rustic furniture.

The name hickory was first referenced in 1671 and is taken from the Algonquian (perhaps Powhatan) as a shortening of *pockerchicory* or a similar word for this genus in the walnut family. Mockernut hickory is so-named because the nuts are large but with thick shells and very small kernels. White hickory refers to the white sapwood.

Carya is the ancient Greek name for walnut; *tomentosa* refers to the tomentose (short, matted, wooly) hairs on the lower surface of the leaves.

Carya tomentosa ❧ a. Leaf, b. Fruit, c. Nut, d. Twig

American chestnut

Castanea dentata (Marshall) Borhk.

Oak family (Fagaceae)

Appearance: Formerly medium to large trees, up to 120 feet tall, with a broad rounded crown but now persisting mostly as stump sprouts 9 to 33 feet high.

Flowers: Late May–July, after the leaves, male and female flowers separate on the same tree, male catkins 4 to 8 inches long; stamens numerous in dense, close clusters; female flowers much smaller and scattered near the base of some of the catkins.

Fruit: September–October, large, spiny burs, 2 to 3 inches in diameter; **spines smooth (without hairs), bur opening into 4 parts and containing 1 to 3 nuts, flattened on one side**, 3/4 to 1 1/4 inches in diameter, broadest at the base, pointed at the tip; seed edible, very sweet; few trees reach fruiting age today.

Leaves: Alternate, simple, 6 to 11 inches long, 1 1/2 to 3 inches wide, lance-shaped, broadest towards the tip; thin and papery, margin coarsely toothed, vein extending beyond each tooth forming a short, curved bristle; leaf tapering to a pointed tip; upper surface yellowish-green, smooth, shiny, **lower surface paler, smooth (without hairs)**.

Twigs: Slender, yellowish-green, slightly hairy when young, becoming reddish-brown to dark brown and smooth with age, shape somewhat zigzag; pores numerous, white.

Trunk: Bark thick, dark brown, with shallow irregular grooves separating the broad flat ridges; **swollen trunks and stems with splitting bark is caused by the fungus canker**; wood reddish-brown, light, soft, very rot resistant.

Habitat: Formerly planted in Missouri on farms, woodlots, and in yards and around buildings but scarce now due to the chestnut blight.

Range: At one time from Mississippi, Alabama, Georgia; north to Maine, and west to New York, Ohio, Michigan, Indiana, and southern Illinois.

Wildlife Uses: The nuts were once an important food for a variety of wildlife.

Remarks: The American chestnut was once a dominant tree in the deciduous forests of eastern North America. Because of its decay-resistant wood, it was used for posts, poles, pilings, railroad ties, and split-rail fences. Tragically, the chestnut blight fungus, *Endothia parasitica*, was introduced about 1900 on seedlings of Asiatic chestnut in New York. Within 50 years, the disease had spread throughout the range of the American chestnut, subsequently killing tens of billions of trees. The fungus attacks the inner bark, and girdles the tree, thereby cutting off circulation. Research is being conducted by various agencies and organizations trying to find resistant strains of the tree for possible reintroduction. Success has been achieved in Virginia by crossing the American chestnut with the Chinese chestnut, *Castanea mollissima*, which is resistant to the blight. Researchers hope to introduce this hybrid to the wild around the year 2005. Chinese chestnut, a smaller tree, is planted as an ornamental in Missouri. It differs from American chestnut by having hairy leaves and buds.

Castanea is the Latin word for Castania, a town in northern Greece, which was known for its trees; *dentata* means "toothed," which refers to the leaves.

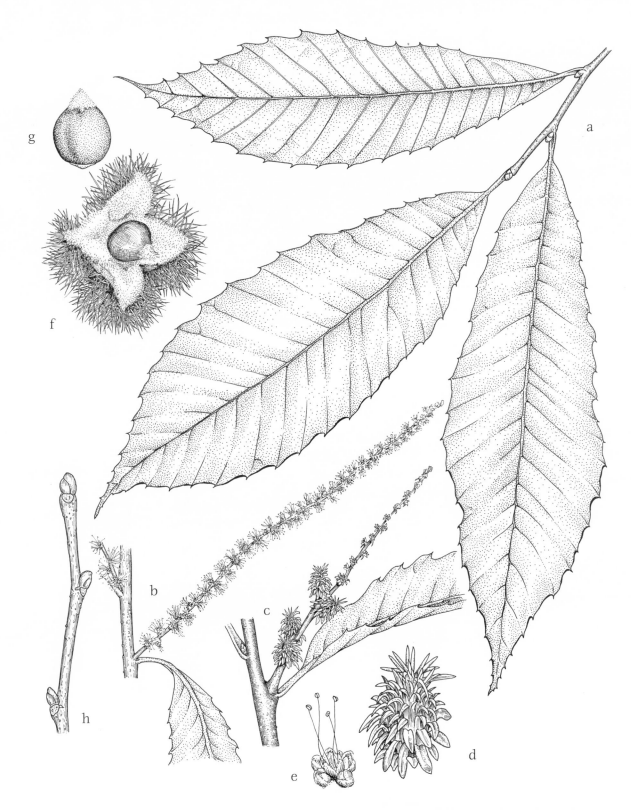

Castanea dentata ❀ a. Leaves, b. Male catkin, c. Female flower clusters with male catkin,
d. Single female flower cluster, e. Single male flower, f. Fruit opened, g. Seed, h. Twig

Ozark chinquapin

Castanea pumila var. *ozarkensis* (Ashe) G. Tucker

Oak family (Fagaceae)

Also called Ozark chestnut

Appearance: Formerly a small to medium-sized tree, up to 50 feet tall, but **now a shrubby stump sprouter due to chestnut blight**.

Flowers: Late May–June, after the leaves, male and female flowers separate on the same tree, male catkins 2 to 8 inches long; stamens numerous in dense, close clusters; female flowers much smaller and scattered near the base of some of the catkins.

Fruit: September–October, spiny burs, often in large, heavy clusters, about 1 1/2 inches across; **bur opening into 2 parts, spines hairy; nut single, rounded, not flattened**, dark brown, egg-shaped, up to 3/4 inch wide; seed edible, very sweet; today, only open-grown stump sprouts attain enough solar energy to produce some seed.

Leaves: Alternate, simple, 6 to 10 inches long, lance-shaped, broadest towards the tip; thin and papery, margin coarsely toothed, teeth about 3/8 inch long, vein extending beyond each tooth forming a short, curved bristle; leaf tapering to a pointed tip; upper surface yellowish-green, smooth, shiny, **lower surface paler, covered with short hairs (velvety)**.

Twigs: Slender, young ones light brown, covered with dense hairs, becoming gray and smooth later, shape somewhat zigzag; pores numerous, white.

Trunk: Gray to light brown, smooth, becoming grooved with flattened scaly plates; **swollen trunks and stems with splitting bark is caused by the fungus canker**; wood dark brown, hard, rather brittle, coarse-grained.

Habitat: Occurs on dry upper slopes and ridges in acidic, cherty soils.

Range: In the Ozark region of southwestern Missouri, Arkansas, and Oklahoma.

Wildlife Uses: The nuts were once an important food for a variety of wildlife.

Remarks: Ozark chinquapin has suffered the same plight as the American chestnut. In the Ozarks, the blight was not noticed until at least the 1960s but the disease spread swiftly and was deadly. Today, only skeletons remain of the Ozark chinquapin with stump sprouts still emerging, trying to begin a new start only to be re-infected with the canker that eventually cuts off its circulation. To date, no disease resistant strains have been found.

Another variety, the Allegheny or downy chinquapin, *Castanea pumila* var. *pumila* differs by having smaller leaves, 4 to 6 inches long, leaf tips more rounded, teeth up to 1/8 inch long; burs small, less than 1 inch in diameter (including the spines), single or paired; nuts up to 1/2 inch wide; small trees, often appearing as shrubs, occasionally in thickets. There is one historic record from Howell County. It's range includes southern Arkansas and southeastern United States.

Chinquapin, or sometimes spelled "chinkapin," is from *chinkomen*, an Algonquin (Native American) term for chestnuts.

Castanea is the Latin word for Castania, a town in northern Greece, which was known for its trees; *pumila* refers to its small size, and *ozarkensis* is for the Ozark Mountains of Arkansas, where it is (was) most abundant.

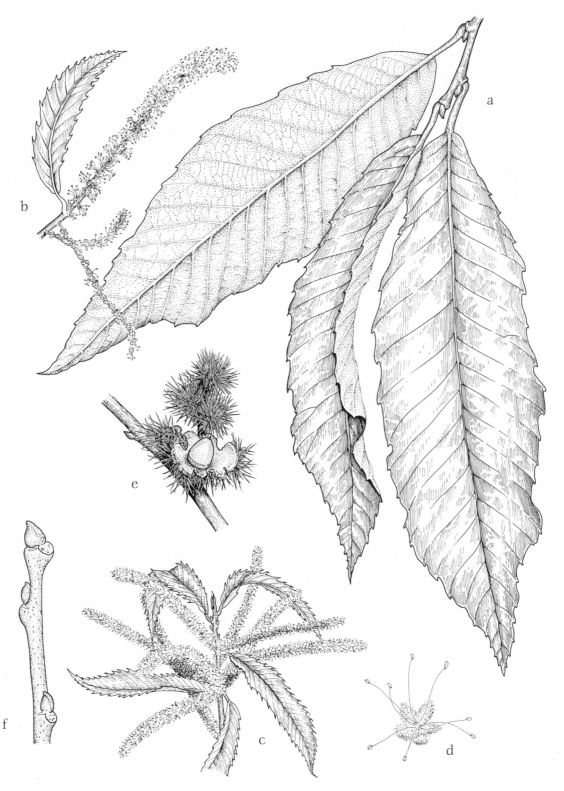

Castanea pumila* var. *ozarkensis ❀ a. Leaves, b. & c. Male catkins, d. Male flower, e. Fruit with seed, f. Twig

Southern catalpa

Catalpa bignonioides Walter

Trumpet creeper family (Bignoniaceae)

Also known as common catalpa, cigartree, catawba tree

Appearance: Medium-sized tree, up to 50 feet tall, with a broad, round crown and a short trunk branching into large limbs, which are brittle and easily broken in storms.

Flowers: May–June, borne on the tips of branches in large, erect, pyramid-shaped clusters, 4 to 10 inches long, flowers opening first at the bottom; flowers white, showy, attractive, fragrant, appearing after the leaves, **bell-shaped, about 1/2 to 2 inches long; upper two lobes with yellow and purple spots and dark lines in throat, lower lobe lacking a notch in the center**; stamens 2.

Fruit: October, produced in clusters, **pod bean-like, narrow, 6 to 15 inches long, 1/4 to 1/2 inch wide**, chestnut brown, splitting in two halves to release the seeds; seeds numerous, flattened, about 1 inch long and 1/4 inch wide, silvery gray, with pointed, fringed wings at each end; pods persist on tree all winter, opening in spring before falling.

Leaves: Simple, opposite or whorled, egg-shaped, with an abruptly pointed tip, 4 to 12 inches long, 3 to 7 inches wide, margin smooth; upper surface light green, smooth, lower surface paler, hairy; **strong scented, unpleasant, when crushed**; leaf stalk 5 to 6 inches long, hairy; leaves turn black and fall with first frost; late to leaf out in the spring.

Twigs: Stout, brittle, green to purplish and hairy when young, becoming light orange or brown and smooth later; pores large, pale.

Trunk: Bark thin, brown to gray, divided into **large, thin irregular scales**; wood soft, light brown, durable.

Habitat: Planted in yards, cemeteries, along streets; escaping along roadsides, railroads, disturbed sites, stream banks.

Range: Introduced in Missouri and widely planted in eastern United States; native in Louisiana, Mississippi, Alabama, Georgia, and Florida.

Wildlife Uses: Leaves are fed on by the large spotted caterpillars of the catalpa sphinx moth, *Ceratomia catalpae*.

Medicinal Uses: Tea from the bark formerly was used as an antiseptic, snakebite antidote, laxative, sedative, and internal worm expellant. Tea from the seeds was used for asthma, bronchitis, and applied externally for wounds.

Remarks: The wood of southern catalpa has been used for posts, poles, rails, crossties, inexpensive interior finish, and cabinetwork. It is a fast growing tree that begins to produce flowers at 6 to 8 years old.

Some catalpas are planted primarily as food for sphinx moth caterpillars or "catalpa worms," which are harvested as a convenient bait for fishing. Hitting the trees with sticks to dislodge the bait often breaks limbs and damages the bark. Fungus cankers easily invade the tree through the wounds and disfigure the tree.

Catalpa is the Native American name; *bignonioides* refers to its flowers, which resemble the bignonia-vine.

Catalpa bignonioides ❀ a. Growth form with flowers, b. Flowers, c. Fruit, d. Twig

Northern catalpa

Catalpa speciosa Warder ex Engelm.

Trumpet creeper family (Bignoniaceae)

Also known as catawba tree, cigartree

Appearance: Medium-sized tree, up to 60 feet tall, with a short trunk and several large, ascending branches forming a narrow, rounded crown.

Flowers: May–June, borne on tips of branches in large, erect, pyramid-shaped clusters, 4 to 8 inches long, flowers opening first at the bottom; flowers, white, showy, attractive, fragrant, appearing after the leaves, **bell-shaped, about 2 inches long; throat of flower with yellow blotches and dark lines, lower lobe with a notch in the center**; stamens 2.

Fruit: October, solitary or 2 to 3 together, **pod bean-like, 8 to 20 inches long, 1/4 to 1/2 inches wide**, light brown, splitting into 2 halves to release seeds; seeds numerous, flattened, about 1 inch long and 1/4 inch wide, light brown to gray, fringed wings at each end; pods persist on tree all winter, opening in spring before falling.

Leaves: Simple, opposite or in threes, egg-shaped, with an abruptly pointed tip, 6 to 12 inches long, 4 to 8 inches wide, margin mostly smooth; upper surface dark green, smooth; lower surface paler and hairy; **mildly scented when crushed**; leaf stalk 4 to 6 inches long, slightly hairy; leaves turn black and fall with first frost; late to leaf out in the spring.

Twigs: Stout, brittle, green to purplish and hairy when young, becoming light orange or brown and smooth later; pores large, pale.

Trunk: Bark thick, brown to gray, **with irregular, short ridges and deep grooves, not scaly**; wood light brown, not strong, soft, durable.

Habitat: Occurs in bottomland woods along streams and base of bluffs, also in upland woods; native in the southeastern Missouri Bootheel counties; planted and escaped elsewhere in the state; found in old fields, abandoned homesites, and disturbed areas.

Range: East Texas, Oklahoma, Arkansas, and Louisiana; east to Tennessee, north to Kentucky, Indiana, and west to Illinois and Missouri. Introduced and naturalized in Virginia, West Virginia, Ohio, Iowa, Nebraska, and Kansas.

Wildlife Uses: Leaves are eaten by the large spotted caterpillars of the catalpa sphinx moth, *Ceratomia catalpae*.

Medicinal Uses: See information under southern catalpa.

Remarks: Uses of the wood is similar to that of southern catalpa. Another species, the Chinese catalpa, *Catalpa ovata*, is a native of Asia; it is known to escape from plantings and naturalize; recorded from Boone County; a shrub to small tree, with yellow flowers and leaves somewhat lobed.

    Catalpa is the Native American name; *speciosa* meaning "showy," is given for the large showy flowers.

Catalpa speciosa ❦ a. Growth form with flowers, b. Flower, c. Fruit, d. Seed, e. Twig

Sugarberry

Celtis laevigata Willd.

Elm family (Ulmaceae)

Appearance: Medium to large tree, up to 90 feet tall, with stout spreading branches forming a broad, irregular head.

Flowers: April–May, appearing with or soon after the leaves; male flowers in clusters, toward the base of the new branch; stamens 5 to 6; female flowers appear toward the tip of the new branch, small, produced singly or in clusters of 2 to 3.

Fruit: September, nearly globe-shaped, **about 1/4 inch in diameter**, persisting through winter, thin-skinned, orange-red to black, flesh thin, dry, sweet; seed solitary, pale brown, surface rough; fruit stalk often longer than the leaf stalk.

Leaves: Alternate, simple, unequal with one side longer or broader than the other half, lance-shaped, broadest at the base, 2 1/2 to 5 inches long, 1 to 2 1/2 inches wide, with 3 principal nerves emerging from the base; middle vein tapers to a long-pointed tip, **margin entire or with a few teeth towards the tip, thin; base uneven; upper surface light green, smooth**; lower surface paler, smooth; leaves turning a drab yellow in autumn.

Twigs: Slender, usually shiny, flexible, zigzag, numerous, light green to reddish-brown.

Trunk: Bark pale gray, thin, smooth or cracked **with irregular warty projections not becoming ridge-like**; wood yellowish, soft, weak, close-grained.

Habitat: Occurs in bottomland forests along streams and in rocky woodlands, glades, and bluffs.

Range: Texas, Oklahoma, Arkansas, and Louisiana; east to Florida, north to Virginia, and west to Indiana, Illinois, Missouri, and southeastern Kansas.

Wildlife Uses: The fruit is eaten by at least 15 species of songbirds, wild turkey, bobwhite quail, ruffed grouse, squirrels, and raccoons. Flocks of cedar waxwings can be seen devouring the fruits in late fall and winter. The larvae of the hackberry butterfly is always associated with sugarberry and hackberry, feeding exclusively on the leaves.

Remarks: Sugarberry has been in cultivation since 1811. A moderate to fast-growing tree that lives up to 150 years, the wood is used to a limited extent for furniture, flooring, crates, fuel, posts, and rough construction. The tree is often used as a shade or street planting in the southern states because it adapts to a wide range of conditions. Hardiness limits its northern range. Sugarberry is not bothered by witches' brooms or leaf galls that attack hackberry.

The name "sugarberry" comes from the sweet pulp of the fruit, which can be nibbled on.

Celtis is a name given by Pliny to a sweet-fruited African lotus; *laevigata* means "smooth" and refers to the leaves.

Celtis laevigata ❊ a. Growth form, b. Flower cluster, c. Flower, d. Fruit, e. Twig, f. Twig closeup

Hackberry

Celtis occidentalis L.

Elm family (Ulmaceae)

Also called northern hackberry, nettle tree

Appearance: Medium to large tree, up to 90 feet tall, with a rounded crown; bark gray with numerous wart-like projections and ridges.

Flowers: April–May, appearing in the spring, with or soon after the leaves, male flowers in clusters towards the base of the new branch; stamens 4 to 6; female flowers towards the tip, small, single or in pairs.

Fruit: September, nearly globe-shaped, **1/4 to 1/2 inch in diameter**, orange-red turning dark purple, persisting through winter, thin-skinned, flesh dry, sweet; seed solitary, pale brown, surface rough; fruit stalk often longer than the leaf stalk.

Leaves: Simple, alternate, unequal with one side longer or broader than the other side, egg-shaped to broadest in the middle, 2 to 4 inches long, 1 1/2 to 2 inches wide, with 3 principal veins emerging from the base; **with 10 to 40 teeth all around the margin except near the base, abruptly pointed at the tip**; base uneven; upper surface light green, **rough to the touch**, lower surface paler green, hairy; leaves turning a drab yellow in autumn.

Twigs: Slender, usually shiny, flexible, zigzag, numerous, light green to reddish-brown.

Trunk: Bark gray, **with numerous wart-like projections along the trunk becoming more prominent with age**; wood yellowish-white, heavy, soft, weak, coarse grained.

Habitat: Occurs in moist woodlands in bottomlands and uplands throughout the state.

Range: Texas, Oklahoma, Arkansas, Missouri, and Louisiana; east to Georgia, north to Quebec, and west to Manitoba, Idaho, and Utah.

Wildlife Uses: The fruit is eaten by at least 25 species of songbirds, wild turkey, bobwhite quail, ruffed grouse, squirrels, and raccoons. Flocks of cedar waxwings can be seen devouring the fruits in late fall and winter. The larva of the hackberry butterfly is always associated with hackberry and sugarberry, feeding exclusively on the leaves.

Remarks: Hackberry has been cultivated since 1656. The tree is drought resistant and often planted for shade in lawns and parks in the south. Hackberry is a relatively fast grower and is moderately long-lived. The tree often develops a type of "witches' broom," which is a proliferation of twigs in clusters that resemble a crudely fashioned, hand-made broom. The brooming is caused by the combined action of a powdery mildew fungus, *Sphaerotheca pytophila*, and a gall mite, *Eriphytes* sp.

The wood is occasionally used for fuel, furniture, veneer, fence posts, boxes, and crates. The Dakota were known to pound up the hard seed and fruit to use as seasoning for meat. The Pawnee pounded the fruit to a fine consistency, added a little fat, and mixed it with parched corn. The fruit is sweet and edible, good for nibbling while trekking through the woods.

The origin of the name "hackberry" is confusing because presumably it is a corruption of the Scottish "hagberry," which, in Britain, is given to the bird cherry, *Prunus avium*.

Celtis is a name given by the Greek, Pliny to a sweet-fruited African lotus; *occidentalis* means "western."

Celtis occidentalis ✼ a. Growth form with fruit, b. Leaf, c. Flower cluster, d. Male flower, e. Female flower, f. Female flowers, g. Twig

Dwarf hackberry

Celtis tenuifolia Nutt

Elm family (Ulmaceae)

Appearance: A shrub to small tree up to 24 feet tall, **often somewhat scraggly.**

Flowers: April–May, small clusters of male flowers in leaf axils, near the base of a short new branch; female flowers in leaf axils, toward the tip of the same new shoot. Female flowers contain disproportionately large stigmas (central column), an adaption useful in capturing the plant's wind-dispersed pollen.

Fruit: September–October, drupe (a seed covered by fleshy pulp), globe-shaped, about 1/4 inch diameter, orange to brown or red; seed brown; stalk hairy, about 3/8 inch long.

Leaves: Simple, alternate, broadly egg-shaped to triangular, **leaf blade lopsided (asymmetrical) with one half longer or broader than the other half**; tip pointed, **base slanting with unequal sides**, with 3 principal veins emerging from the base, margin mostly entire, blade length 3/4 to 4 inches, width 1/2 to 1 3/4 inches, thin, sometimes leathery in texture, upper surface dark green, rough, lower surface hairy to smooth; leaf stalk 1/4 to 3/8 inch long, hairy, leaves turn a dull yellow in autumn.

Twigs: Slender, reddish-brown, hairy at first, later smooth and darker brown to gray; **bark often with corky ridges**.

Trunk: Bark light gray, with grooves, the ridges short, warty, and with vertical sides; wood light, soft, nearly white, with a wide, white sapwood.

Habitat: Occurs in rocky open woods, dolomite glades and along bluffs.

Range: East Texas, Oklahoma, Arkansas, and Louisiana; east to Florida, north to Virginia, and west to Kentucky, Indiana, Illinois, Missouri, and Kansas.

Wildlife Uses: Fruits are eaten by raccoons, squirrels, wild turkeys and ruffed grouse.

Remarks: On dry, thin-soiled glades, dwarf hackberry exhibits an interesting stunted, gnarly appearance. On better soils, it resembles a miniature hackberry and is suitable as an ornamental, especially with its colorful fruit. The fruits are edible, and probably were used by Native Americans to flavor meat, as other species of hackberries were. The berries were pounded fine and mixed with a little fat and parched corn.

The origin of the name "hackberry" is confusing because presumably it is a corruption of the Scottish "hagberry," which, in Britain, is given to the bird cherry, *Prunus avium.*

Celtis is the name given by the Greek, Pliny, to a sweet-fruited African lotus; *tenuifolia* refers to the thin leaves.

Celtis tenuifolia ❀ a. Section of trunk showing growth form, b. Branch with leaves, c. Male flowers, d. Female flower, e. Fruit

Eastern redbud

Cercis canadensis L.

Senna family (Caesalpiniaceae)

Appearance: Shrub or small tree to 40 feet. Distinctly ornamental in spring with small, clustered, rose-purple flowers covering the bare branches before the leaves.

Flowers: Late March–early May, **flowering before the leaves**, in clusters of 2 to 8, on stalks 1/4 to 3/4 inch long; flowers 1/4 to 2/5 inch long, **rose-purple**, petals 5, of the three upper petals, the two outer ones longer than the central one, the two lower petals joined together to form a keel; stamens 10, shorter than the petals.

Fruit: September–October, persistent on the branches, often abundant; pod 3 to 4 inches long, about 1/2 inch wide, tapering at both ends, leathery, reddish-brown; seeds several, egg-shaped, flattened, 1/6 to 1/5 inch long.

Leaves: Simple, alternate, 2 to 6 inches long, 1 1/4 to 6 inches, **oval to heart-shaped or as broad as or broader than long**, tip pointed, base heart-shaped, margin entire; upper surface dark green, smooth; lower surface paler and smooth with some hairs along the veins and in the vein axils; leaf stalk 1 1/4 to 5 inches long, smooth.

Twigs: Slender, smooth, brown to gray, often zigzag, pith white.

Trunk: Bark reddish-brown to gray, thin and smooth when young, older ones with long grooves and short, thin, blocky plates; wood heavy, hard, brown, with a thin, white sapwood.

Habitat: Found in open woodland, borders of woods, thickets, dolomite glades, and along rocky streams and bluffs. Occurs in every county in Missouri.

Range: Texas, Oklahoma, Arkansas, and Louisiana; east to Florida, north to Connecticut, and west to Ontario, Michigan, Illinois, Iowa, Nebraska, and Kansas; also northeastern Mexico.

Wildlife Uses: The seeds are eaten by several species of birds, and the foliage browsed by white-tailed deer. Eastern redbud also is a nectar source for bees.

Remarks: Eastern redbud has been used as an attractive ornamental since 1641. It usually blooms a couple of weeks before flowering dogwoods, and, on rare occasions, the two overlap in flowering. Eastern redbuds begin to bear pods at five years of age; the maximum age is about 75 years. Good crops of pods generally occur on alternate years. The leaves turn a yellow or pale greenish-yellow in autumn. The sour- or pea-flavored flowers are sometimes used raw or pickled in salads; in Mexico they are fried.

Cercis is the ancient name of the closely related Judas-tree of Europe and Asia. According to legend, Judas hanged himself from a branch of the tree. The species name, *canadensis*, literally means "of Canada," where it is rather uncommon. Or perhaps it refers to northeastern North America, before political boundaries were drawn.

Cercis canadensis ❀ a. Growth form, b. Flowers, c. Fruit

Fringe tree

Chionanthus virginicus L.

Olive family (Oleaceae)

Also called old man's beard, graney graybeard

Appearance: Usually a shrub with crooked branches, but sometimes a tree to 35 feet.

Flowers: April–May, **in delicate drooping bundles along the twig at the leaf axils,** 4 to 6 inches long; stalks hairy; petals 4 to 6, narrow, tip pointed, about 1 inch long, white with purple spots near the base, fragrant; stamens 2.

Fruit: August–October, drupe (a seed covered by fleshy pulp) borne in clusters, bluish-black, smooth, globe- to egg-shaped, to 3/4 inch long, 1 to 3 seeds each about 1/3 inch long, oval, brown. Plants 5 to 8 years old begin to produce seed.

Leaves: Simple, opposite, **may appear whorled near the tip, large**, 4 to 8 inches long, 1 to 4 inches wide, oval to egg-shaped or lance-shaped, tip blunt to pointed, base wedge-shaped, margin entire or wavy, dark green and smooth above, paler below with hairs on the veins; leaf stalk to 1 inch long, hairy.

Twigs: Stout, hairy, light brown to orange, later gray.

Trunk: Bark brown to gray, thin, close, flattened, broken into small thin scales; wood light brown, sapwood lighter, hard, heavy, close-grained.

Habitat: Occurs along rocky dolomite wooded ledges and bluffs, and along the edges of dolomite glades in southwestern Missouri, and along wooded slopes of small creeks and wet woods in southeastern Missouri.

Range: East Texas, Oklahoma, Arkansas, and Louisiana; east to Florida, north to New Jersey, and west to Pennsylvania, Ohio, Kentucky, and Missouri.

Wildlife Uses: The fruit is eaten by several songbirds including robins and mockingbirds; also wild turkey and bobwhite quail; and white-tailed deer.

Medicinal Uses: Native Americans boiled the bark in water and used the liquid to bathe wounds and treat fever associated with malaria. Pioneers applied an application of crushed bark to cuts and bruises. In Appalachia, a solution from boiled bark is used to treat skin inflammations. The leaves and flowers have been used to treat inflammations and sores, ulcers in the mouth and throat, and diarrhea.

Remarks: Fringe tree provides a showy display of late spring flowers clustered in drooping fringes. Fruits resemble small olives, at first green but turning black at maturity. It does well in landscaped settings. The leaves turn a rich yellow in autumn. Fringe tree has been grown as an ornamental since 1736, but is often difficult to find at nurseries.

The name fringe tree refers to the "fringe" of delicate, showy flowers that hang from the twigs.

Chionanthus is a combination of two Greek words meaning "snow flower"; *virginicus* refers to the state of Virginia, probably where it was first found and described.

Chionanthus virginicus ❊ a. Growth form with flower clusters, b. Flower, c. Fruit

Yellowwood

Cladrastis kentukea (Dumond de Courset) Rudd

Bean family (Fabaceae)

Also known as American yellowwood, yellow-tree, virgilia

Appearance: Medium-sized tree, up to 60 feet tall, with a short trunk and a broad, open, rounded crown.

Flowers: May–June, in elongated, hanging clusters, 10 to 14 inches long; **flowers white, fragrant, about 1 inch long, pea-shaped with 5 petals; upper petal rounded with a yellow blotch at the base**, 2 side petals straight, remaining 2 forming a nearly straight keel; stamens 10.

Fruit: August–September, **a pod, 3 to 4 inches long, flattened, late to split into two halves, persisting into winter**; seeds 2 to 6, longer than broad, flattened, dark brown.

Leaves: Alternate, feather-like arrangement, 8 to 12 inches long, with 5 to 11 leaflets, **not always in opposite pairs**; leaflets oval- to egg-shaped to broadest in the middle, 2 to 4 inches long, 1 1/2 to 3 1/2 inches wide; margin entire, abruptly pointed at the tip; upper surface dark green, smooth, lower surface pale, smooth; **leaf stalk enlarged at the base, enclosing a bud**; leaves yellow to gold-orange in autumn.

Twigs: Slender, smooth, shiny, zigzag, brittle, reddish-brown; pores numerous; **bud at end of twig absent, side buds usually 2 to 4, clumped, appearing as one, hairy**.

Trunk: Bark gray to light brown, thin, smooth, similar to American beech; wood yellow to brown, heavy, hard, strong, close-grained.

Habitat: Occurs along moist wooded slopes and bluffs and along rocky drainages in somewhat sheltered areas. Primarily limited in Missouri to a few southwestern counties.

Range: Northeastern Oklahoma, Arkansas, and Missouri; east to Alabama, north to Kentucky, southern Indiana, and southern Illinois. Uncommon to endangered throughout its range.

Remarks: Formerly known as *Cladrastis lutea* K. Koch., yellowwood has been in cultivation since 1812. The tree is often planted as an ornamental in the United States and Europe for its attractive flowers and foliage. It grows well in partial shade or sun and is relatively free of serious insects and diseases. Yellowwood grows slowly and its branches are somewhat brittle, making them more susceptible to storm damage. The wood has been used for fuel and gunstocks. Early Appalachian settlers made a yellow die from the root bark. In February 1796, André Michaux was the first botanist to encounter the tree, admiring its form and smooth bark during an icy rain.

The name yellowwood is in reference to its ability to yield a clear yellow dye.

Cladrastis is from the Greek "kladros" (branch) and "thraustos" (fragile) for fragile branches; *kentukea* refers to the state of Kentucky.

Cladrastis kentukea ❧ a. Growth habit with flowers, b. Fruit, c. Twig, d. Leaf scar with multiple hairy buds

Alternate-leaved dogwood

Cornus alternifolia L.

Dogwood family (Cornaceae)

Also known as pagoda dogwood, green osier, pigeon berry and blue dogwood

Appearance: Shrub or small tree to 18 feet. Branches often in tierlike layers. Easily mistaken for flowering dogwood when not in flower.

Flowers: May–June, white to cream-colored, inflorescence broad or flat-topped, 1 1/4 to 2 1/2 inches broad, sepals minute or absent; petals 4, small, about 1/8 inch long; stamens 4.

Fruit: July–September, borne on a red stalk, drupe (a seed covered by fleshy pulp) bluish-black, about 1/3 inch long stone deeply pitted at the summit.

Leaves: Mostly alternate, a few opposite, but often crowded near the end of twig, margin entire, leaves 2 to 5 inches long, 3/4 to 2 1/2 inches wide, either egg-shaped, longer than broad, or widest in the middle, tip pointed, base wedge-shaped; upper surface smooth, dark green; lower surface paler, hairy, **lateral veins 4 to 6 on each side, conspicuous; leaf stalk 3/4 to 2 1/4 inches long**, somewhat hairy.

Twigs: Often horizontal or ascending, slender, smooth, green, pith white and small.

Trunk: Bark thin, dark reddish-brown, smooth or grooved and broken into irregular narrow ridges; wood hard, with reddish-brown heartwood and thick, paler sapwood.

Habitat: Found along wooded north-facing slopes and along wooded banks of streams.

Range: Arkansas and Louisiana; east to Florida, north to Nova Scotia, and west to Ontario, Michigan, Wisconsin, Minnesota, Iowa, and Missouri.

Wildlife Uses: Its leaves are browsed by white-tailed deer and cottontail rabbit. The fruit are eaten by at least 11 species of birds, including warbling vireos and ruffed grouse. Black bears may be especially fond of this fruit.

Remarks: Alternate-leaved dogwood is a popular ornamental, first introduced into cultivation in 1760. It prefers naturalized plantings in partial shade. It is a good replacement for the cold-sensitive flowering dogwood in the northern part of the state. In the fall, the leaves turn yellow to red.

The name alternate-leaved dogwood refers to its alternate leaf arrangement along the twigs, while all other dogwoods have opposite leaves.

Cornus is from the Latin word *cornu*, "a horn," in reference to the hard wood; *alternifolia* means "alternate leaves."

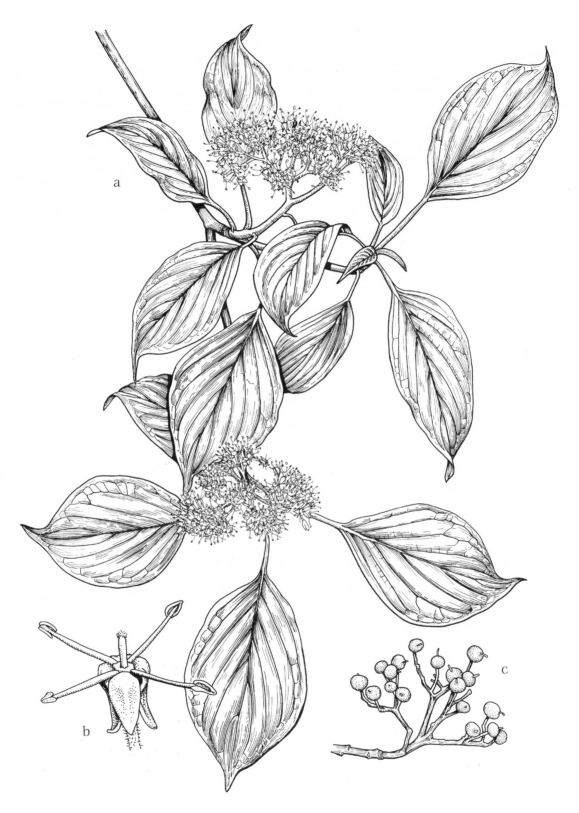

Cornus alternifolia ❧ a. Growth form with flower clusters, b. Flower, c. Fruit

Swamp dogwood

Cornus amomum Miller ssp. *obliqua* (Raf.) J. Wilson

Dogwood family (Cornaceae)

Also known as pale dogwood, silky dogwood, kinnikinnik

Appearance: Open, irregularly branched shrub to 9 feet; rarely taking the appearance of a small tree.

Flowers: May–July, **in flat or sometimes indented**, to round-topped clusters, stalks 1 to 2 inches long, very hairy, **yellowish-brown**; petals 4, white, 1/8 to 3/16 inch long, stamens 4.

Fruit: June–October, a drupe (a seed covered by fleshy pulp), **blue**, globe-shaped, about 1/4 inch in diameter, style (small stalk) on end of drupe persistent.

Leaves: Simple, opposite, leaves 1 1/2 to 3 1/4 inches long, 1/2 to 1 1/2 inches wide, egg- to lance-shaped or longer than broad, tip pointed, base terminating with a sharp angle or narrow wedge shape, margin entire; upper surface smooth and green, lower surface whitish and smooth or with minute appressed, white hairs, lateral veins 3 to 5 on each side; leaf stalk 1/8 to 1/3 inch, hairy.

Twigs: Slender, light to dark brown, smooth; when young whitish with dense appressed hairs, when older lacking hairs.

Trunk: Bark tight on most stems, red, with tan horizontal pores; some stems with longitudinal splits in the outer bark; wood hard, fine-grained, white.

Habitat: Occurs along rocky banks of streams, spring branches, wet places in prairies, fens, wet thickets, swamps and low woodland. Absent from the lowlands of southeastern Missouri.

Range: Oklahoma, Arkansas, and Kentucky; east to New Jersey, north to New Brunswick, and west to Michigan, Minnesota, Nebraska, and Kansas.

Wildlife Uses: The fruit is used by at least 10 species of birds (including ruffed grouse, bobwhite quail and wild turkey), cottontail rabbit, woodchuck, raccoon and squirrels. Wood ducks are known to eat the fruits in late summer and fall, before and after ripening. They have been seen reaching as far as they can from the water to strip the shrubs of fruit. The swamp dogwood on streambanks provides escape for wood ducks and cover for their broods. The thicket-forming swamp dogwood also provides cover for woodcock.

Remarks: Swamp dogwood is also known as *Cornus obliqua* Raf. The reddish-brown or dark brown young branchlets and blue fruit, conspicuous in late fall, are characteristic of this dogwood. The Native American name for tobacco, kinnikinnik, is applied to this and several other species of dogwood. Native Americans removed the outer bark, and scraped and dried the inner bark for smoking. It is fragrant, and many tribes were fond of it.

Cornus is from the Latin word *cornu*, "a horn," in reference to the hard wood; *amomum* is a Greek name of a spice plant and means "purifying," referring to its ritual use by Native Americans; *obliqua* indicates the leaf base is often uneven.

Cornus amomum* spp. *obliqua ✻ a. Growth form, b. Flower cluster, c. Fruit cluster

Rough-leaved dogwood

Cornus drummondii C. Meyer

Dogwood family (Cornaceae)

Appearance: Irregularly branched shrub or small spreading tree.

Flowers: May–June, yellowish-white, borne in terminal spreading, long-stalked clusters 1 to 3 inches across; flower stalks 1 to 2 inches long, hairy, petals 4, spreading, pointed at the tip.

Fruit: August–October, globe-shaped drupe (a seed covered by fleshy pulp), **white**, style (small stalk) on tip of drupe persistent, 1 to 2 seeds, slightly furrowed.

Leaves: Simple, opposite, margins entire, leaves 1 to 5 inches long, 1/2 to 2 1/2 inches wide, conspicuously veined, egg- to lance-shaped, or longer than broad to widest in the middle, tip pointed, base rounded to wedge-shaped, upper surface olive-green and rather **rough-hairy above**, lower surface paler with **woolly, loose curled or curving hairs**; leaf stalk 1/4 to 3/4 inch long, slender, rough-hairy, green to reddish.

Twigs: Young ones green and hairy, older ones reddish-brown and smooth.

Trunk: Bark gray-brown with shallow grooves and short, thin plates; wood pale brown, with sapwood paler, heavy, hard, strong, durable, close-grained.

Habitat: Occurs in dry or rocky woods, thickets, old fields, limestone and dolomite glades, prairies, bluff escarpments, occasionally low wet ground, along ponds, streams and at the base of bluffs. Probably in every county.

Range: East Texas, Louisiana, and Mississippi; north to Ohio and Ontario; and west to Iowa, Nebraska, and Kansas.

Wildlife Uses: Although seldom planted in windbreaks or around farmsteads, its dense thickets are excellent cover for birds and small mammals. Many birds, including Bell's vireo, nest in the thickets. The fruit is eaten by at least 40 species of birds, including bobwhite quail, wild turkey and greater prairie chicken.

Medicinal Uses: This species and flowering dogwood are known to contain a highly active antibiotic substance that is effective in preventing toothy decay and treating other aliments. Chewsticks are made by cutting off a small stem several inches long, removing the outer bark, and chewing on the tip to soften the fibers, which can then be used to massage the gums.

Remarks: The leaves of rough-leaved dogwood emit a faint odor which resembles sour milk. This dogwood is one of the hardiest of Missouri shrubs, and will withstand drought or extreme cold. It spreads by underground stems, sending up sprouts at the margin of the thicket. By virtue of its tenacity, it is difficult to manage in prairies, especially hill prairies in northwestern Missouri. It has been in cultivation since 1836. The wood is used for small woodenware articles, especially shuttleblocks and charcoal.

Cornus is from the Latin word *cornu,* "a horn," in reference to the hard wood; *drummondii* is in honor of Thomas Drummond (1780–1835), a Scottish botanical explorer.

Cornus drummondii ❧ a. Growth form with flower cluster, b. Flower, c. Fruit

Flowering dogwood

Cornus florida L.

Dogwood family (Cornaceae)

Appearance: Shrub to small tree to 40 feet with a straggling, spreading crown.

Flowers: Mid–April to mid–May, in terminal clusters with buds formed the previous year; flowers perfect with four stamens and a pistil, small, with four light- to greenish-yellow petals, about 1/8 inch wide **in clusters of 25 to 30 located above four white bracts (often mistaken for flower petals)**, the bracts are 1 1/4 to 2 1/2 inches long, notched at the tip; flower buds developed the previous year.

Fruit: August–November, **brilliant red drupe** (a seed covered by fleshy pulp), oval, shiny, in clusters of 2 to 6, 1/4 to 1/2 inch long; seeds 1 to 2, cream-colored with 5 to 7 shallow longitudinal grooves.

Leaves: Simple, opposite, margins entire, sometimes barely toothed, leaves 3 to 5 inches long, 1 1/2 to 2 1/2 inches wide, oval to egg-shaped, tip pointed, base wedge-shaped and often unequal; shiny-green and somewhat hairy above; much paler and hairy below, heavily veined; leaf stalk stout, grooved, about 3/4 inch long.

Twigs: Flexible, slender, reddish-gray to purplish, or greenish with red dots, hairy. Flower buds terminal. Leaf buds compressed and oval.

Trunk: Bark dark gray to brown with thin, squarish plates; wood brownish, strong, hard, not easily dented.

Habitat: Found along wooded slopes, ravines, along bluffs, upland ridges, successional fields; less common on glades, valleys and low ground; prefers well-drained, acid-based soils.

Range: Texas, Oklahoma, Arkansas, and Louisiana; east to Florida, north to Maine, and west to Ontario, Michigan, Illinois, Missouri, and Kansas; also northeastern Mexico.

Wildlife Uses: The fruit of flowering dogwood is eaten by squirrels and white-tailed deer. It is a preferred food for wild turkey and at least 28 other species of birds, including quail.

Medicinal Uses: Native Americans used the dried bark of the root to treat malaria, and the early European settlers fought chills and fevers with it; at one time it also was used as a quinine substitute.

Remarks: Missouri's official state tree, flowering dogwood blooms in April shortly after, but sometimes overlapping, redbud.

A rare pink-flowered form has been found in Jasper, Jefferson, McDonald, Newton, Reynolds and Taney counties. The deep red-colored form commonly sold at nurseries is reported to have originated earlier in the last century from a single cutting from a tree growing wild in Tennessee.

The name dogwood comes from the old word "dag," meaning skewer. As the name suggests, this hard, tough, splinter-free wood was used in making skewers to hold meat together while cooking. Native Americans prepared a scarlet dye from the roots to color their quills and feathers.

Cornus is from the Latin word *cornu*, "a horn," in reference to the hard wood; *florida* means "flowering," indicating the large "flowers."

Cornus florida ❁ a. Branch with flowers, b. Flower, c. Twig with leaves and fruit cluster

Stiff dogwood

Cornus foemina Miller

Dogwood family (Cornaceae)

Appearance: Shrub with stiff, upright irregular branches, or sometimes a small tree to 15 feet.

Flowers: May–June, in round-topped, rather open clusters 1 1/4 to 2 inches broad; stalk below flower cluster smooth, 1 to 2 3/4 inches long; petals 4, small, white, longer than broad; stamens 4.

Fruit: August–October, drupe (a seed covered by fleshy pulp) almost spherical, 1/4 inch in diameter, **pale blue**; single seed, longer than broad, slightly grooved.

Leaves: Simple, opposite, margins entire, leaves 1 to 3 inches long, 1 to 1 3/4 inches wide, blade lance-shaped to widest at the middle, tip pointed, green on both sides, lower surface slightly paler, smooth or slightly hairy; leaf stalk 1/4 to 1 inch long, smooth or slightly hairy.

Twigs: Young ones reddish, later greenish to brown or gray; older ones gray and smooth; pith white.

Trunk: Bark gray, smooth when young, developing shallow grooves with age; wood white, hard, fine-grained.

Habitat: Occurs along edges of **swamps and low, wet woodlands and wet open ground in the lowland counties of southeastern Missouri.**

Range: East Texas, Arkansas, and Louisiana; east to Florida, north to Virginia and Delaware; and west to Indiana, Illinois, and Missouri.

Wildlife Uses: The fruit is eaten by a variety of songbirds and wood duck; also cottontail rabbit, swamp rabbit, raccoon, and squirrels.

Remarks: Stiff dogwood is also known as *Cornus foemina* Miller ssp. *foemina* because gray dogwood, *Cornus racemosa* Lam., was added as a subspecies of *Cornus foemina*. The two sometimes hybridize and produce fertile seeds which indicates a close relationship, hence they are put under the same species. Others feel that the status of the name *Cornus foemina* is still in question and use the name *Cornus stricta* Lam. For simplicity, the traditional name of *Cornus foemina* Miller is used here.

Stiff dogwood can be found in association with bald cypress, water tupelo, swamp red maple, pin oak, basket oak, water elm, American snowbell, ladies' eardrops, wisteria, Virginia willow, swamp rose, and climbing dogbane.

The name dogwood comes from the old word "dag," meaning skewer. As the name suggests, this hard, tough, splinter-free wood was used in making skewers to hold meat together while cooking. The name "stiff" refers to the stiff, upright stems of this dogwood.

Cornus is from the Latin word *cornu*, "a horn," in reference to the hard wood; *foemina* means "female," a name that 1730s herbalists chose to distinguish it from what they considered to be the "male" flowering dogwood.

Cornus foemina ✽ a. Growth form with fruit cluster, b. Branch with flower cluster

Gray dogwood

Cornus racemosa Lam.

Dogwood family (Cornaceae)

Appearance: Thicket-forming shrub, up to 12 feet tall; occasionally a small tree. Stems many-branched, ascending, smooth and light gray to brown.

Flowers: May–July, clusters dome- or globe-shaped, in open, branching pattern 1 1/4 to 2 1/2 inches high or broad; stalk below flower cluster 1/3 to 1 1/2 inches long, **conspicuously red**; individual flowers small, white; petals 4, 1/8 to 1/6 inch long, spreading and recurved; stamens 4.

Fruit: July–October, drupe (a seed covered by fleshy pulp) **white to gray or greenish on red stalks**, rather persistent, resembling a depressed globe, about 1/4 inch in diameter, 1 to 2 seeded sometimes shallowly furrowed, about 1/6 inch long and wide.

Leaves: Simple, opposite, lance-shaped, widest at the middle, tip pointed, base ending at a sharp angle to occasionally rounded, margins entire, blade length 1 to 4 inches, width 1/2 to 1 1/2 inches, upper surface olive-green, lower surface somewhat whitened to grayish; leaf stalk 1/8 to 3/4 inch, smooth or with flattened hairs.

Twigs: Older branches gray and smooth or somewhat angled, **younger ones lacking hairs**, brown to red; pith white to brown.

Trunk: Bark gray or gray-brown, tight, roughened by pores called lenticels; old bark with small, squarish, thin flakes; wood hard, fine-grained, white.

Habitat: Occurs in moist or rocky soil along streams, ponds, fens, glades and prairies, thickets along fence rows and roadsides and along bluffs.

Range: Oklahoma, Missouri, and Arkansas; east to Virginia, north to Maine, and west to Ontario, Manitoba, the Dakotas, and Nebraska.

Wildlife Uses: The fruit of gray dogwood is eaten by at least 25 species of birds, including ruffed grouse and bobwhite quail. It is an important cover plant for woodcock and ruffed grouse. Unlike the sprawling branches of other dogwoods, the fine upper twigs of gray dogwood provide excellent support for the woven grass nests of various sparrows and the bulky nests of catbirds, mockingbirds and red-wing blackbirds.

Remarks: Gray dogwood is also known as *Cornus foemina* Miller ssp. *racemosa* (Lam.) J. Wilson. See discussion under stiff dogwood, *Cornus foemina*. This species of dogwood forms thickets from new shoots that emerge from the spreading roots. Gray dogwood is persistent on unfavorable sites and endures city smoke. It has been cultivated as an ornamental since 1758. The leaves turn a purplish-red to rose-red or purplish-brown in autumn.

The wood of gray dogwood is hard, heavy and durable, but does not get large enough for commercial use. Some of the tips of the upper branches may have an enlarged or swollen portion the size of a marble. This is the dogwood bud gall, caused by a gall gnat, and it occurs only on this species.

Cornus is from the Latin word *cornu*, "a horn," in reference to the hard wood; *racemosa* is for the racemelike (cluster) of flowers.

Cornus racemosa ❦ a. Growth form with fruit cluster, b. Flower cluster

Smoke tree

Cotinus obovatus Raf.

Cashew family (Anacardiaceae)

Also called American smoke tree, yellowwood

Appearance: Tall shrub to small tree with slender, spreading branches attaining a height of 35 feet.

Flowers: May, greenish-yellow, borne in loose, few-flowered clusters at the end of stems, clusters 5 to 6 inches long, 2 1/2 to 3 inches broad; **flower stalks with feathery, gland-tipped hairs and purplish**, flowers about 1/8 inch across, petals 5; stamens 5.

Fruit: June–July, small, hard-cased drupes (a seed covered by fleshy pulp) 1/8 to 1/4 inch long, kidney-shaped, flattened, smooth, pale brown; **fruit stalk slender, conspicuously purple or brown with gland-tipped hairs**.

Leaves: Simple, alternate, most abundant toward the tip of twigs, 1 1/2 to 6 inches long, 2 to 3 1/2 inches wide, broadest in the middle and tapering at both ends to oval; **tip round to blunt**, base broadly wedge-shaped or rounded, margin entire or somewhat wavy; **upper surface bluish- or olive-green** and smooth to hairy; lower surface hairy early and smooth with age, veins conspicuous; leaf stalk 1/4 to 2 inches, yellowish-green to reddish, smooth or hairy; bruised leaves somewhat fragrant.

Twigs: Slender, green to reddish or purple when young, gray and smooth with age; pores small, abundant, pale.

Trunk: Bark gray to black, roughly breaking into thin, longer than broad scales; wood orange to yellow, sapwood cream-white, coarse-grained, soft, light.

Habitat: Occurs on dolomite glades and wooded, rocky dolomite bluffs along what was once the White River and its tributaries.

Range: Central Texas, east Oklahoma, northwest Arkansas, southwest Missouri, Kentucky, Tennessee, and Alabama. Nowhere is it abundant or widespread.

Remarks: The brilliant orange and red colors of the leaves in autumn make it a worthwhile ornamental. Most smoke trees sold at nurseries are the European smoke tree, *Cotinus coggygria*, and not the native. The European species is typically a smaller tree with smaller leaves, which are purplish in at least one variety. The "smoke" from smoke tree is often mistaken for a spray of flowers but are actually the hairy, colorful stalks of the flowers after the blossoms have fallen away, imparting a smoky hue from a distance. The tree is called "yellowwood" by some, although that name is more correctly applied to another tree, *Cladrastis kentuckea*. The wood yields a yellow dye, and was used during the Civil War period. The wood is also very durable in contact with the soil and has been used for fence posts.

   Cotinus is the Latin name for European wild olive; *obovatus* refers to the leaf shape, which is described as an inverted egg shape.

Cotinus obovatus ❧ a. Growth form with fruit, b. Flowers and leaf, c. Hairy stalks with one bearing a fruit, d. Fruit

Urn-tree hawthorn

Crataegus calpodendron (Ehrh.) Medikus

Rose family (Rosaceae)

Also known as pear hawthorn

Appearance: Shrub or small tree, up to 18 feet tall, with scaly branches, thorns present or absent.

Flowers: May–early June, after the leaves appear, in many-flowered clusters; **flowers 1 to 2 inches across**; petals 5, white, rounded, stamens about 20.

Fruit: September, **pear- to urn-shaped**, about 1/3 inch thick, hairy at first, later smooth, bright red or orange-red; flesh thin, sweet, and juicy; seeds small, 2 to 3.

Leaves: Simple, alternate, **broadest at or above the middle**, 2 to 3 1/2 inches long, 1 1/2 to 3 inches wide; margin coarsely toothed often with 3 to 5 pairs of irregular lateral lobes above the middle; young leaves with short dense hairs above, dull yellowish-green; hairy below; leaf stalk stout, **sometimes with the margins winged to the base**.

Twigs: Slender, straight, gray, with dense hairs when young, smooth later; spineless or with spines, 1/2 to 2 inches long, stout, slender, sharp, straight or slightly curved.

Trunk: Bark on old trunks and limbs thick and grooved, scaly on the larger branches.

Habitat: Rocky open woodlands and bluffs.

Range: East Texas, Arkansas, and Missouri; east to Georgia, north to New York and Ontario, and west to Minnesota.

Wildlife Uses: The fruit is eaten by fox sparrow, cedar waxwing, robin, ruffed grouse, wild turkey, mice, woodrat, gray and fox squirrel, flying squirrel, gray fox, skunk, raccoon, and white-tailed deer. Deer also browse on the foliage and twigs. The thorniness, dense branching, and heavy foliage provide good cover and nesting sites for many birds.

Medicinal Uses: Hawthorn fruits and flowers are famous in herbal folk medicine (American, Indian, Chinese, European) as a heart tonic. Studies confirm its use in reducing hypertension associated with weak heart, angina pectoris, and arteriosclerosis. It is known to dilate coronary vessels, reduce blood pressure and act as a direct and mild heart tonic. A tea or tincture (dilated alcohol solution of plant parts) is used. Hawthorn products are very popular in Europe and China.

Remarks: Hawthorns make up a tough group of small, thorny trees that can brighten an urban landscape with profuse, applelike spring blossoms and colorful fall/winter fruits. Although not usually good eaten raw, the small fruit make an excellent jam or jelly and they contain their own pectin. A tea is made with the fruit and steeped along with a little peppermint.

The "haw" from hawthorn is from the Old English "haga," for hawthorn or other trees with small apple-like fruits.

Crataegus is from the Greek "kratos" (strength) and refers to the hard wood of some species; *calpodendron* means "urn-tree" and refers to the shape of the fruit.

Crataegus calpodendron ❈ a. Growth form with flowers, b. Flowers, c. Fruit, d. Twig

Cockspur thorn

Crataegus crus-galli L.

Rose family (Rosaceae)

Appearance: Shrub or small tree, up to 20 feet tall, with stout, nearly horizontal branches forming a broad crown.

Flowers: May–early June, after the leaves appear, in many-flowered clusters; flowers about 1/2 inch across; petals 5, white, margin often irregular; stamens 10.

Fruit: September, persist over winter, globe-shaped, greenish- to dull red, about 3/8 inch long, tip depressed; **flesh thin and dry**; seeds 2, small, ends rounded, about 1/4 inch long.

Leaves: Simple, alternate, **thick and leathery, broadest above the middle**, 1 to 2 inches long, 1/2 to 1 inch wide; margin finely toothed, tip rounded to slightly pointed; **upper surface dark green, shiny**; lower surface pale, smooth; leaf stalk 1/2 to 3/4 inch long, stout, **winged along the margin**; leaves turn orange to red in autumn.

Twigs: Stout, reddish or gray, smooth, **with numerous sharp, straight or slightly curved spines 1/2 to 3 inches long**, chestnut brown to ashy.

Trunk: Bark dark brown, grooved, with the ridges short and scaly, often peeling; wood salmon-colored, heavy, hard, fine-grained.

Habitat: Rocky open woodlands, borders along creeks, in thickets and rocky pastures.

Range: East Texas, Oklahoma, Arkansas, Missouri, and Louisiana; east to Georgia, north to southern Quebec, and west to Ontario, Michigan, southern Minnesota, and eastern Kansas.

Wildlife Uses: The fruit is hard and not as widely used as some of the other more fleshy hawthorns.

Medicinal Uses: See discussion under urn-tree hawthorn, *Crataegus calpodendron*.

Remarks: Cockspur hawthorn has some of the longest thorns of any hawthorn. It is possibly the most widely planted hawthorn in the United States and Europe because of its broad crown, shiny leaves, conspicuous flowers, and thorny bold texture. There are several varieties of this hawthorn because of its variable characteristics appearing over such a wide distribution. In Missouri, there are 2 to 5 varieties depending on which classification is followed.

The "haw" from hawthorn is from the Old English "haga," for hawthorn or other trees with small apple-like fruits.

Crataegus is from the Greek "kratos" (strength) and refers to the hard wood of some species; *crus-galli* translates as "cock's spur" in reference to the stem thorns resembling a rooster's spur.

Crataegus crus-galli ❀ a. Growth form with flowers, b. Flower, c. Fruit, d. Twig

Downy hawthorn

Crataegus mollis (Torrey & A. Gray) Scheele

Rose family (Rosaceae)

Also called red haw, summer haw, turkey crab apple

Appearance: Small tree, up to 30 feet tall, with stout branches and spreading to form a round-topped crown.

Flowers: April–early May, with or after the leaves emerge, in many-flowered clusters; flowers about 1 inch across; petals 5, white; stamens 20.

Fruit: September, solitary or in small clusters, somewhat globe-shaped, red, about 3/8 to 1/2 inch in diameter; flesh thick, yellow, dry, mealy when fully ripe, edible; seeds small, 3 to 5, light brown.

Leaves: Simple, alternate, broadly egg-shaped, 3 to 5 inches long and wide; **margin somewhat lobed, densely toothed**; upper surface dark yellowish-green; **lower surface paler and very hairy; leaf stalk hairy**, leaves turn red in autumn.

Twigs: Stout, **densely hairy at first**, becoming smooth when older; spines stout, shiny, chestnut-brown, 1 to 2 inches long.

Trunk: Bark reddish-brown to yellowish-brown, with shallow grooves and flat-topped, somewhat blocky and flaky ridges; wood light brown, hard, heavy.

Habitat: Occurs in open woods, along small streams, pastures.

Range: Eastern Oklahoma, Missouri, Arkansas, and Louisiana; east to Alabama, north to Ontario, and west to Michigan, Minnesota, eastern Dakotas, Nebraska, and Kansas.

Wildlife Uses: The fruit is eaten by fox sparrow, cedar waxwing, robin, ruffed grouse, wild turkey, mice, gray and fox squirrel, flying squirrel, gray fox, skunk, raccoon, and white-tailed deer. Deer also browse on the foliage and twigs. The thorni-ness, dense branching, and heavy foliage provide good cover and nesting sites for many birds.

Medicinal Uses: See discussion under urn-tree hawthorn, *Crataegus calpodendron.*

Remarks: Downy hawthorn was approved as the state flower by the 52nd General Assembly of Missouri on March 16, 1923. One of the largest of the hawthorns, they tolerate a wide variety of situations from different soil types, full sun or partial shade, and droughty conditions.

The "haw" from hawthorn is from the Old English "haga," for hawthorn or other trees with small apple-like fruits.

Crataegus is from the Greek "kratos" (strength) and refers to the hard wood of some species; *mollis* refers to the soft-hairy foliage.

Crataegus mollis ❦ a. Growth form with fruit, b. Flowers, c. Flower, d. Twig

Washington thorn

Crataegus phaenopyrum (L. f.) Medikus

Rose family (Rosaceae)

Appearance: Shrub to small tree, up to 30 feet tall, with a short trunk and ascending branches forming a rounded crown.

Flowers: May–early June, after the leaves appear, in many-flowered clusters; flowers about 1/2 inch across; petals white; stamens 20.

Fruit: September, persistent into winter, globe-shaped, shiny, bright red, about 1/4 inch in diameter; seeds 3 to 5, small, tip rounded, about 1/8 inch long.

Leaves: Simple, alternate, **broadest near the base, triangular, thin**, 1 1/2 to 2 inches long, 1 to 1 1/2 inches wide; margin coarsely toothed and **mostly with 3 main lobes**, sometimes smaller lobes present; **lobes sharply pointed at the tip, base broadly-rounded to nearly flattened; upper surface dark green, shiny**, smooth; lower surface paler, hairy; leaves turn red in autumn.

Twigs: Slender, brown to gray, smooth, with short, slender spines 1 1/2 to 2 inches long.

Trunk: Brownish-gray, thin, scaly.

Habitat: Occurs scattered in open woods, thickets, and edges of woods.

Range: Arkansas, east to Florida, north to Virginia, and west to Kentucky, southern Illinois, and Missouri.

Wildlife Uses: The fruit is eaten by fox sparrow, cedar waxwing, robin, ruffed grouse, wild turkey, mice, woodrat, gray and fox squirrel, flying squirrel, gray fox, skunk, raccoon, and white-tailed deer. Deer also browse on the foliage and twigs. The thorniness, dense branching, and heavy foliage provide good cover and nesting sites for many birds.

Medicinal Uses: See discussion under urn-tree hawthorn, *Crataegus calpodendron.*

Remarks: Washington thorn is often planted as an ornamental tree for its distinctive foliage and bright red, long-persisting fruit. This species seems resistant to the leaf diseases that develop on some of the other hawthorns. Washington thorn was first described to science in 1691 from a garden specimen, which had been growing in England for some time where it had been planted by some unknown or forgotten botanical explorer. At a later date, it became popular in cultivation around Washington, D.C., where it got its common name.

The "haw" from hawthorn is from the Old English "haga," for hawthorn or other trees with small apple-like fruits.

Crataegus is from the Greek "kratos" (strength) and refers to the hard wood of some species; *phaenopyrum* translates as "pear-like," possibly referring to its pendulous branches when weighted down with ripe fruits that somewhat resemble the strained appearance of pear tree *(Pyrus communis)* branches when fully loaded with ripe fruits.

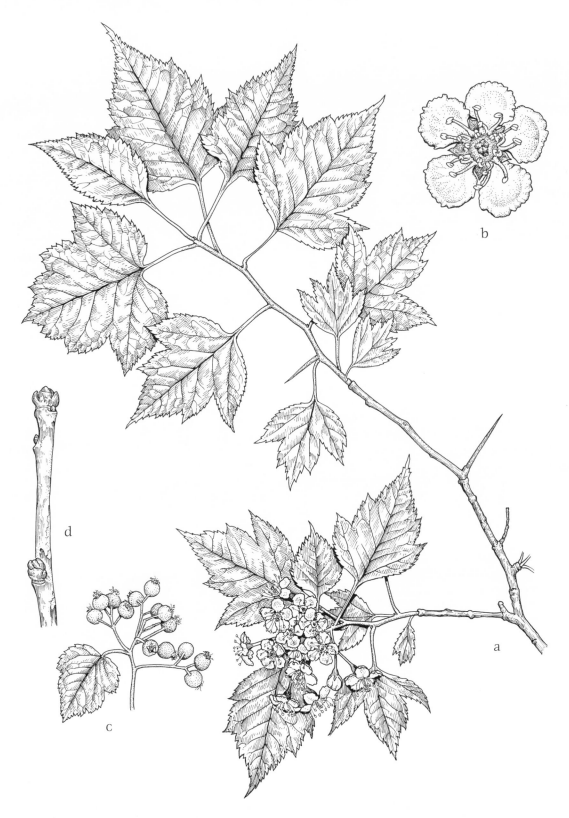

Crataegus phaenopyrum ❧ a. Growth form with flowers, b. Flower, c. Fruit, d. Twig

Frosty hawthorn

Crataegus pruinosa (Wendl.) K. Koch

Rose family (Rosaceae)

Appearance: Thorny shrub or small tree, attaining a height of 20 feet and a diameter of 4 to 8 inches.

Flowers: Late April–May, clusters smooth and few-flowered, stalks slender, bearing white, 5-petaled flowers 3/4 to 1 inch across, rounded, showy; stamens 20.

Fruit: September–October, few-fruited, stalks green or red; fruit globe-shaped, about 1/2 inch across, dark red at maturity, smooth, shiny, with a white waxy coating, often dotted, pulp yellow; nutlets (seeds with bony covering) 5, about 1/4 inch long.

Leaves: Simple, alternate, blade length 1 to 1 1/2 inches, width 3/4 to 1 inch; broadest in the middle, tip pointed, base rounded or broadly flattened, **margin densely toothed and also short-lobed**; mature leaves firm and leathery, dark green above, lower surface paler; leaf stalk slender green or reddish, somewhat winged by the leaf base, 1/2 to 1 inch long; leaves turn dull yellow in autumn.

Twigs: Slender, smooth, reddish-brown, with **stout, straight, brown thorns 1/2 to 1 1/2 inches long.**

Trunk: Bark dark gray and scaly; wood hard, fine-grained.

Habitat: Rocky open woods and thickets.

Range: Northern Arkansas, east to Kentucky and North Carolina; north to New England and Newfoundland; and west to Ontario, Wisconsin, Missouri, and east Kansas.

Wildlife Uses: The thorniness and dense branching make hawthorns favorite nesting sites for many birds. The small applelike fruits are not used by wildlife to nearly so great an extent as might be expected. Fox sparrows and cedar waxwings are the principal songbird users. Other birds include wild turkey, ruffed grouse and American robin. Coyote, gray fox, cottontail rabbit, raccoon and smaller mammals eat the fruit. White-tailed deer eat the foliage, twigs and fruit.

Remarks: The hawthorn group is complicated, with many variations and hybrids. Estimates as to the number of Missouri species have varied from 15 to 50. Sixteen species of hawthorn are included here based on work by Ladd 1988. Only two are considered as shrubs to small trees, frosty hawthorn and one-flower hawthorn.

Some hawthorn species are used as ornamentals, but most are subject to infection by cedar apple rust, a fungus that produces rusty-orange spots on the leaves and deforms the fruits.

The "haw" from hawthorn is from the Old English "haga," for hawthorn or other trees with small apple-like fruits.

Crataegus is from the Greek "kratos" (strength) and refers to the hard wood of some species; *pruinosa* means "frosty" and refers to the waxy, whitish coating of the fruit.

Crataegus pruinosa ❀ a. Growth form with thorns and flower clusters, b. Flower, c. Fruit

Littlehip hawthorn

Crataegus spathulata Michaux

Rose family (Rosaceae)

Also called pasture hawthorn

Appearance: Shrub or small tree, up to 25 feet tall, with a broad open crown and bearing sparse straight spines.

Flowers: May, after the leaves appear, in many-flowered clusters; flowers about 1/2 inch in diameter; petals 5, white; stamens about 20.

Fruit: September, persistent into winter, globe-shaped, bright red, about 1/4 inch or less in diameter; flesh dry, thin, mealy; seeds small, 3 to 5.

Leaves: Simple, alternate, broadest above the middle, **spatula-shaped, sometimes with 3 to 5 lobes at the end, but not symmetrically 3-lobed**; 1 to 2 inches long, 1 to 1 1/2 inches wide; margin toothed, **tip pointed to somewhat rounded, gradually tapering to a narrow base**; upper surface dark green, smooth, shiny; lower surface paler, smooth or bearing long, soft, shaggy hairs; leaf tapering to the base with a **winged leaf stalk**.

Twigs: Slender, reddish-brown, hairy, crooked; **spines sparse**, slender, more or less straight, brown, 1 to 1 1/2 inches long.

Trunk: Bark light brown to gray, smooth, with large, **thin plates that flake off exposing an orange-brown inner bark**; wood orange-brown, heavy, hard, strong.

Habitat: Endangered, occurring in moist soil in thickets and open woods.

Range: Occurs from east Texas, Oklahoma, southern Missouri, and Arkansas; east to Florida, and north to South Carolina and Virginia.

Wildlife Uses: The fruit is eaten by fox sparrow, cedar waxwing, robin, wild turkey, mice, gray and fox squirrel, flying squirrel, gray fox, skunk, raccoon, and white-tailed deer. Deer also browse on the foliage and twigs. The thorniness, dense branching, and heavy foliage provide good cover and nesting sites for many birds.

Medicinal Uses: See discussion under urn-tree hawthorn, *Crataegus calpodendron*.

Remarks: Although there are few known occurrences for littlehip hawthorn in Missouri, it is commonly encountered in east Texas pastures and in the southwestern quarter of Arkansas. It appears to be on the northern edge of its range in Missouri and possibly was never very common. Littlehip hawthorn is a species of conservation concern in Missouri and is considered endangered.

The name "littlehip" refers to the small fruit that resembles the fruit of wild rose called rose-hips. The "hip" is an Old English word *heope* or *hiope*, which means "seed pod."

The "haw" from hawthorn is from the Old English "haga," for hawthorn or other trees with small apple-like fruits.

Crataegus is from the Greek "kratos" (strength) and refers to the hard wood of some species; *spathulata* refers to the spatula- or spoon-shaped leaves.

Crataegus spathulata ✻ a. Growth form, b. Flowers, c. Flower, d. Fruit, e. Twig, f. Short spur shoot twig

One-flower hawthorn

Crataegus uniflora Muenchh.

Rose family (Rosaceae)

Also called dwarf hawthorn

Appearance: Slender shrub 3 to 12 feet, rarely a small tree, with crooked, thorny, small branches. Usually each small branch with a single flower or fruit.

Flowers: May, **flower stalk short, densely hairy with matted wool; flower single or rarely 2 to 3 together**, 3/8 to 5/8 inch wide, petals 5, white, rounded; stamens 20 or more.

Fruit: October, tip with 5 small leafy lobes, fruit body 3/8 to 1/2 inch thick, globe-shaped, hairy, greenish yellow to dull red, pulp firm, dry and mealy; nutlets (seeds with bony coverings) 3 to 5, about 1/3 inch long.

Leaves: Simple, alternate, somewhat leathery, leaf varying in shape from egg-shaped to gradually narrowed downward from a rounded summit, tip rounded to somewhat pointed, base wedge-shaped, margin toothed, unlobed, upper leaf surface dark green and shiny, lower leaf surface hairy, especially along the veins, **3/4 to 1 1/4 inches long, 1/2 to 1 inch wide or larger; leaf stalk stout, hairy, less than 1/4 inch long;** leaves turn dull yellow in autumn.

Twigs: Slender, reddish-brown to gray and very hairy when young, gray and smooth later; **twigs bearing one thorn at the base of a leaf stalk,** thorns slender, straight or slightly curved, gray to black, 1/2 to 2 1/4 inches long.

Trunk: Bark gray or dark brown.

Habitat: Thickets and open woods, usually in sandy or rocky ground.

Range: Texas, Oklahoma, Arkansas, and Louisiana; east to Florida, north to New York, and west to Ohio, Kentucky, southern Illinois, and Missouri.

Wildlife Uses: The small applelike fruits are eaten by fox sparrows, cedar waxwings, American robin, wild turkey and ruffed grouse. Coyote, gray fox, cottontail rabbit and smaller mammals eat the fruit. White-tailed deer eat the foliage, twigs and fruit.

Remarks: The hawthorn group is complicated, with many variations and hybrids. Estimates as to the number of Missouri species have varied from 15 to 50. Sixteen species of hawthorn are included here based on work by Ladd 1988. Only two are considered as shrubs to small trees, frosty hawthorn and one-flower hawthorn.

This is the smallest hawthorn in Missouri, both in leaf size and overall height. It is frequently found without flowers or fruit, probably due to growing in too much shade. Its small leaves and hairy young twigs are useful characters for identification.

The "haw" from hawthorn is from the Old English "haga," for hawthorn or other trees with small apple-like fruits.

Crataegus is from the Greek "kratos" (strength) and refers to the hard wood of some species; *uniflora* means "one-flowered."

Crataegus uniflora ❀ a. Growth form with thorns and fruit, b. Twig with leaves and flower, c. Fruit

Green haw

Crataegus viridis L.

Rose family (Rosaceae)

Appearance: Small tree, up to 35 feet tall, with a broad, rounded crown, *fluted trunk and branches with few or no spines.*

Flowers: May, after the leaves appear, in many-flowered clusters; flowers about 3/4 inch in diameter; petals 5, white; **sepals (flower structure below petals) narrow, entire (without teeth)**; stamens 15 to 20.

Fruit: September, persistent in winter, globe-shaped, in drooping clusters, bright red to orange, about 1/4 inch in diameter; seeds small, 4 to 5, about 1/8 inch long.

Leaves: Simple, alternate, broadly egg-shaped, 2 to 3 1/2 inches long and wide; **margin densely toothed, often with small lobes towards the tip;** tip pointed; **base narrowing**; upper surface dark green, shiny, smooth; lower surface paler usually with some hair in the axils of the veins; leaf stalk about 1 inch long, flattened or grooved above; the leaves turn purplish-red in autumn.

Twigs: Rigid, gray or reddish-brown, smooth; pores pale, elongated; with or without spines; spines when present slender, pale, sharp, 1/4 to 1 inch long.

Trunk: Bark gray to reddish-brown, thin, grooves shallow, ridges flat, scaly and somewhat loose; wood pale brown, hard, heavy, tough, fine-grained.

Habitat: Occurs in bottomland forests along larger streams, edges of swamps, sometimes on slopes with seepage water.

Range: East Texas, Oklahoma, Arkansas, and Louisiana; east to Florida, north to Virginia, and west to Indiana, Illinois, Missouri, and southeastern Kansas.

Wildlife Uses: The fruit is eaten by a variety of songbirds.

Medicinal Uses: See discussion under urn-tree hawthorn, *Crataegus calpodendron.*

Remarks: An Indiana-cultivated variety of green hawthorn called "Winter King" is the most commonly available hawthorn on the market. The persistent red fruit, rounded shape, fall color, spring flowers and distinct gray bark are its assets. Fruits and leaves of green hawthorn are susceptible to rust.

Green hawthorn grows in the wild on low ground, which is often quite wet, a characteristic that sets it apart from most of the other hawthorns.

The "haw" from hawthorn is from the Old English "haga," for hawthorn or other trees with small apple-like fruits. Green probably refers to its dark green leaves.

Crataegus is from the Greek "kratos" (strength) and refers to the hard wood of some species; *viridis* means "green."

Crataegus viridis ❀ a. Growth form with flowers, b. Flower, c. Fruits, d. Twig

Other Hawthorns

Crataegus species

Kansas hawthorn, *Crataegus coccinioides* Ashe

Characteristics: Flowers about 1 inch across; sepals (flower structure below petals) broad, toothed; leaves broadest near the base, 1 1/2 to 2 1/2 inches wide, 1 1/4 to 2 inches wide with 4 to 5 pairs of shallow lateral lobes.

Occurs in thickets and open woods, mostly on limestone hills. Ranges from southeastern Kansas, northern Arkansas, and Missouri, to southern Illinois.

Dotted hawthorn, *Crataegus collina* Chapm.

Characteristics: leaves broadest above the middle, 1 1/2 to 2 1/2 inches long, 1/2 to 1 1/2 inches wide; upper surface dull, veins noticeably indented; lower surface hairy; margin both finely and coarsely toothed; leaf stalk more than 1/4 as long as the leaf blade; fruit dull red or orange with pale dots.

Occurs in thickets and open woods along small streams. Ranges from eastern Oklahoma and Arkansas, east to Georgia, north to Virginia, and west to Indiana, Illinois, and Missouri.

Barberry-leaved hawthorn, *Crataegus engelmannii* Sarg.

Characteristics: Leaf margins finely toothed; upper surface of leaf shiny, veins not noticeable; lower surface hairy; twigs flexible.

Occurs in thickets and rocky open woods. Ranges from eastern Oklahoma, Missouri, and Arkansas, east to Mississippi, and north to Illinois

Thicket hawthorn, *Crataegus intricata* Lange

Characteristics: Flowers, leaves, and leaf stalks with minute glands (minute structures that secrete sticky or oily substances).

Occurs in rocky open woods and hillsides. Ranges from Missouri and Arkansas, east to North Carolina, north to Vermont, and west to Indiana and Illinois.

Round-leaved hawthorn, *Crataegus margaretta* Ashe

Characteristics: Leaves extremely variable but mostly oval to broadest above the middle; tip blunt or rounded; flowers 3/8 to 1/2 inch across, 6 to 10 flowers in a cluster; stamens about 20.

Occurs in rocky open woods and thickets. Ranges from Missouri, east to Pennsylvania, north to Michigan and southern Ontario, and west to Iowa.

Parsley haw, *Crataegus marshallii* Eggl.

Characteristics: Flowers in simple to slightly branched, 4- to 7-flowered clusters; flowers about 1 inch across; leaves deeply lobed, base of some of the lobes almost reaching the central vein; twigs stout.

Occurs in bottomland forests in the Bootheel of southeastern Missouri. Ranges from eastern Texas, Oklahoma, and Arkansas; east along the coastal plain to Florida, north to Virginia, and west to Missouri.

Hawthorn, *Crataegus sicca* Sarg.

Characteristics: Leaves fairly consistent in shape, broadest at or above the middle; tip pointed; flowers 1/2 to 3/4 inch across, 3 to 6 flowers in a cluster; stamens about 10.

Occurs on dry limestone or dolomite hills or rocky ground above streams; uncommon. Ranges from southern Missouri to Ohio.

Red haw, *Crataegus succulenta* Schrader ex Link

Characteristics: Leaves broadest at the middle, up to 1 1/2 times as long as wide; margin both coarsely and finely toothed above the middle; lower surface smooth.

Occurs in rocky woods and bluffs. Ranges from eastern Kansas and Missouri, east to North Carolina, north to southern Ontario, and west to Illinois and Iowa.

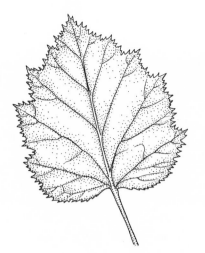

Crataegus coccinioides

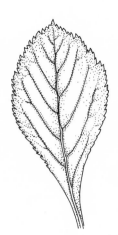

Crataegus collina

Crataegus engelmannii

Crataegus intricata

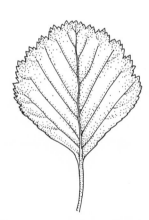

Crataegus margaretta

Crataegus marshallii

Crataegus sicca

Crataegus succulenta

Persimmon

Diospyros virginiana L.

Ebony family (Ebenaceae)

Appearance: Medium-sized tree, up to 60 feet tall, or, in open-grown situations, up to 30 feet tall, with a shorter trunk and broad crown.

Flowers: Late May–June, after the new leaves have emerged, male and female flowers on separate trees; male flowers in clusters of 2 to 3, greenish-yellow, urn-shaped, about 1/4 to 1/2 inch long; stamens about 16; **female flowers solitary, urn-shaped with tips recurved**, greenish-yellow to cream white, fragrant, about 1/4 to 1/2 inch long.

Fruit: September–October, **about 3/4 to 1 1/2 inch long and wide, globe-shaped, orange to orange-purple, often with a whitish coating; astringent and puckery to taste when green; when ripe, sweet, edible**; seeds 4 to 8, large, longer than broad, flat, wrinkled, dark brown, about 1/2 inch long.

Leaves: Simple, alternate, egg-shaped to broadest in the middle, 2 to 6 inches long, 1 to 3 inches wide; margin entire, tip pointed; upper surface dark green, shiny; lower surface paler, smooth to somewhat hairy; leaf stalk up to 1 inch long; leaves reddish-yellow to greenish-yellow in autumn.

Twigs: Slender, gray to reddish-brown, somewhat zigzag; pores orange; end bud absent.

Trunk: Bark dark brown to black, grooves deep, ridges broken into thick, square to rectangular blocks; wood dark brown, hard, strong, fine-grained.

Habitat: Occurs in rocky, dry open woods, edges of woods, glades, prairies, old fields, thickets, bottomland woods and valleys along streams.

Range: East Texas, Oklahoma, Arkansas, and Louisiana; east to Florida, north to Maryland, and west to Indiana, Illinois, Missouri, and eastern Kansas.

Wildlife Uses: The fruit is eaten by at least 16 species of birds, also by small rodents, raccoon, opossum, red fox, skunk, gray, fox, and flying squirrels, and white-tailed deer.

Medicinal Uses: Tea from the bark once was used as a folk remedy for stomachaches, heartburn, diarrhea, and dysentery.

Remarks: The edible fruit was well known by explorers and early settlers, being mentioned in the writings of De Soto in 1539, and Jan de Laet in 1558. Captain John Smith, in the 17th century near Jamestown, commented "If it be not ripe, it will draw a man's mouth awrie with much torment."

Fruit is eaten fresh when ripe or used to make jam, pudding, and nut bread. The dried leaves can be made into a tea rich in vitamin C. The wood is used for golf club heads, textile shuttles, billiard cues, and brush handles.

The name persimmon first appeared in press in 1612. Derived from the Algonquian word *pasimenan* which means "fruit dried artificially."

Diospyros is translated "fruit-of-the-gods," and *virginiana* refers to the state of Virginia.

Diospyros virginiana ❀ a. Growth form with flowers, b. Flower, c. Fruit, d. Twig

Russian olive

Elaeagnus angustifolia L.

Oleaster family (Elaeagnaceae)

Also called oleaster

Appearance: Small tree up to 25 feet tall, with low branches and a trunk that often leans; **easily recognized by its silvery leaves**.

Flowers: May–July, scattered on the branches in leaf axils, in clusters of 1 to 3 flowers; flowers small, up to 1/4 inch, **silvery yellow**, fragrant; petals absent; sepals 4; stamens 4.

Fruit: August–October, oval, about 1/2 inch long, yellow to tan but **densely covered with silvery scales**; flesh yellow, waxy, mealy, sweet; stony pit solitary, broadest in the middle, about 3/8 inch long, brown.

Leaves: Simple, alternate narrow, widest near the base, 2 to 3 1/2 inches long, 3/8 to 3/4 inch wide; margin entire, tip somewhat pointed; upper surface dull gray green, sometimes with silvery scales; **lower surface covered with silvery white scales**; leaf stalk with dense scales, about 1/2 inch long

Twigs: Slender, reddish, coated with gray, scaly hairs, later becoming smooth; **twigs often with short spines**.

Trunk: Bark thin, dark gray to brown, with shallow grooves, ridges flat, shedding in long strips; wood dark brown, light.

Habitat: Planted in yards and escaping into disturbed sites and idle ground where it spreads by seed or root sprouts often forming thickets.

Range: A native of southern Europe and western Asia to the Himalayan Mountains. Introduced and naturalized in the central and western states; rarely escaping in the eastern states.

Wildlife Uses: Birds feed on the fruits and distribute the seeds.

Remarks: Russian olive was first cultivated in Germany in 1736. It was introduced into the United States in the late 1800s, and was planted as an ornamental and subsequently escaped into the wild. Until recently, many state and federal agencies in the Great Plains and West once recommended Russian olive for wildlife planting and windbreaks. Although not a serious threat in Missouri yet, it may eventually become one like its cousin, autumn olive, *Elaeagnus umbellata* Thunb.

West of Missouri, Russian olive outcompetes native vegetation, disrupts natural plant succession and the distribution of nutrients, and stresses water supplies. Because Russian olive is capable of fixing nitrogen in its roots, it can grow on bare, mineral substrates and dominate stream-edge vegetation. Although it provides a plentiful source of edible fruits for birds, similar to autumn olive, ecologists have found that bird diversity is actually higher in stream-edge vegetation dominated by native plants. Both Russian olive and autumn olive have become nuisance weeds in many areas and should not be planted. Efforts should be made to eradicate them where they are found.

The common name reflects the general origin of the tree and the fruit, which resembles small olives.

Elaeagnus is from the Greek word *elaia* ("olive") and the Latin *agnus* ("lamb"), probably in reference to the dense silvery white hairs underneath the leaves; *angustifolius* refers to the narrow leaves.

Elaeagnus angustifolia ❦ a. Growth form with flowers, b. Flower, c. Fruit and leaves,
d. Winter fruit, e. Single fruit, f. Twig with spines, g. Twig

Wahoo

Euonymus atropurpureus Jacq.

Staff-tree family (Celastraceae)

Also called burning bush, eastern wahoo

Appearance: Usually a shrub, but sometimes a small tree to 25 feet, with spreading branches and an irregular crown.

Flowers: Late April–June, in clusters of 7 to 15, from axils of leaves, stalks slender, 1 to 2 inches long; flowers about 1/2 inch broad, petals 4, spreading, **purple**; stamens 4, alternating with the petals and arising from the edge of the disk.

Fruit: September–October, capsule deeply 4-lobed, smooth, about 1/2 inch across, persistent into winter on long stalks, purple to rose-colored, splitting open to expose brown seeds about 1/4 inch long enclosed by a **scarlet seed covering**.

Leaves: Opposite, simple, 2 to 5 inches long, 1 to 2 inches wide, egg-shaped to broadest in the middle and tapering at both ends, tip pointed, base tapering sharply, margin finely toothed; bright green above; pale and **hairy beneath**; leaf stalk 1/2 to 1 inch long; leaves turn yellow in autumn.

Twigs: Slender, somewhat **4-angled, purplish-green** turning brownish later; pores pale and prominent.

Trunk: Bark smooth, thin, gray, with minute scales; wood almost white, tinged with yellow or orange, close-grained, heavy, hard, tough.

Habitat: Occurs on wooded slopes, bluffs, open woods, alluvial soils along streams, and in thickets. Throughout Missouri, doubtless in every county.

Range: East Texas, Oklahoma, Arkansas, and Mississippi; east to Georgia, north to New York, and west to Ontario, Michigan, Wisconsin, Minnesota, Nebraska, and Kansas.

Wildlife Uses: The fruit is eaten by a number of species of birds, including wild turkey. The leaves and stems are eaten by white-tailed deer and cottontail rabbits.

Medicinal Uses: Native American women drank a solution of the inner bark for uterine discomfort and used the same preparation as an eye lotion. Pounded stem bark or root bark was applied to facial sores. Settlers used the bark as a liver stimulant and a laxative, and for fever and indigestion. An oil from the seed was used, both in Europe and the United States, to destroy head lice.

Remarks: Wahoo has been cultivated since 1756. It is a relatively fast-growing, short-lived shrub to small tree. Often sprouting from the roots, wahoo can form loose clonal thickets. It is sometimes used as an ornamental because of its beautiful scarlet fruit in autumn. The Native Americans used the powdered bark for tobacco and the wood for arrows.

The name wahoo is Dakota for *wãhu* from *wã* for "arrow" and *hu* for "wood," referring to the straight stems of the plant, which were used for arrows.

Euonymus is the Greek name meaning "true name;" *atropurpureus* is from the Latin *atro* (dark) and the Latin *purpureus* "purple" referring to the flowers and fruits.

Euonymus atropurpureus ✺ a. Growth form with fruit capsules, b. Flower, c. Capsule with fruit

American beech

Fagus grandifolia Ehrh.

Oak family (Fagaceae)

Appearance: Medium to large tree, up to 80 feet tall, with a long trunk supporting a wide, spreading crown.

Flowers: April–May, after the leaves have emerged, in separate male and female flower clusters on the same twigs; **male flowers in globe-shaped clusters, about 1 inch across**, hanging on stalks; stalks hairy, 1 to 2 inches long; stamens 8 to 10; female flowers usually in pairs on stout spikes, about 1 inch long, usually at the tip of the twigs.

Fruit: September–October, borne on short, hairy stalks, burlike husk, with straight or curved prickles; husk reddish-brown, 1/2 to 3/4 inch long, splitting into four sections; **nuts 2, brown, 3-angled**, sweet, edible, dispersed after first frost; good seed crops every 2 to 3 years.

Leaves: Simple, alternate, with straight veins, **very thin**, usually broadest at or just below the middle, 3 to 6 inches long, 1 1/2 to 3 inches wide; margin coarsely toothed, tip pointed, becoming papery; upper surface dull bluish-green, shiny, smooth; lower surface yellow green, smooth; **persisting on younger trees through winter**; leaves turning yellow or brown in autumn.

Twigs: Slender, somewhat zigzagged, green and hairy at first, later reddish-brown or gray and smooth; pores elongated, orange; **buds slender, 3/4 to 1 inch long, sharp pointed**.

Trunk: Bark light- to steel-gray, smooth, unfortunately a favorite tree for carving initials; wood reddish-brown, heavy, hard, strong, not durable, close-grained.

Habitat: Occurs on lower slopes and ravines of Crowley's Ridge, also mesic (moist) woods of slopes, ravines, and small valleys bordering streams and spring branches in the river hills bordering the Mississippi River in southeastern Missouri.

Range: From east Texas, east Oklahoma, Arkansas, and Louisiana; east to Florida, north to Nova Scotia, and west to Michigan, Wisconsin, Illinois, and Missouri.

Wildlife Uses: Fruit is eaten by a variety of songbirds, wild turkey, gray, fox and flying squirrels, small rodents, raccoon, opossum, and white-tailed deer.

Medicinal Uses: Native Americans chewed nuts as a worm expellant. Bark tea was used for lung ailments. Leaf tea was used as a wash for burns, frostbite, and poison ivy rash.

Remarks: American beech was first cultivated in the United States in 1800. It is a very impressive tree with its large, smooth trunk, huge limbs, and large, spreading canopy. The tree is long-lived (300 to 400 years) and fairly disease resistant. The wood is used for chairs, tool handles, woodenware, flooring, crates, toys, and fuel. Beech is especially good for containers since it does not impart taste or color to the contents (hence the famous "beechwood aged" Budweiser beer!). Rainfall seems to be a limiting factor for its distribution in Missouri, with the southeastern part of the state receiving the highest amount.

Beech is from the Old English *bece* for "edible." *Fagus* is from a Greek word referring to the edible nuts; *grandifolia* refers to the large leaves.

Fagus grandifolia ❧ a. Growth form, b. Male flower clusters, c. Female flower, d. Fruit, e. Seed, f. Twig

Swamp privet

Forestiera acuminata (Michaux) Poiret

Olive family (Oleaceae)

Appearance: Straggly shrub or small tree to 30 feet, growing in wet to swampy ground.

Flowers: Late March–April, **appearing before the leaves on stem of previous year**, male and female flowers mostly appearing on separate trees; male flowers in dense yellow to greenish yellow clusters above yellow bracts (modified leaves), petals lacking; stamens 4; female flowers in clusters 3/4 to 1 1/4 inches long.

Fruit: June, purplish, sometimes curved, longer than broad, tip pointed, about 1 inch long; single seed, light brown, about 1/3 inch long, one side flatter than the other.

Leaves: Simple, opposite, 2 to 4 1/2 inches long, 1 to 2 inches wide, longer than broad to egg-shaped, tip pointed, **base narrowly wedge-shaped**, margin with few teeth, leaf blade smooth, yellowish-green above, paler with occasional hairs on veins beneath; leaf stalk slender, 1/4 to 1/2 inch long, slightly winged by leaf bases; leaves turn yellow in autumn.

Twigs: Light brown to gray, smooth, slender, warty, with numerous pores; twigs sometimes rooting on contact with the mud.

Trunk: Bark dark brown, thin, close, slightly ridged; wood yellowish to reddish-brown, close-grained, light, weak, soft.

Habitat: Occurs in swamps, low wet woods, alluvial and rocky borders of streams, ponds, sloughs and bayous. In Missouri, mainly along the Mississippi River and in the Bootheel.

Range: Texas, Oklahoma, Arkansas, and Louisiana; east to Florida, north to South Carolina, and west to Tennessee, Indiana, Indiana, Illinois, Missouri, and southeastern Kansas.

Wildlife Uses: The fruit is considered to be a good wild duck food.

Remarks: Swamp privet often occurs in small stands due to its ability to sprout from the roots. It is quite noticeable in early spring, with the clusters of yellow flowers and bracts appearing along the gray branches before the leaves come out. In this way, it is similar in aspect to spice bush.

The name privet is of unknown origin. It was first used in print in 1542.

Forestiera is in honor of the French physician and botanist, Charles Le Forestier; *acuminata* refers to the pointed leaves.

Forestiera acuminata ❧ a. Growth form with fruit clusters, b. Fruit, c. Branch with flowers

White ash

Fraxinus americana L.

Olive family (Oleaceae)

Appearance: Medium to large trees, up to 90 feet tall, with a straight, tall trunk and narrow, rounded or pyramid-shaped crown.

Flowers: April–May, male and female flowers in clusters on different trees, appearing before or at leaf development; male flowers small, green to red, no petals; stamens 2 to 3; female flowers similar to male flowers.

Fruit: August–September, produced in dense clusters up to 8 inches long; fruit is a samara with wing partially around the seed; seed yellowish-brown, 1 to 2 inches long, smooth, flat.

Leaves: Opposite, feather-like arrangement, 8 to 12 inches long with 5 to 9 (usually 7) leaflets; leaflets broadest near the base or middle, 3 to 5 inches long, 1 1/2 to 3 inches wide; margin often with rounded teeth, tip pointed; **upper surface dark green, dull to somewhat shiny; lower surface paler, whitish, smooth**; leaf stalk smooth; leaves turn yellow or purple in autumn.

Twigs: Stout, rigid, brittle, green to brown, or gray, smooth; pores pale; bud at tip about 1/4 inch long.

Trunk: Bark light gray to dark brown, grooves deep, with narrow, interlacing ridges that are flat-topped, forming a diamond pattern; wood brown to nearly white, tough, strong, heavy, close-grained.

Habitat: Occurs in bottomland forests along streams, slopes, base of bluffs, upland and rocky woods, and glades.

Range: Texas, Oklahoma, Missouri, Arkansas, and Louisiana; east to Florida, north to Nova Scotia, and west to Ontario, Minnesota, south-eastern Nebraska, and eastern Kansas.

Wildlife Uses: The fruit is eaten by a variety of songbirds, bobwhite quail, wild turkey, wood ducks, and small mammals. White-tailed deer sometimes browse white ash heavily.

Medicinal Uses: Native Americans used the inner-bark tea as an emetic or strong laxative, also to relieve stomach cramps and fevers. A wash was used for sores, itching, lice, and snakebites.

Remarks: White ash has been in cultivation since 1724. It is an important timber tree and widely planted as an ornamental. The male trees flower every year but the female trees flower and produce large amounts of seed every few years. The seeds sprout prolifically in disturbed sites and unkempt yards. Often, white ash leaves turn color in autumn before the peak arrives in late October in Missouri. The wood is used for baseball bats, tool handles, musical instruments, cabinets, doors, frames, veneer, fuel, handles, ships, boats, and fuel.

The "white" of white ash possibly refers to the color of the undersurface of the leaf; "ash" is from the Old English *aesc* or "spear" made of ash wood.

Fraxinus is the ancient Latin name of the ash, from phraxix (a separation), referring to its use in hedges; *americana* is for its origin.

Fraxinus americana ❧ a. Leaf with fruit clusters, b. Male flower clusters, c. Male flower, d. Female flower variations, e. Seed, f. Twig

Green ash

Fraxinus pennsylvanica Marshall

Olive family (Oleaceae)

Also called red ash

Appearance: Medium to large tree, up to 90 feet tall, with a straight, tall trunk, high branches, and a round-topped crown.

Flowers: April–May, male and female flowers in clusters on different trees, appearing before or at leaf development; male flowers small, green, no petals; stamens 2; female flowers similar to male flowers.

Fruit: August–September, produced in dense clusters up to 8 inches long; fruit is a samara with wing partially around the seed; seed yellowish-brown, 1 to 2 inches long, smooth, flat.

Leaves: Opposite, feather-like arrangement, 8 to 12 inches long with 5 to 9 (usually 7) leaflets; leaflets lance-shaped to uniformly broad, 4 to 6 inches long, 1 to 2 inches wide; margin often with rounded teeth, tip pointed; **upper surface dark green, dull**, smooth; **lower surface paler green, more or less hairy; leaflet stalks, at least the lower ones, narrowly winged**; leaves turn bright yellow in autumn.

Twigs: Stout, rigid, gray, smooth; pores pale.

Trunk: Bark brown, grooves shallow, with narrow, interlacing ridges that are flat-topped, forming a diamond pattern; wood yellowish, heavy, hard, strong, coarse-grained.

Habitat: Occurs in bottomland soils, commonly along streams, borders of sloughs, edges of swamps and ponds.

Range: New Mexico, Texas, Oklahoma, Arkansas, and Louisiana; east to Florida, north to Nova Scotia, and west to Manitoba, Montana, Wyoming, and Colorado.

Wildlife Uses: The fruit is eaten by a variety of songbirds, bobwhite quail, wild turkey, wood ducks, and small mammals.

Remarks: Green ash is the most widely distributed of all native American ashes. It was first cultivated in 1823. It is often planted as a shade tree and is also much used for windbreak planting in the prairie/plains states. Female green ash trees produce a tremendous amount of seeds and are considered messy. In areas, such as yards, where this would be a problem, planting male trees is recommended. The wood is not as desirable as that of white ash but can be used for the same purposes.

Green ash is a common tree of bottomland forests across the state. It grows in association with bur oak, hackberry, box elder, shellbark hickory, pin oak, cottonwood, and silver maple.

The "green" of green ash probably refers to the undersurface color of the leaf; "ash" is from the Old English *aesc* or "spear" made of ash wood.

Fraxinus is the ancient Latin name of the ash, from phraxix (a separation), referring to its use in hedges; *pennsylvanica* is for the state.

Fraxinus pennsylvanica ❁ a. Leaf, b. Leaf variation, c. Winged leaf stalks, d. Flower clusters, e. Female flower, f. Male flower, g. Seed, h. Twig

Pumpkin ash

Fraxinus profunda (Bush) Bush

Olive family (Oleaceae)

Appearance: Large tree, up to 120 feet tall, with a narrow, open crown, and **a swollen or pumpkin-shaped base**.

Flowers: April–May, male and female flowers in clusters on different trees, appearing before or at leaf development; male flowers small, green, no petals; stamens 2 to 3; female flowers similar to male flowers. For an illustration of the flower clusters, see one of the other ashes because they are all similar.

Fruit: August–September, produced in dense clusters up to 8 inches long, fruit is a samara, with the wing partially around the seed, yellowish-green, 2 to 3 inches long, smooth, flat.

Leaves: Opposite, feather-like arrangement, 9 to 18 inches long with 7 to 9 leaflets; leaflets broadest near the base or middle, 5 to 10 inches long, 1 1/2 to 5 inches wide; margin mostly entire but sometimes slightly toothed, tip pointed; upper surface yellowish-green, smooth; **lower surface paler with soft hairs; leaf stalk very hairy**; leaves turning yellow in autumn.

Twigs: Stout, light gray, often hairy when young, smooth later; pores large, pale; **end bud reddish-brown, hairy**.

Trunk: Bark light gray, grooves shallow, ridges flattened or rounded, with small, fattened scales, bark somewhat similar to white ash; wood brown, heavy, hard, strong, close-grained.

Habitat: Occurs in swamps and wet bottomland forests.

Range: Louisiana, east to northern Florida, north to New York, and east to Ohio, Indiana, Illinois, and southeastern Missouri.

Wildlife Uses: The fruit is eaten by a variety of songbirds, wood ducks, and small mammals.

Remarks: Pumpkin ash is also known as *Fraxinus tomentosa*. It has the largest leaves and fruits of any of the Missouri ashes. The name "pumpkin ash" is derived from the enlarged base or buttress that the tree develops when growing on sites that remain wet for most of the growing season. Buttresses are also found on water tupelo and bald cypress. The buttress provides extra stability for the tree, which is rooted in mucky, wet, and generally unstable soil. In swamps, pumpkin ash grows with bald cypress, water tupelo, Drummond's red maple, swamp cottonwood, water elm, and water locust. Understory plants include buttonbush, swamp privet, Virginia willow, and swamp rose. In wet bottomland forests, overcup oak, swamp chestnut oak, willow oak, water oak, water hickory, and Nuttall's oak are present.

The wood is not as desirable as that of white ash but can be used for the same purposes.

The name "ash" is from the Old English *aesc* or "spear" made of ash wood.

Fraxinus is the ancient Latin name of the ash, from phraxix (a separation), referring to its use in hedges; *profunda* is Latin for "deep," probably referring to its aquatic environment.

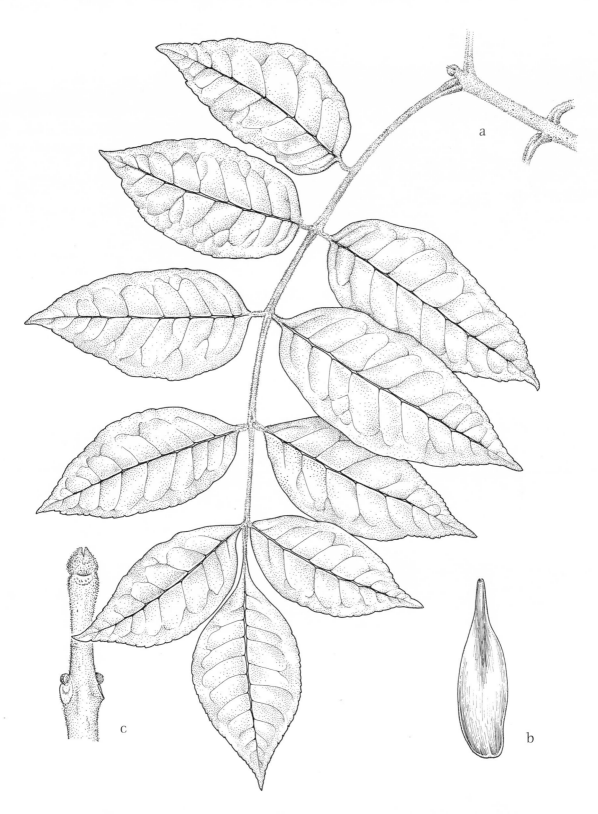

Fraxinus profunda ❧ a. Leaf, b. Seed, c. Twig

Blue ash

Fraxinus quadrangulata Michaux

Olive family (Oleaceae)

Appearance: Small to medium-sized tree, up to 60 feet tall, with a relatively short trunk and small branches which spread into a slender or small crown.

Flowers: March–April, in clusters before the leaves appear, flowers perfect or with male and female flowers; male flowers small, dark purple, no petals; stamens 2; female flowers similar to male flowers.

Fruit: August–September, produced in loose clusters up to 4 inches long; fruit is a samara with the wing partially surrounding the seed; seed tan, 1 to 2 inches long, 1/4 to 1/2 inch wide, smooth, flat.

Leaves: Opposite, feather-like arrangement, 8 to 12 inches long, with 5 to 11 (usually 7) leaflets; leaflets lance-shaped, broadest near the base or uniformly wide, 3 to 5 inches long, 1 to 2 inches wide; margin with small teeth, tip pointed; upper surface dark green, smooth, shiny; lower surface paler, smooth or slightly hairy along the midrib and veins; leaf stalk slightly two-ridged, smooth to hairy; leaves turn a clear, bright yellow in autumn.

Twigs: Stout, 4-sided, the angles often winged, light gray to brown, smooth or finely hairy; pores pale, scattered; **bud at tip densely hairy**.

Trunk: Bark light brown to gray, **with irregular, shallow grooves, ridges narrow and flat-topped with smaller, thin scales**; wood yellowish-brown, hard, rather brittle, very durable.

Habitat: Occurs on ledges and rock outcrops on limestone and dolomite bluffs, glades, dry rocky woodland, and, less frequently, along streams and at the base of bluffs.

Range: Oklahoma, Missouri, and Arkansas; east to Alabama, north to Ontario, and west to Michigan, Wisconsin, and Illinois.

Wildlife Uses: The fruit is eaten by a variety of songbirds, bobwhite quail, wild turkey, and small mammals.

Remarks: Blue ash has been in cultivation since 1823. It is sometimes planted in parks and gardens as an ornamental and for shade. The wood is used for flooring and interior finishing.

Of all the ashes, this one is the easiest to identify, because it is the only one with square and sometimes winged twigs.

The name "ash" is from the Old English *aesc* or "spear" made of ash wood. The "blue" comes from the fact that a blue dye is obtained by immersing the inner bark in water and/or the sap, which turns bluish when exposed to air. Early settlers used this blue dye for cloth.

Fraxinus is the ancient Latin name of the ash, from phraxix (a separation), referring to its use in hedges; *quadrangulata* refers to the 4-angled twigs.

Fraxinus quadrangulata ❧ a. Leaf with seeds, b. Flower clusters, c. Flower, d. Seed, e. Twig

Water locust

Gleditsia aquatica Marshall

Senna family (Caesalpiniaceae)

Appearance: Medium-sized tree, up to 60 feet tall, with a long trunk and an irregular, spreading crown, and armed with large spines.

Flowers: May, appearing after the leaves emerge, mostly with male and female flowers on different trees or with some flowers complete; male flowers in many-flowered clusters 3 to 4 inches long; petals 5, greenish-white; stamens 3 to 10; female flowers in slender, few-flowered clusters 2 to 3 inches long, greenish-white.

Fruit: September–October, brown, **shiny, thin, flat, somewhat oval, 1 to 3 1/2 inches long; seeds 1, (rarely with 2 or 3)**, orange to brown, about 1/2 inch wide, circular.

Leaves: Alternate, feather-like arrangement, sometimes divided again, 5 to 10 inches long with 5 to 12 pairs of leaflets; leaflets broadest near the base to even throughout, 1/2 to 1 inch long, 1/4 to 1/2 inch wide; upper surface dark green, shiny, smooth; lower surface paler, smooth; margins entire or sometimes with very small, rounded teeth, tips rounded; leaves turn yellow in autumn.

Twigs: Gray or reddish-brown, smooth; pores raised; spines dark red, shiny, simple or branched, up to 10 inches long.

Trunk: Bark dull gray or reddish-brown, firm, grooves narrow, between small, flat scales; often bearing heavy, simple to multi-branched spines; wood light reddish-brown, strong, heavy, hard, close-grained.

Habitat: Occurs in bottomland forests, swamps, and edges of sloughs in southeastern Missouri up to St. Charles County.

Range: East Texas, Louisiana, and Mississippi; north to Arkansas, Missouri, and southern Illinois; also Florida, Georgia, and South Carolina.

Wildlife Uses: The seeds are eaten by squirrels, small rodents, and white-tailed deer.

Remarks: The wood is extremely durable in contact with the soil, and farmers have been known to make fence posts that have lasted over a century.

In swamps, water locust grows with bald cypress, water tupelo, Drummond's red maple, swamp cottonwood, water elm, and water hickory. Understory plants include buttonbush, swamp privet, Virginia willow, and swamp rose. In wet bottomland forests, overcup oak, swamp chestnut oak, willow oak, water oak, water hickory, and Nuttall oak are present.

The name "locust" is from the Greek *akris*, which was first used in 1615 as a reference to the carob tree, *Ceratonia siliqua* L., with its pod-shaped fruit.

Gleditsia is a word modification and is named in honor of Johann Gottlieb Gleditsch, an 18th Century German botanist who was affiliated with the Berlin Botanic Garden; *aquatica* refers to the plant's habitat.

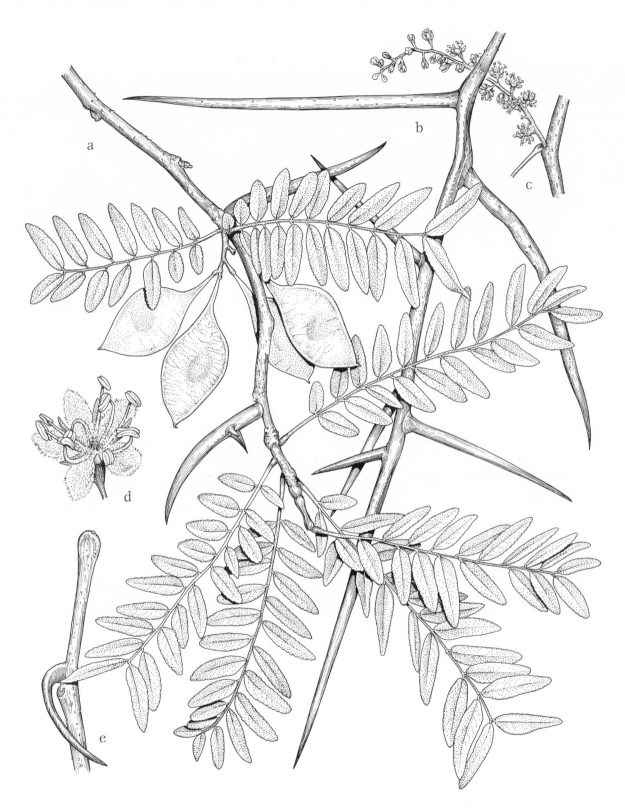

Gleditisia aquatica ❊ a. Growth form with fruit, b. Single spine, c. Flower cluster, d. Flower, e. Twig with spine

Honey locust

Gleditsia triacanthos L.

Senna family (Caesalpiniaceae)

Appearance: Medium-sized tree, up to 60 feet tall, with a short, thorny trunk and thorny branches, and a loose, open crown.

Flowers: May–June, appearing after the leaves, mostly with male and female flowers on different trees or with some flowers complete; male flowers in many-flowered clusters 2 to 5 inches long; petals 3 to 5, hairy, greenish-white; stamens 10; female flowers in slender few-flowered clusters 2 to 3 inches long; petals 3 to 5, hairy, greenish-white.

Fruit: September–October, **leathery pod, 6 to 18 inches long, narrow, flattened, many-seeded, dark brown, twisting at maturity**; seeds 6 to 27, oval, brown, flattened, hard, about 1/2 inch long, surrounded by pulp.

Leaves: Alternate, feather-like arrangement, sometimes divided again on more vigorous shoots, 5 to 10 inches long, with leaflets 15 to 30; leaflets 3/4 to 2 inches long, 1/2 to 1 inch wide, broadest near the base to lance-shaped to even throughout; upper surface dark green, shiny, smooth; lower surface paler, often hairy; margin entire or sometimes with very small rounded teeth, tip rounded; leaves turn yellow in autumn.

Twigs: Greenish- or reddish-brown, shiny, stout, often zigzag, with solitary or branched spines which are rigid, sharp, straight, shiny, purplish-brown, up to 12 inches long.

Trunk: Bark grayish-brown to black, on older trees with grooves deep, narrow, **separating into scaly ridges with the sides or ends free and curved outward; often bearing heavy, simple to multibranched spines**; wood reddish-brown, stiff, hard, durable, highly shock resistant, shrinks little, coarse-grained.

Habitat: Occurs in bottomlands along streams and their valleys, also upland slopes and open or wooded pastures.

Range: Texas, Oklahoma, Arkansas, and Louisiana; east to Alabama, north to Pennsylvania and New York, and west to Illinois, Iowa, Nebraska, and Kansas.

Wildlife Uses: Seeds and pulpy seed pods provide winter food for cottontail rabbits, gray squirrel, and white-tailed deer. The flowers are reported to be a good bee food.

Medicinal Uses: Pods once were made into tea to treat indigestion, measles, and inflammation of the lungs. Inner-bark tea (with sycamore bark) once was used for hoarseness and sore throats.

Remarks: Honey locust has been in cultivation since 1700. It is a popular shade and ornamental tree, planted along city streets, yards, and landscaped areas, but it is the cultivated varieties that are used because they are thornless. Native Americans ate the fleshy sweet pulp of the young pods. Honey locust is a common and troublesome invader of pastures and idle fields.

Gleditsia is a word modification and is named in honor of Johann Gottlieb Gleditsch, an 18th Century German botanist who was affiliated with the Berlin Botanic Garden; *triacanthos* refers to the commonly three-branched thorns.

Gleditsia triacanthos ❀ a. Growth form with flower clusters, b. Single spine, c. Male flower, d. Female flower, e. Fruit, f. Twig with spine

Kentucky coffee tree

Gymnocladus dioica (L.) K. Koch

Senna family (Caesalpiniaceae)

Appearance: Medium-sized tree, up to 60 feet tall, with stout, blunt branches, forming a narrow, round-topped crown.

Flowers: May–June, after the leaves, on the tips of new twigs, male and female flowers separate and on the same or separate trees, both similar in size and shape; flowers 14 to 20, **greenish-white**; male flowers in clusters 3 to 5 inches long; flowers about 1/4 inch long; petals 5; stamens 10; female flowers in clusters up to 12 inches long.

Fruit: October, **persisting through winter in large pods 4 to 10 inches long**; pods brownish-black, thick, leathery, with 3 to 5 seeds; **seeds blackish, rounded, flattened, large, 3/4 inches long, very hard-shelled in a sweet, sticky pulp; pods fall to the ground in late winter unopened**.

Leaves: Alternate, **feather-like arrangement and divided again, 1 to 3 feet long, 1 to 2 feet wide, with 5 to 9 branches; each branch contains 7 to 14 leaflets**; leaflets 3/4 to 3 inches long, 1 to 1 1/2 inches wide, egg-shaped to oval; margin entire, tip often abruptly pointed at the tip; upper surface dark green, smooth; lower surface paler, smooth; **opening late in the spring, early to drop in autumn** with yellow leaves.

Twigs: Short, blunt, contorted, reddish-brown, hairy, later grayish-brown, smooth; pores numerous, orange; buds barely protruding from a silky-lined cavity.

Trunk: Bark gray to brown, shallow grooved, **with scaly ridges that curl away on one edge from the trunk**; wood reddish-brown, heavy, moderately strong and durable, coarse-grained.

Habitat: Occurs in bottomland forests along streams and in moist woods at the base of bluffs.

Range: Nowhere common; Oklahoma, Arkansas, Missouri, and Tennessee; north to New York and Ontario; and west to Wisconsin, Iowa, South Dakota, Nebraska, and Kansas.

Wildlife Uses: Little wildlife use, although squirrels and white-tailed deer have been reported in the Ozarks to eat the pods and seeds. Some speculate that some large, Ice-age mammals, now extinct, were the seed dispersers.

Medicinal Uses: The pulp from the pod was used by Native Americans to treat "lunacy." Leaf and pulp tea formerly were used for reflex troubles and as a laxative.

Remarks: Kentucky coffee tree leaves are the largest of any native Missouri tree. The tree was first introduced into cultivation in 1748. The first specimens sent back to Europe were welcomed as a botanical curiosity. This is a handsome shade tree with a unique appearance and unusual bark. Small clones can occur from root sprouts. The wood has been used for posts, furniture, fuel, cabinetmaking, interior finish, and construction.

The Meskwaki and other tribes made coffee from roasted, ground seeds (raw seeds are toxic), and European settlers apparently learned from them, hence the common name.

Gymnocladus is from the Greek *gymos* (naked) and *klados* (a branch) and refers to the thick, blunt, naked branches; *dioica* refers to the separate male and female flowers.

Gymnocladus dioica ❀ a. Leaf, b. Flowers, c. Single flower, d. Fruit, e. Seed, f. Twig

Ozark witch hazel

Hamamelis vernalis Sarg.

Witch hazel family (Hamamelidaceae)

Also called vernal witch hazel

Appearance: Shrub attaining a height of up to 9 feet, often sending up sprouts from the base; or uncommonly a small tree, especially in cultivation.

Flowers: January–April, fragrant, flower stalks short to absent, flowers clustered or solitary; petals 4, **yellow to dark red**, 1/4 to 1/2 inch long, narrow, strap or ribbon-shaped; stamens usually 8.

Fruit: September–October, capsule hard, woody, about 1/2 inch long, splitting down a two-parted tip; seeds 1 or 2, large, hard, black, forcibly discharged to a distance of up to 30 feet.

Leaves: Simple, alternate, blade length 2 to 5 inches, width about 3 inches on the average, inverted egg-shaped to oval, tip rounded to blunt, base wedge-shaped to rounded, uneven; margin strongly wavy; upper surface dull green with veins lying below the general surface; lower surface paler green, smooth to hairy, veins prominent beneath. Some forms with lower surface densely velvety-hairy. The leaves turn yellow to brownish-yellow in autumn.

Twigs: Rather stout, light brown to reddish-brown or gray, **densely velvety-hairy**, later smooth and light or dark gray.

Trunk: Bark tight not peeling, gray to brown, often with gray blotches, pores narrow, cream-colored.

Habitat: In gravel and rocky streambeds, at the base of rocky slopes along streams, and rarely on wooded hillsides in rocky draws.

Range: From Missouri and Arkansas to Oklahoma

Wildlife Uses: The leaves and shoots are browsed in varying degrees by white-tailed deer. The bark is occasionally eaten by beaver, squirrels and cottontail rabbits. The seeds and flowers are eaten by wild turkey and ruffed grouse.

Medicinal Uses: Like the Eastern witch hazel, the twigs, leaves and bark are the basis of witch hazel extract, which is included in shaving lotions and in many medicinal lotions for bruises and sprains.

Remarks: Ozark witch hazel differs noticeably from Eastern witch hazel in that the flowers are produced in late winter or early spring. The latter produces flowers in late autumn to early winter. Both witch hazels make attractive shrubs in cultivation. The Ozark witch hazel is the first woody species to be found in bloom in Missouri, often blooming while snow is on the ground.

Hamamelis is from the Greek words *hama* ("at the same time") and *melon* ("apple"), possibly because of the presence of both fruit and flower simultaneously; *vernalis* ("spring") refers to its early-blooming habit from midwinter to spring.

Hamamelis vernalis 🌿 a. Growth form, b. Twig with flower clusters, c. Flower, d. Twig with seed capsules and next year's flower buds

Eastern witch hazel

Hamamelis virginiana L.

Witch hazel family (Hamamelidaceae)

Appearance: Tall shrub to small tree, up to 30 feet tall, with a short trunk, soon branching to form a broad, rounded shape.

Flowers: October–December, fragrant, flower stalks short to absent, flowers clustered, petals 4, **bright yellow**, 1/2 to 3/4 inches long, narrow, strap or ribbon-shaped; stamens 8.

Fruit: Ripens the following September–October, capsule hard, woody, about 1/2 inch long, splitting down a two-parted tip; seeds 1 or 2, large, hard, black, forcibly discharged to a distance of up to 30 feet.

Leaves: Simple, alternate, blade length 6 inches, width 3 inches on the average, or on older branches much smaller, inverted egg-shaped to oval, tip pointed, base wedge-shaped, uneven; margin wavy, sometimes toothed; usually smooth above; somewhat hairy beneath; leaf stalk hairy, about 1/4 to 3/4 inch long; leaves turn yellow in autumn.

Twigs: Slender, zigzag, reddish or orange, **smooth or slightly hairy**.

Trunk: Brown, thin, smooth when immature, and scaly when mature; wood reddish-brown, hard, close-grained, sapwood almost white.

Habitat: Occurs in moist woods on north- or east-facing slopes or in wooded valleys along streams. Uncommon in Missouri and restricted to the extreme southeastern part of the Ozarks.

Range: East Texas, Oklahoma, Arkansas, southeastern Missouri, and Louisiana; east to Florida, north to Nova Scotia, and west to Michigan, Wisconsin, and northern Illinois.

Wildlife Uses: The leaves and shoots are browsed in varying degrees by white-tailed deer. The bark is occasionally eaten by beaver, squirrels and cottontail rabbits. The seeds and flowers are eaten by wild turkey and ruffed grouse.

Medicinal Uses: The twigs, leaves and bark are the basis of witch hazel extract, which is included in shaving lotions and in many medicinal lotions for bruises and sprains. Native Americans used this plant profusely. They applied the bark to skin tumors and skin inflammations, used the inner bark as a treatment for irritated eyes, and chewed the bark to freshen their mouths. A boiled solution was rubbed on the legs of young athletes to keep them limber; it also was used to treat a lame back.

Remarks: Eastern witch hazel has been in cultivation since 1736. Eastern witch hazel differs noticeably from Ozark witch hazel in that the flowers are produced in late autumn or early winter. The latter produces flowers in late winter or early spring. Both witch hazels make attractive shrubs in cultivation. The Eastern witch hazel is the last woody species to bloom in Missouri. In superstitious lore, the twigs are used as divining rods or witching sticks to locate water or mineral deposits.

Hamamelis is from the Greek words *hama* ("at the same time") and *melon* ("apple"), possibly because of the presence of both fruit and flower simultaneously; *virginiana* refers to the state of Virginia, where the plant was first described.

Hamamelis virginiana ✻ a. Growth form, b. Flowers, c. Seed capsules, d. Winter twig

Rose of Sharon

Hibiscus syriacus L.C.

Mallow family (Malvaceae)

Also called shrubby althaea

Appearance: Many-branched shrub or small tree 3 to 18 feet. Not native, sometimes spreads from plantings.

Flowers: July–September, showy, emerging from axils of leaves, flower stalk variable in length; **flowers large, showy**, 2 to 4 inches across, solitary on new year's growth; petals 5, variable in color in the many horticultural forms—white, pink, lavender, rose, with a crimson or purplish blotch at the base, 1 3/4 inches long, rounded to inverted egg-shaped, margins wavy; **central column prominent with stamens along it and a 5-parted tip (stigma)**.

Fruit: September–October, capsule egg- to oval-shaped, **persisting into winter, splitting into five-parts**, 3/4 to 1 inch long, hairy.

Leaves: Alternate, simple, triangular to broadest in the middle, usually more or less 3-lobed, 1 1/2 to 4 3/4 inches long, margin with rounded or pointed teeth; upper surface medium green, often shiny; lower surface smooth except for a few hairs on the veins; young leaves hairy, becoming smooth later; leaf stalk 1/4 to 1 inch long, generally shorter than the blades; leaves turn yellow in autumn.

Twigs: Smooth, gray to brown, somewhat roughened, broadened at the tip.

Habitat: Commonly planted as an ornamental shrub, known to spread along roadsides, railroads, thickets and woods.

Range: Native of Asia. Escaped in Texas, Oklahoma, Arkansas, and Louisiana; east to Florida, north to Massachusetts, and west to Missouri; also in coastal regions of Canada.

Wildlife Uses: Rose of Sharon has little wildlife value although it is reported that hummingbirds are attracted to the flowers.

Remarks: Rose of Sharon was introduced into cultivation about 1600. This is one of the less aggressive shrubs, rarely competing with native vegetation; although, in one instance, it has spread into the woods at Castlewood State Park, St. Louis County. There are two native hibiscus in Missouri, *Hibiscus lasiocarpos* and H. *militaris,* but neither are considered woody. They occur along borders of streams, ponds, sloughs, ditches in wet soil or shallow water.

Hibiscus is the ancient name of the European Marsh-mallow; *syriacus* is for Syria, where it was once supposed to be native; however, more recent investigations prove it to be originally from China and India.

Hibiscus syriacus ❀ a. Growth form with flower, b. Twig with seed capsules

Possum haw

Ilex decidua Walter

Holly family (Aquifoliaceae)

Also called deciduous holly

Appearance: Usually a shrub with a spreading open crown, but sometimes a small tree to 30 feet.

Flowers: April–May, flowering when leaves are about half grown, single or in clusters, some plants may be male, others female, or flowers may be perfect (see illustration); petals 4 to 6, white, egg-shaped, about 1/4 inch long; stamens 4 to 6.

Fruit: September–October, persistent on branches most of the winter after leaves are shed, berry globe-shaped, orange to red, 1/4 inch across, solitary or 2 to 3 together; seeds usually 4, pale yellow.

Leaves: Simple, alternate or often in clusters on short lateral spurs; 2 to 3 inches long, 1/2 to 1 1/2 inches wide, widest at the middle and tapering at both ends, **tip blunt**, base wedge-shaped or narrowly tapering, **margin mostly with round or blunt teeth**; upper surface dark green, smooth or with a few hairs, main vein lying below the general surface; lower surface paler, smooth or hairy on the veins; leaf stalk slender, grooved, smooth to densely hairy, length up to 1/2 inch long.

Twigs: Drawn out, slender, often with many short spurlike lateral twigs, light to dark gray, smooth or slightly hairy.

Trunk: Bark smooth, thin, mottled gray to brown, sometimes with numerous warty protuberances; wood pale yellow to white, heavy, hard, close-grained.

Habitat: Occurs on dolomite glades, rocky upland open woods, fencerows, borders of upland and lowland ponds, swamps, sloughs, valleys and low wet woods along streams.

Range: East Texas, Oklahoma, Arkansas, and Louisiana; east to Florida, north to Maryland, and west to Kentucky, Indiana, Illinois, Missouri, and Kansas.

Wildlife Uses: Small mammals, opossums and at least 9 species of birds feed upon the fruit, including the bobwhite quail. The female shrub is a heavy producer of fruits, most of which persist until late winter. Often in a particularly hard winter, or when the regular food supply is scarce, birds will clean the fruits from the branches in a short period. On warm, early spring days, intoxicated robins and mockingbirds are sometimes seen after they have eaten the fermenting fruits. White-tailed deer are known to browse the branches.

Remarks: Possum haw is occasionally planted as an ornamental, and is attractive in winter because of its orange to red berries. Some shrubs will have all male flowers, which lack the showy berries. It is best to plant more than one plant to ensure that some will be female. The foliage turns dull purplish and green in autumn.

Ilex is the ancient Latin name of the holly oak rather than of the holly; *decidua* refers to the autumn-shed leaves; many hollies are evergreen.

Ilex decidua ❧ a. Growth form, b. Twig with flowers, c. Flower, d. Winter twig with fruit, e. Stem

American holly

Ilex opaca Sol.

Holly family (Aquifoliaceae)

Appearance: Small to medium-sized **evergreen tree**, up 50 feet tall, with short, crooked branches and a rounded or pyramidal crown.

Flowers: May–June, in short-stalked clusters, male and female flowers either on separate trees or both on the same tree; male flowers in clusters of 3 to 9, small, white, petals 4; stamens 4; female flowers single or 2 to 3 together, small, white, petals 4.

Fruit: October, berry-like, rounded to egg-shaped, bright red, rarely yellow or orange, 1/4 to 1/2 inch long; seeds 4.

Leaves: Alternate, **evergreen, thick, leathery**, egg-shaped to widest in the middle, 2 to 4 inches long, 1 to 1 1/2 inches wide; **margin with large, sharp, spine-tipped teeth**, tip pointed; upper surface dark green, dull, smooth; lower surface paler green, smooth to somewhat hairy; leaf stalk short, stout, grooved, sometimes hairy.

Twigs: Stout, green to light brown or gray, covered with fine, rust-colored hairs when young, smooth later; pores small.

Trunk: Bark light or dark gray, thin, smooth or with small, wart-like projections; wood ivory white to pale brown, tough, highly shock resistance, close-grained.

Habitat: Occurs naturally only in southeastern Missouri on the lower slopes and edges of Crowley's Ridge on sandy-gravelly soils that remain moist from seepage.

Range: East Texas, Oklahoma, Arkansas, and Louisiana; east to Florida, north to Massachusetts and New York, and west through Pennsylvania, Ohio, Indiana, Illinois to southeastern Missouri.

Wildlife Uses: At least 20 species of birds eat the fruit after it is exposed to a hard frost.

Medicinal Uses: Native Americans chewed the fruit for colic and indigestion. Fruit is considered poisonous. Leaf tea used for measles, flu, colds, and pneumonia; externally for sores, itching. Bark tea once used in malaria and epilepsy.

Remarks: American holly is one of the rarest trees in Missouri, however, hundreds of cultivated varieties developed throughout its range are commonly planted as an ornamental for its evergreen leaves and bright red fruit that can add comfort to a cold winter day. It was a favorite tree of George Washington who germinated and planted a grove of holly in the South Semicircle at Mount Vernon.

Holly is one of the whitest woods known. It is used to make wood engravings, handles, carvings, some veneer and cabinetwork, small furniture, and measuring scales and rules for scientific instruments; when dyed black to resemble ebony, it is used for piano keys, violin pegs, and fingerboards. Holly makes attractive Christmas decorations but wild populations can quickly be devastated.

Holly is Old English for "holy," perhaps referring to its use at Christmas time.

Ilex is the Latin name for holly oak, *Quercus ilex; opaca* (opaque, shaded) refers to the dull green leaf.

Ilex opaca ❧ a. Growth form, b. Flowers, c. Flower, d. Fruit, e. Twig

Winterberry

Ilex verticillata (L.) A. Gray

Holly family (Aquifoliaceae)

Also called black alder

Appearance: A shrub or small, rounded tree to 25 feet.

Flowers: April–May, small, male flowers in clusters of 2 to 10, female flowers in clusters of 1 to 3; some plants may be male, others female, or flowers may contain both sexes (see illustration); petals 4 to 8, greenish-white, egg-shaped or rounded, 1/4 inch across; stamens usually the same number as the petals and alternating with them.

Fruit: September–October, persistent in winter, globe-shaped, about 1/4 inch in diameter, shiny red to orange or yellow; seeds usually 3 to 6.

Leaves: Simple, alternate, thin to leathery in texture, length 1 1/2 to 4 inches, width about 1 inch, egg-shaped to broadest in the middle and tapering at both ends to lance-shaped, **tip tapering to a point**, base tapering to sometimes rounded, **margin with sharp-pointed teeth;** upper surface smooth; lower surface downy; leaf stalk about 1/4 inch long, somewhat hairy. Leaves turning black in autumn.

Twigs: Gray to reddish-brown, smooth at first but usually roughened by warty pores later.

Habitat: Occurs along igneous shut-ins, rocky stream beds and sandstone bluffs of the St. Francois Mountains.

Range: Missouri, Arkansas, and southeastern Louisiana; east to Florida, north to Maine and Nova Scotia; and west to Illinois, Wisconsin, and Minnesota.

Wildlife Uses: The fruit is eaten by small mammals and at least 48 species of birds including bluebirds, American robin, cedar waxwing, bobwhite quail and ruffed grouse.

Medicinal Uses: The fruit and bark were used as an astringent internally for diarrhea and locally in ulcerated skin lesions.

Remarks: Winterberry is the most popular of the red-fruited, deciduous hollies. There are many varieties and horticultural forms. It has been cultivated since 1736, and is used for ornamental planting in moist places. It is rather free of insects and disease.

The native winterberry found in Missouri is *Ilex verticillata* var. *padifolia* (Willd.) Torrey & Asa Gray. *Padifolia* is Greek for "leaves like Padus," in reference to *Padus*, a European genus of cherry trees.

Ilex is the ancient Latin name of the holly oak rather than of the holly; *verticillata*, meaning whorled, refers to the axillary clusters of flowers.

Ilex verticillata ❀ a. Twig with flowers, b. Flower, c. Twig with fruit

Butternut

Juglans cinerea L.

Walnut family (Juglandaceae)

Also called white walnut

Appearance: Medium-sized tree, up to 60 feet tall, with a short trunk dividing into several ascending limbs that form an irregular or round-topped crown.

Flowers: April–May, male and female flowers on the same tree; male flowers in catkins, 1 1/2 to 5 inches long, appearing when the leaves are half grown from buds of the previous year, yellowish-green; stamens 7 to 15; female flowers 1 to 6 in a short spike, each about 1/2 inch long; emerging at the end of current year's growth.

Fruit: September–October, from 1 to 5 in a cluster, drooping, odor strong, 1 1/2 to 3 inches long, broadest in the middle and narrowing at two equal ends, with 2 to 4 ridges, light brown, **sticky with rust-brown hairs, not splitting open to expose the nut**; nut conspicuously 4-ribbed, sometimes with 4 fainter ribs, light brown, broadest in the middle and narrowing at both ends, 1 to 2 1/2 inches long; seed sweet, oily, edible.

Leaves: Alternate, feather-like arrangement, 10 to 25 inches long, **with sticky hairs on the leaf stalk; leaflets 11–19**, 2 to 4 times longer than broad to lance-shaped, 2 to 5 inches long, 1 1/2 to 2 inches wide; margin with small teeth, tip pointed; **upper surface yellow-green with fine hairs**; lower surface paler, with sticky hairs when young; leaves turn yellow in autumn.

Twigs: Stout, brown to grayish-brown, hairy; pores white, conspicuous; **end bud large, 1/2 to 3/4 inches long, hairy; pith of twig dark brown, separating into chambers when cut lengthwise**.

Trunk: Bark gray to light brown, sometimes whitish, grooves deep, **ridges broad, smooth, flat, short, roughly forming diamond-shaped patterns, chocolate-colored when cut**.

Habitat: Occurs in moist woods at the base of slopes and bluffs, and along streams.

Range: Arkansas and Missouri; east to Georgia, north to New Brunswick, and west to Minnesota and Iowa.

Wildlife Uses: The nuts are eaten by mice and squirrels.

Medicinal Uses: Native Americans used bark tea for rheumatism, headaches, toothaches; applied to wounds to stop bleeding and to promote healing. Butternut contains the active component, juglone, which has been shown to have antiseptic and anti-tumor properties.

Remarks: Butternut has been cultivated since 1633. Several varieties have been developed for their nuts, which are more valued than their wood products. Unfortunately, butternut is in precipitous decline throughout its range because of butternut canker, a fungal disease that girdles the branches and stems. Butternut is on the road to extinction unless a cure is found.

Native Americans and European settlers harvested the buttery fat left from boiling the nuts, hence the name. The other name, white walnut, is for the sometimes whitish broad ridges of the bark.

Juglans is from the Latin *Jovis glans*, meaning "acorn (or any nut of similar shape) of Jove (of the god Jupiter);" *cinerea* (gray) refers to the color of the bark.

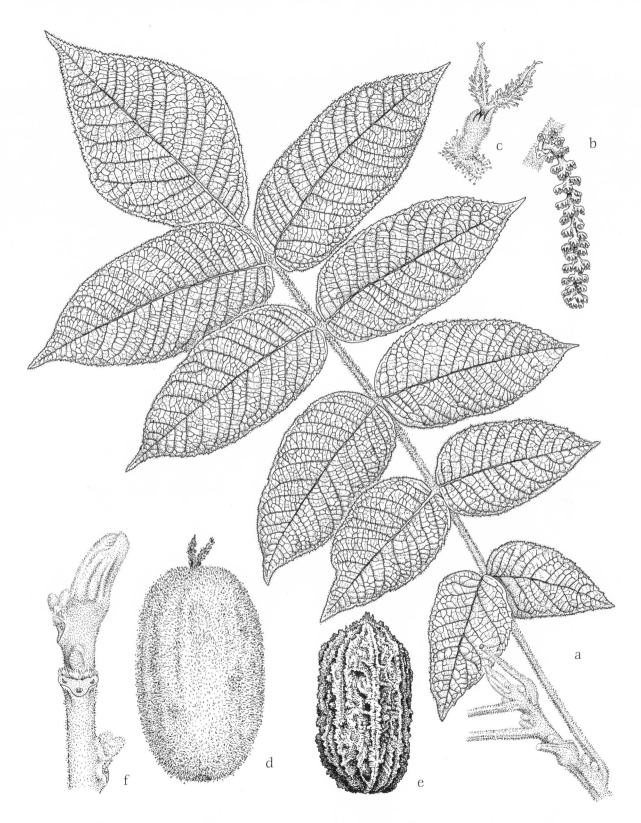

Juglans cinerea ❦ a. Leaf, b. Male catkin, c. Female flower, d. Fruit, e. Nut, f. Twig

Black walnut

Juglans nigra L.

Walnut family (Juglandaceae)

Appearance: Large tree, up to 90 feet tall, with a straight trunk and rounded, open crown.

Flowers: April–May, male and female flowers on the same tree; male flowers in catkins, 2 to 5 inches long, stout, yellow-green, usually hairy, appearing when the leaves are half grown from buds of the previous year; stamens 20 to 30; female flowers 1 to 5 in a short spike, each about 1/4 inches long, yellowish-green, emerging at the end of current year's growth.

Fruit: September–October, single or in pairs, large, **rounded**, 1 1/2 to 2 1/2 inches in diameter, outer husk thick, green to yellow-green, turning dark brown at maturity, slightly hairy, not splitting open to expose the nut; nut shell globe-shaped, hard, bony, 1 to 1 1/2 inches long, dark brown to black; kernel oily, sweet, edible.

Leaves: Alternate, feather-like arrangement, 1 to 2 feet long, **with an odor, leaf stalk hairy, with 11 to 23 leaflets, end leaflet smaller than side ones or absent**; leaflets broadest near the base to broadly lance-shaped, 3 to 5 inches long, 1 to 2 inches wide; margin toothed, tip pointed; upper surface yellow-green, smooth; lower surface paler, hairy; leaves are late to emerge in the spring, turn yellow in autumn, and simultaneously drop after first hard frost.

Twigs: Stout, rigid, brown to gray-brown, hairy; end bud about 1/2 inches long, hairy; **pith light brown, chambered when cut lengthwise**.

Trunk: Bark grayish-brown or black, grooves deep, **ridges broad, sharp or rounded edges, roughly forming diamond-shaped patterns, chocolate-colored when cut**; wood attractive, dark rich brown, heavy, hard, coarse-grained.

Habitat: Occurs in moist woods at the base of slopes or bluffs, in valleys along streams, and in open and upland woods; sometimes planted or persisting in old fields and pastures.

Range: Texas, Oklahoma, Missouri, Arkansas, and Louisiana; east to Florida, north to New York and Ontario; west to Minnesota, Nebraska, and Kansas.

Wildlife Uses: The nuts are eaten by mice and squirrels. It is a preferred host by caterpillars of the luna moth, and the regal moth whose larva is the hickory horned devil.

Medicinal Uses: Native Americans used inner-bark tea as an emetic (induces vomiting) and lax-ative; bark was chewed for toothaches. The husk was used on ringworm and chewed for colic. Leaf tea is an astringent (causes tissue to contract) and insecticidal against bedbugs.

Remarks: Black walnut has been in cultivation since 1686. It makes a fine ornamental because of its shape and large leaves. Over 70 varieties have been developed. Walnut manufactures a substance called juglone that is lethal to and pre-vents the growth of many other plants within the trees rooting zone. The wood is used to make cabinets, veneers, furniture, interior finishing, and gunstocks. The leaves of walnut can be heav-ily attacked by the walnut caterpillar, *Datana inte-gerrima*.

Juglans is from the Latin *Jovis glans*, meaning "acorn (or any nut of similar shape) of Jove (of the god Jupiter);" *nigra* (black) refers to the dark wood.

Juglans nigra ❀ a. Leaf with fruit, b. Female flowers, c. Male catkins, d. Male flower, e. Nut, f. Twig

Ashe's juniper

Juniperus ashei Buchholz

Cypress family (Cupressaceae)

Also called Ozark white cedar

Appearance: Shrub to small **evergreen** tree rarely more than 30 feet. Usually irregular, **main branches emerging at the base**, with a fluted and twisted trunk.

Flowers: March–May, minute, male and female cones usually appearing on separate trees; male cones small, golden brown, about 1/8 inch long, cones produced at tips of twigs; female cones smaller.

Fruit: August–September, fleshy, berrylike cone about 1/4 inch long, bluish-green, covered with a white, waxy coating, globe-shaped; single seed, egg-shaped, tip pointed, base rounded, shiny, light to dark brown, about 1/8 inch diameter.

Leaves: Usually at the ends of the twigs, minute, scalelike, opposite in 2 to 4 ranks, flatly pressed against the small stem, egg-shaped, tip pointed, margin minutely toothed, lacking glands but resinous, aromatic; leaves retain their green color in winter.

Twigs: Gray to reddish, scaly, aromatic, rather stiff.

Trunk: Bark gray to reddish-brown beneath, shredding into shaggy, lengthwise strips, **white blotches ringing the stems and branches;** wood streaked reddish-brown, sapwood lighter colored, close-grained, hard, light, not strong, but rot resistent, somewhat aromatic.

Habitat: On dolomite bluffs and glades, and limestone glades on knobs along the reservoirs of the former White River and its tributaries in southwestern Missouri.

Range: Southwestern Missouri, north Arkansas, Arbuckle Mountains and bluffs of Pryor Creek in Oklahoma and in parts of Texas, especially the Edwards Plateau. Southward and westward into Mexico and Guatemala.

Wildlife Uses: The foliage is browsed occasionally by white-tailed deer. The sweet fruit is eaten by several species of birds and mammals, including the bobwhite quail, American robin, bluebird, cedar waxwing, gray fox and raccoon.

Remarks: The best example of a stand of old growth Ashe's juniper in Missouri is protected at Ashe Juniper Natural Area, Stone County, where trees have been aged between 350 and 500 years old.

Mostly in Texas, where it is abundant on the Edwards Plateau, the wood is used for fuel, poles, posts, crossties and small woodenware articles. Ashe's juniper is occasionally cultivated as an ornamental, and is apparently resistant to the cedar-apple rust.

Juniperus is the classical name; *ashei* is in honor of William Willard Ashe (1872–1932) a pioneer forester who collected botanical specimens in Arkansas.

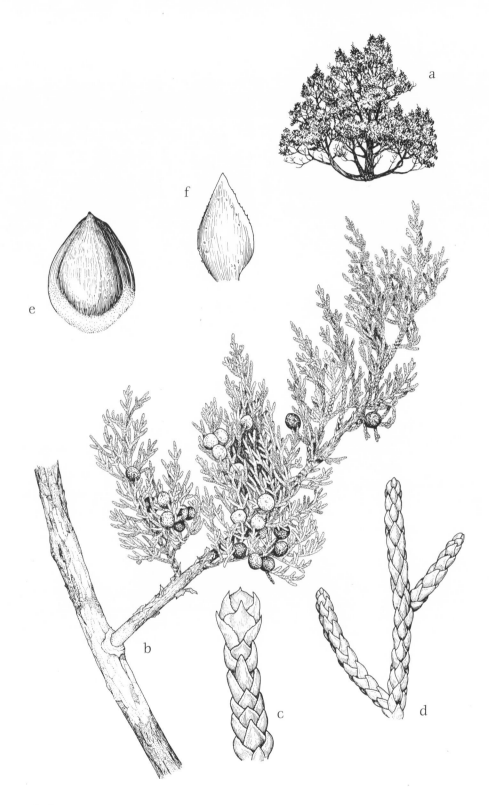

Juniperus ashei ❀ a. Growth form, b. Branch with fruit, c. Male cone at tip of small branch, d. Small female cones at tip of small branches, e. Seed, f. Scalelike leaf

Red cedar

Juniperus virginiana L.

Cypress family (Cupressaceae)

Also called Easter red cedar

Appearance: Small to medium-sized tree, up to 50 feet tall, **aromatic, evergreen** with a dense crown; crown pyramid-shaped but sometimes cylindrical; trunk single, tapering, and spreading at the base.

Flowers: March–May, minute, male and female cones usually appearing on separate trees; male cones small, often abundant, golden brown, about 1/16 inch long with 8 to 10 pollen sacs, cones produced at tips of twigs; female cones smaller, purplish, about 1/16 inch long.

Fruit: August–September, fleshy, berry-like cone, about 1/4 inch long, **dark blue**, covered with a white, waxy coating, globe-shaped; **seeds 1 to 2**, egg-shaped, tip pointed, 1/16 inch long, smooth, shiny; **flesh sweet, resinous, with odor of gin**.

Leaves: Usually at the end of the twigs, minute, dark green, **margin entire**; scale-like leaves opposite each other, 1/16 to 1/8 inch long, flatly pressed against the twig; needle-like leaves 1/8 to 3/8 inches long; **green leaves turn bronze color after cold spells in early winter**.

Twigs: Flexible, green first year, reddish-brown second year, aromatic.

Trunk: Bark light reddish-brown, shredding into long, thin, flat strips, trunk tapering and spreading at the base; wood at center red, outer wood white, light, brittle, soft, fragrant, durable, close-grained.

Habitat: Occurs on glades and bluffs; open, rocky woods, pastures, old fields, roadsides, fencerows.

Range: Almost throughout the eastern United States; west to Texas, Oklahoma, Kansas, Nebraska, and the Dakotas.

Wildlife Uses: The fruit (female cone) is eaten by at least 20 species of birds; also gray fox, opossum, and raccoon. The thick crowns provide nesting and roosting cover for many birds. Cedar waxwings earned their name from their preference for the fruits.

Medicinal Uses: Native Americans used fruit tea for colds, worms, rheumatism, coughs, and to induce sweating. Fruit was chewed for canker sores.

Remarks: Red cedar has been cultivated since 1664. Some gnarled cedars, living on bluffs in the Ozarks, have been aged at over 1,000 years old. The aromatic wood is used for chests, closets, interior finish, posts, poles, pencils, woodenware, and novelties. The resin is refined to produce an oil that is used for ointments, liniments, soaps, and shoe polishes. The tree is host to cedar-apple rust, which in certain stages attacks the leaves of apple, hawthorn, and crabapple trees.

Red cedar will invade glades and prairies that have not been burned for some time. The dense cedar canopy shades out herbaceous plants and the resin in the fallen needles leaches out into the soil and restricts plant growth. The smaller fire-sensitive trees can easily be managed by prescribed burning but larger trees may have to be cut, stacked, and burned. Once cut below the lowest branch, red cedar will not grow back.

Juniperus is the classical Latin name; *virginiana* refers to the state of Virginia.

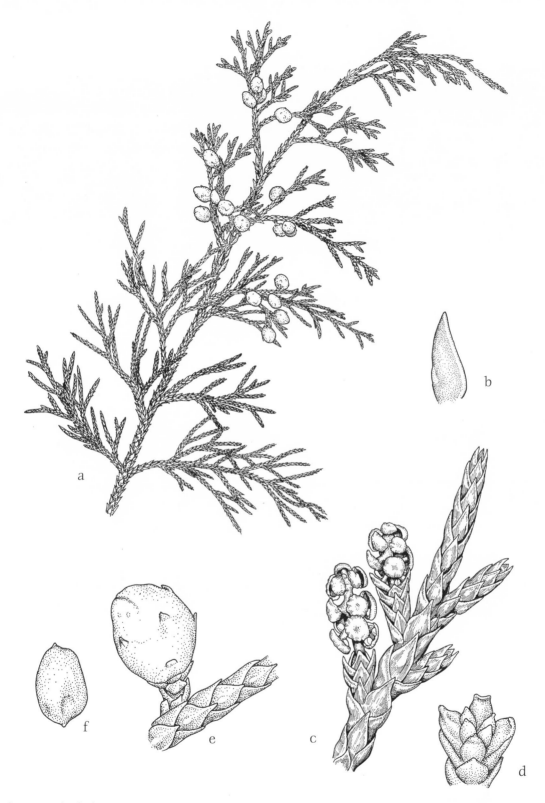

Juniperus virginiana ❀ a. Growth form with fruit, b. Scalelike leaf, c. Twig with male cones, d. Female cone at tip of twig, e. Fruit, f. Seed

Goldenrain tree

Koelreuteria paniculata Laxm.

Soapberry family (Sapindaceae)

Appearance: Small to medium-sized tree, up to 40 feet tall, with an equal spreading crown, in a broad, somewhat irregular globe-shape.

Flowers: June–July, complete, with both male and female parts, small, produced in loose, upright, branched clusters, 12 to 15 inches long; **flowers yellow with red center, showy**, 1/4 to 3/4 inch wide.

Fruit: September–October, in clusters of brown, **3-sided bladder-like, papery capsules**, 1 to 2 inches long; seeds black, round, 1 to 3; **capsules or pods appear as Chinese lanterns and persist into winter**.

Leaves: Alternate, **feather-like arrangement, sometimes split again**, 6 to 15 inches long; leaflets 7 to 15, broadest near the base, 1 to 3 inches long, less than 2 inches wide; **margin coarsely toothed**, sometimes lobed, tip pointed; upper surface emerging bronzed, maturing to dark green, smooth; lower surface paler, smooth; leaves turn greenish-yellow, yellow, or golden yellow in autumn.

Twigs: Stout, somewhat zigzag, olive to light brown, smooth; pores, raised, prominent, orange to brown; prominent leaf scars but no end bud.

Trunk: Bark light gray-brown, thin, older branches and trunk with significant ridges and grooves; **trunk short, branching early, quickly losing its central leader**.

Habitat: Ornamental tree planted in urban areas and escaping from cultivation.

Range: Native to China, Japan, and Korea; widely planted in the United States in plant hardiness zones 5 to 9 which includes all of Missouri up to the southern half of Iowa.

Wildlife Uses: Of little wildlife value other than serving as a nectar food source for insects.

Remarks: Goldenrain tree was first introduced into the United States in 1763. It is used as an ornamental landscape tree and sometimes naturalizes on disturbed sites. Young trees are sensitive to dieback or death in severe winters.

While serving as Minister to France from 1784 to 1789, Thomas Jefferson became friends with Madame de Tessé, the aunt of the Marquis de Lafayette, and maintained an active correspondence with her until her death in 1814. On June 12, 1809, Jefferson received from her seeds of the "Koelreuteria," and two years later was able to report that a tree had grown from that shipment and was planted at his Monticello Estate.

Goldenrain tree currently does not appear to be as aggressive as some of the other exotics that have become naturalized in Missouri. However, multiflora rose, bush honeysuckle, autumn olive, and others appeared conformable at first but soon became troublesome weeds after years of acclimation to their new environment.

Goldenrain is named for the appearance of the clusters of bright yellow flowers.

Koelrueteria is named for Joseph Gottlieb Koelreuter, a German professor of botany; *paniculata* means a branched cluster of flowers with flowers maturing from the bottom upwards.

Koelreuteria paniculata ❧ a. Growth form with flowers, b. Leaflet, c. Flower, d. Fruit, e. Twig

Corkwood

Leitneria floridana Chapman

Corkwood family (Leitneriaceae)

Appearance: Shrub or small tree attaining a height of 20 feet and often forming thickets by root suckers.

Flowers: March–April, male and female flowers on separate plants, male catkins many-flowered, each catkin 1 to 2 inches long, light brown; stamens 3 to 12; female catkins few-flowered, shorter than the male catkins; **catkins flowering before leaves emerge**.

Fruit: June–July, in clusters of 2 to 6, flattened, about 3/4 inch long, 1/4 to 1/3 inch wide, longer than broad, tip pointed to blunt, brown; seed light brown, flattened.

Leaves: Simple, alternate, in terminal clusters, 3 to 6 inches long, 1 to 3 inches wide, longer than broad, tip pointed or rounded, base narrowed; leaf hairy above when young and with densely matted hairs beneath, when mature rather leathery, dark olive to dull green; smooth or hairy above; bearing long, soft hairs beneath; leaf stalk 1/4 to 1 1/4 inches long with long, soft hairs; leaves turn yellow in autumn.

Twigs: Reddish-brown to gray, smooth, finely furrowed, pores numerous. The large flower buds that over winter resemble small pine cones.

Trunk: Bark gray to brown, ridges narrow, grooves shallow; wood pale yellow, soft, close-grained and light weight.

Habitat: Occurs in wooded or open wetlands and wet ditches along roadsides in the lowlands of southeastern Missouri.

Range: Southeast Texas, east Arkansas, southeast Missouri, northern Florida, and south Georgia.

Remarks: Corkwood is a species of conservation concern throughout its entire range. It is classified as rare in Missouri. Once more widespread in the swamps of the Bootheel, only remnant populations remain due to destruction of habitat. Corkwood Conservation Area, in Butler County, was purchased to protect the largest population of corkwood left in Missouri, along with excellent dune and swale forest.

The buoyant fruit of corkwood is timed to drop in late spring when floodwaters begin receding, leaving the fruit to germinate on exposed soil.

The wood, lighter than cork and second only to balsawood, is sometimes used for fishing-net floats, bobbers and bottle stoppers.

Corkwood is the only species in the genus *Leitneria,* and *Leitneria* is the only genus in the family *Leitneriaceae.*

Leitneria is in honor of the German naturalist E. F. Leitner; *floridana* refers to the early so-called "Floridian Provinces" of the southeastern states.

Leitneria floridana ❀ a. Growth form with fruit, b. Male catkins, c. Female catkins

Sweet gum

Liquidambar styraciflua L.

Witch hazel family (Hamamelidaceae)

Appearance: Large tree, up to 130 feet tall, with a long, cylindrical trunk, pyramid-shaped crown, and corky wings on branches and twigs.

Flowers: April–May, appearing with emerging leaves, male and female flowers on same twig; male flowers greenish-yellow, petals absent, on an upright stalk in several tight, rounded clusters; stalks 2 to 3 inches long; stamens numerous; female flowers in a single, drooping, round cluster about 1/2 inch in diameter.

Fruit: September–October, persists through winter, light brown, **globe-shaped, formed by the union of multiple individual fruits, hard, spiny due to numerous woody, horn-like projections**, somewhat shiny, 1 to 1 1/2 inches in diameter; seeds, from each individual fruit in head, 1 to 2, flat with a wing at the tip, 1/4 to 1/2 inch long, light brown.

Leaves: Alternate, **star-shaped, with 5 (sometimes 7) lobes**, 3 to 6 inches wide, deeply lobed; margin toothed, **tips long pointed**; upper surface dark green, smooth, glossy, **slightly aromatic when bruised**; lower surface paler, hairy along the veins; leaf stalk 3 to 6 inches long, slender; leaves turn various shades of gold, red, pink, and purple, often on the same tree.

Twigs: Slender to moderate, reddish- or yellowish-brown becoming gray, aromatic, **often with corky wings on second-year's growth**; pores raised, dark; end bud 1/4 to 1/2 inch long, pointed, shiny, reddish-brown, cone-shaped.

Trunk: Bark brown to gray, very rough with deep grooves and narrow, slightly scaly ridges.

Habitat: Occurs in rich, moist bottomland soils in valleys and along streams.

Range: East Texas, Oklahoma, Arkansas, and Louisiana; east to Florida, north to New York and Connecticut; west to Illinois and Missouri. Also in the mountains of Mexico and Central America.

Wildlife Uses: The seeds are eaten by at least 25 species of birds including goldfinch, purple finch, wood duck; also gray squirrel and Eastern chipmunk.

Medicinal Uses: The gum (hardened sap) was traditionally chewed for sore throats, coughs, colds, diarrhea, ringworm; used externally for sores, skin ailments, wounds. It is the ingredient in "compound tincture of benzoin," available from pharmacies.

Remarks: Sweetgum has been cultivated since 1681. It is ornamental, rapid growing, long-lived, and relatively free from insects and disease damage. A popular urban tree, the town of St. James is called the sweetgum capital of Missouri for its streets lined with the tree. The tree's "gumballs" can be a messy problem in lawns but creating a mulch bed under the tree can solve that problem plus repel cats seeking an outdoor litter box. Gumballs are also sprayed various colors and used as ornaments. The wood is used for flooring, furniture, veneers, cabinets, musical instruments, and many other products.

The sweet gummy sap is sometimes chewed by children as a substitute for chewing gum.

Liquidambar refers to the amber-colored liquid sap; *styraciflua* is from *styraci* ("storax") and *flua* ("fluidus") or flowing like storax or styrax, which is an Asiatic tree.

Liquidambar styraciflua ❦ a. Leaves, b. Male flower clusters, c. Female flower cluster, d. Fruit, e. Twig

Tulip tree

Liriodendron tulipifera L.

Magnolia family (Magnoliaceae)

Also called yellow poplar, tulip poplar

Appearance: Large, stately tree, over 100 feet tall, with a long, clear trunk and a pyramid-shaped crown.

Flowers: May–June, **large, greenish-yellow, orange-banded at the base, tulip-shaped, showy**, 3 to 4 inches across, with 6 upright petals; stamens numerous, long; flower stalk, stout, upright, 1 to 2 1/2 inches long.

Fruit: September–October, brown, **woody, cone-shaped**, longer than broad, tapering to a point, 2 to 3 inches long; seeds numerous, winged, light brown, about 1 1/2 inches long.

Leaves: Alternate, simple, 4 to 6 inches long and broad, **tip notched or V-shaped at the center, with two lobes near the tip and 2 or 4 lobes on the lower sides**; upper surface dark green, shiny, smooth; lower surface pale, whitish, smooth; margin entire, lobes pointed; leaf stalk 2 to 4 inches long; leaves turn clear yellow in autumn.

Twigs: Stout, brittle, greenish- to reddish-brown, sometimes with whitish coating, aromatic, bitter; pores pale; **end bud flattened, resembling a duck's bill, 1/2 inch long**.

Trunk: Bark gray at first, thin tight, later gray to brown with rounded ridges and long, deep grooves; wood light, soft, fairly stiff, somewhat brittle, light yellow or brown.

Habitat: Occurs in moist woods of ravines, in upland woods, and along streams of Crowley's Ridge, and at the base of wooded bluffs along the Mississippi River in southeastern Missouri.

Range: Louisiana and Arkansas; east to Florida, north to Massachusetts and Vermont, and west to Michigan, Indiana, Illinois, and southeastern Missouri.

Wildlife Uses: The seeds are known to be eaten by at least 10 species of birds, also by gray squirrel and small rodents; leaves are eaten by white-tailed deer and cottontail rabbit. It is a favorite nesting tree of many birds. A considerable amount of nectar is produced and harvested by bees.

Medicinal Uses: Native Americans used bark tea for indigestion, dysentery, rheumatism, pinworms, fevers, and in cough syrups; used externally, as a wash on fractured limbs, wounds, boils, and snakebites. In medicine, an alkaloid extract from the bark was once used as a heart stimulant.

Remarks: Tulip tree has been cultivated since 1663. It is an important ornamental tree for lawns, parks, and cemeteries and one of the most attractive and tallest of eastern hardwoods. Fast growing, trees may reach 300 years of age in cove forests of the Appalachians. The wood is used for veneer, plywood, boxes, crates, furniture, cabinets, musical instruments, toys, and novelties.

Early lumberman called it "poplar" for its lightweight wood similar to poplars and birches. Daniel Boone utilized a tulip tree to build a 60-foot long canoe to carry his family and gear down the Ohio River from Kentucky into Spanish territory.

Liriodendron means "lily-tree," referring to the lily-like flowers; *tulipifera* is translated as "tulip-bearing."

Liriodendron tulipifera ❧ a. Growth form with flowers, b. Flower, c. Fruit, d. Seed, e. Twig

Osage orange

Maclura pomifera (Raf.) C. Schneider

Mulberry family (Moraceae)

Also called bois d'arc, bowwood, hedge apple

Appearance: Medium-sized tree, up to 50 feet tall, with a short trunk, dense, round or irregular crown, milky sap, and bearing stout thorns.

Flowers: May–June, after the leaves, **no petals**, male and female flowers produced on separate trees; male flowers in densely packed, small, light green clusters, 1 to 1 1/2 inches long; stamens 4; female flowers in dense, solitary heads, about 1 inch across, globe-shaped.

Fruit: September–October, compound (resulting from the union of multiple, individual fruits) **large, fleshy or pulpy, 4 to 5 inches in diameter, globe-shaped, yellowish-green; surface covered with numerous, small rounded projections (resembling an orange or a brain); juice of fruit milky and bitter**; seeds small, flattened, imbedded in the fleshy fruit, cream colored, egg-shaped, 1/4 to 1/2 inch long.

Leaves: Alternate, simple, broadest below the middle and **tapering to a long-pointed tip**, 3 to 5 inches long, 2 to 3 inches wide; margin entire; upper surface dark green, smooth, shiny; lower surface paler, smooth, with some hairs along the veins; leaf stalk 1/2 to 2 inches long; leaves turn yellow in autumn.

Twigs: Slender, green turning light orange-brown, young twigs hairy, becoming smooth later, **sap milky; spines stout, straight, about 1/2 inches long, emerging above leaf attachment**.

Trunk: **Bark brown to orange**, becoming deeply grooved with age, ridges rounded, interconnecting, often peeling into long, thin strips; **exposed roots bright orange**; wood bright orange or yellow, heavy, hard, durable, flexible, strong.

Habitat: Occurs in low woods in valleys along streams, edge of woods, pastures, fencerows, and in thickets.

Range: Originally from Texas, Louisiana, Arkansas, and Oklahoma; now planted and escaping from cultivation throughout the eastern United States.

Wildlife Uses: Squirrels tear apart the fleshy fruit to eat the seeds.

Medicinal Uses: Native Americans used root tea as a wash for eye sores.

Remarks: Osage orange has been in cultivation since 1818, primarily for windbreaks or hedgerows. The name "Bois d' Arc" was given to it by the French, meaning "wood of the bows," with reference to the fact that the Osage Indians made bows from the wood. The wood is the heaviest of native woods and the most decay-resistant. A yellow dye can be extracted from the roots and has been used to dye cloth and baskets. The fossil record shows that Osage orange once extended to southern Canada as recently as 100,000 years ago and was pushed back by the last glaciers. It is speculated that mastodons, one of the only animals large enough to eat the large, heavy fruits, did not have a chance to spread the seeds north again after the last glacial period because they went extinct.

Maclura is in memory of William Maclure, an early American geologist; *pomifera* means "fruit-bearing."

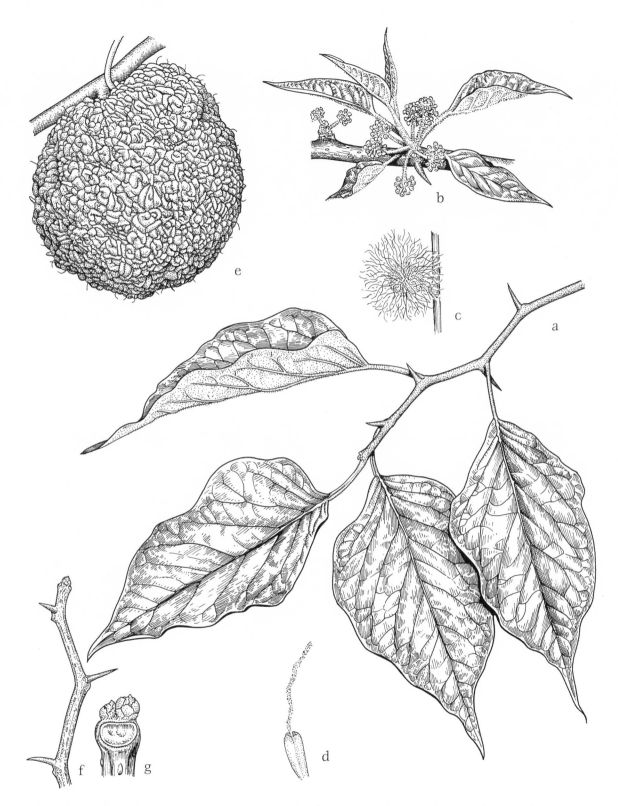

Maclura pomifera ❧ a. Growth form, b. Male flower clusters, c. Female flower cluster, d. Female flower, e. Fruit, f. Twig with spines, g. Leaf scar with buds

Cucumber magnolia

Magnolia acuminata L.

Magnolia family (Magnoliaceae)

Also called cucumber tree

Appearance: Medium-sized tree, up to 80 feet tall, with rather slender branches and a dense, pyramid-shaped crown.

Flowers: April–May, **at the tip of the twig after the leaves appear, solitary**, slightly fragrant, cup-shaped, upright, smooth, with 6 petals; **petals greenish-yellow, 2 to 3 inches long**, broadest near the tip; stamens numerous; flower stalk 3/4 to 1 1/2 inches long.

Fruit: August–October, **cucumber-shaped cone** composed of a tightly-packed cluster of dried fruits, red to brown, 2 to 3 inches long, 3/4 to 1 1/4 inches wide, often curved, smooth; **seeds red, each hanging by a thread after fruit splits open**, globe-shaped, flattened, about 3/8 inch long.

Leaves: Alternate, simple, scattered along the twig, broadest near the base or middle, **large, 5 to 10 inches long, 2 1/2 to 6 inches wide**; margin entire, often wavy, tip pointed; upper surface yellow-green, smooth; lower surface paler, somewhat hairy; leaf stalk densely hairy, 1/2 to 1 1/2 inches long; leaves turn yellow or a bright tan in autumn.

Twigs: Stout, red to brown, hairy and shiny at first, brown to gray and smooth later; pores small, numerous; **bud at tip about 1/2 inch long, densely hairy**.

Trunk: Bark dark brown to gray, thin, long grooves separated by narrow scaly ridges; wood light yellow-brown, light, soft, close-grained.

Habitat: Occurs in low woods in valleys of streams and on lower slopes.

Range: Oklahoma, Arkansas, and Louisiana; east to Georgia, north to New York and Ontario, and west to Ohio, southern Illinois, and southern Missouri.

Wildlife Uses: The seeds are eaten by birds and small mammals.

Medicinal Uses: Bark tea was used for malarial and typhoid fevers; also for indigestion, rheumatism, worms, and toothaches. Bark was chewed to break tobacco addiction.

Remarks: Cucumber magnolia has been in cultivation since 1736 after it was first discovered in Virginia by botanist John Clayton. It is often planted as a street and park tree in the Eastern states and in Europe. They are fast-growing trees that take at least 25 years to reach flowering size and may live up to 150 years of age. They withstand cold winters better than other magnolias. The wood is used in boxes, crates, paneling, inexpensive furniture, and cabinets. The red cone and seeds have a fragrant, citrus-like aroma.

Southern magnolia, *Magnolia grandiflora*, is native to the southern coastal states. It is often planted in yards in the southern half of Missouri but can suffer dieback in extremely cold winters. It is recognized by its large, showy, white flowers and large, glossy, evergreen leaves. It does not escape from cultivation in Missouri.

Magnolia is in honor of Pierre Magnol (1638–1715), a physician, botanist, and director of the botanical garden at Montpellier, France; *acuminata* refers to the pointed leaves.

Magnolia acuminata ❀ a. Growth form with flower, b. Flower bud, c. Fruit, d. Twig

Narrow-leaved crab apple

Malus angustifolia (Aiton) Michaux

Rose family (Rosaceae)

Also called wild crab, southern crab-apple

Appearance: A large shrub to small tree up to 26 feet tall, with rigid, thorny branches forming a broad, open crown; sometimes thicket-forming.

Flowers: April–May, very fragrant, in clusters of 3 to 5 flowers; flower stalks 3/4 to 1 inch long, slender, hairy at first, smooth later; flowers about 1 inch across, white to pink; petals 5, about 1/4 inch wide, broadest at or above the middle, narrowing at the base; stamens about 40 to 60, shorter than the petals.

Fruit: August–September, a kind of fleshy fruit, applelike, small, about 3/4 to 1 inch across, often broader than long, waxy, pale yellowish-green, fragrant, flesh bitter, sour.

Leaves: Simple, alternate, 1 to 3 inches long, 1/2 to 2 inches wide, **narrow, broadest in the middle and tapering at both ends to lance-shaped**, tip pointed to rounded, base wedge-shaped, margin with rounded teeth; late in the season's growth, tips of twigs with leaves round to inverted egg-shaped and with lobes as well as sharp teeth on the margins; blade firm and leathery; dull green above; lower surface hairy when young, smooth later, main vein sometimes remaining hairy; leaf stalk slender, about 3/4 to 1 inch long, green to reddish, hairy at first, smooth later.

Twigs: Stout, light brown to reddish-brown, hairy at first, smooth later; pores scattered, orange-colored; spur shoots (short, thick, slow-growing, reduced branches) present.

Trunk: Bark dark reddish-brown to gray, with deep grooves, ridges narrow, separating into small, platelike scales; wood with yellow sapwood and reddish-brown heartwood, close-grained, hard, heavy.

Habitat: Occurs in sandy soil in upland or lowland woods and thickets on Sikeston Ridge and Crowleys Ridge in the southeastern Missouri Bootheel.

Range: Oklahoma, Arkansas, and Louisiana; east to Florida, north to New Jersey, and west to Kentucky, Missouri, and Kansas.

Wildlife Uses: The fruit is eaten by many species of birds and mammals including the bob-white quail, blue jay, cardinal, ruffed grouse, skunk, opossum, raccoon, cottontail rabbit, and red and gray fox.

Remarks: The narrow-leaved crab apple is classified as state endangered. Before the destruction of much of its habitat in the Bootheel, this plant—like so many others—probably was more common.

The wood, because of its fine grain and hardness, has been used for levers, tools and small woodenware objects. The bitter, sour fruit is made into preserves and cider.

Malus is the classical Latin name of the apple; *angustifolia* is Latin ("angust" for narrow and "folia" for leaf) and refers to the narrow leaves. Some authors place this species in the genus *Pyrus*.

Malus angustifolia ❦ a. Growth form with flowers, b. Flower, c. Fruit

Sweet crab apple

Malus coronaria (L.) Miller

Rose family (Rosaceae)

Also called wild crab

Appearance: A large shrub to small bushy tree to 26 feet, stiffly-branched with a broadly rounded crown.

Flowers: April–May, fragrant, produced in clusters of 2 to 5 flowers; flower stalks smooth, slender, about 1 inch long; flowers pink at first, maturing to white, about 1 inch across; petals 5, egg-shaped; **green cup-shaped receptacle at the base of the petals smooth**; stamens numerous.

Fruit: August–September, a fleshy fruit, apple-like, small, about 1 to 1 1/4 inches long, rounded to globe-shaped, yellowish-green when mature, with a waxy coating, flesh firm, bitter.

Leaves: Simple, alternate, 1 1/4 to 3 inches long, 1/2 to 1 1/2 inches wide, egg-shaped to sometimes triangular-shaped, tip pointed, base rounded to heart-shaped, margin occasionally with shallow lobes, coarsely toothed; upper surface bright green, hairy when young; **lower surface paler, hairy when young, smooth later**; leaf stalk stout, 1 1/2 to 2 inches long.

Twigs: Slender, spreading, often with angles in cross section, reddish brown to light brown, smooth; twigs often with numerous short lateral shoots or spurs, some of the spurs ending in a thorn.

Trunk: Bark about 1/4 inch thick, reddish-brown, with lengthwise grooves and ridges that separate in long scales; wood heavy, close-grained, not strong, light red, with a yellow sapwood.

Habitat: Occurs in low open or upland woods, thickets along streams and prairie openings.

Range: Missouri and Tennessee; east to Georgia and North Carolina; north to New York, and west to Ontario, Michigan, and Wisconsin.

Wildlife Uses: The fruit is of considerable value as wildlife food, eaten by at least 25 species of birds and mammals, including bobwhite quail, ruffed grouse, gray and red fox, skunk, opossum, raccoon, cottontail rabbit, woodchuck, fox squirrel and white-tailed deer. Songbirds use the dense thickets for cover.

Remarks: The sweet crab apple is slow-growing and short-lived. The fragrant, attractive flowers, dense form and spicy odor makes this plant a popular ornamental for cultivation.

The wood has been used for levers, tool handles, and many small domestic articles. The fruits are used to make cider and tart jelly or marmalade.

Malus is the classical Latin name of the apple; *coronaria* means suitable for a wreath, probably referring to its showy clusters of flowers. Some authors place this species in the genus *Pyrus*.

Malus coronaria ❀ a. Twig with flowers and thorns, b. Twig with fruit

Prairie crab apple

Malus ioensis (Alph. Wood) Britton

Rose family (Rosaceae)

Also called wild crab

Appearance: A large shrub to small tree to 20 feet tall with low, crooked branches and thicket forming from sucker shoots.

Flowers: April–May, fragrant, in clusters of 2 to 5 flowers; flowers stalks very hairy, 1 to 1 1/2 inches long; petals 5, white or pink, about 1/2 inch wide, broadest at the middle, base narrowed, margin wavy; **green cup-shaped receptacle at the base of the petals densely hairy on the outside**; stamens numerous.

Fruit: August–September, a kind of fleshy fruit, applelike, small, about 3/4 to 1 1/4 inches long, 3/4 to 1 1/2 inches wide, globe-shaped, greenish to yellow, sometimes with minute, yellow dots, surface waxy and greasy to the touch; pulp bitter, sour.

Leaves: Simple, alternate, 1 1/2 to 5 inches long, 3/4 to 4 inches wide, variable depending if shoot is weak or vigorous; egg-shaped to widest in the middle and tapering at both ends, tip pointed to blunt, base wedge-shaped to rounded, margin with shallow lobes, toothed; upper surface dark green, shiny, smooth; **lower surface pale with white, densely matted hairs**; leaf stalk slender with white, densely matted hairs early, almost smooth later.

Twigs: Reddish-brown to gray, with densely matted hairs early, less so later; pores small and pale; twigs often with numerous short lateral shoots or spurs, some of the spurs ending in a thorn.

Trunk: Bark thin, reddish-brown to gray, grooves shallow, scales narrow and persistent; wood hard, heavy, reddish-brown, with a yellowish sapwood.

Habitat: Occurs in prairies, open woods, thickets, along streams, borders of woods and pastures.

Range: Texas, Oklahoma, Arkansas, and Louisiana; north to Missouri, Illinois, Indiana, and Wisconsin; and west to Minnesota, east Nebraska, and east Kansas.

Wildlife Uses: The fruit is of considerable value as wildlife food, eaten by at least 20 species of birds and mammals, including bobwhite quail, ruffed grouse, gray and red fox, skunk, opossum, raccoon, cottontail rabbit, woodchuck, fox squirrel and white-tailed deer. Songbirds use the dense thickets for cover.

Remarks: The prairie crab apple is an attractive plant, occasionally cultivated for ornamental use since 1885. A variety called Bechtels crab apple, a double-flowering form, is often planted in parks and gardens. The hard, bitter fruit is used for making jellies, cider and vinegar.

Malus is the classical Latin name for apple; *ioensis* refers to the state of Iowa where it was first described. Some authors place this species in the genus *Pyrus*.

Malus ioensis ❀ a. Growth form, b. Twig with flowers, c. Fruit

Apple

Malus pumila Miller

Rose family (Rosaceae)

Also called wild apple, common apple

Appearance: Medium-sized tree, up to 40 feet tall, with a short trunk and broad, rounded crown.

Flowers: April–May, appearing with the leaves in short clusters; flowers 1/2 to 3 inches across, fragrant; petals 5, **rosy or pink, fading to white**, rounded at the tip; stamens numerous.

Fruit: September–October, **an apple, 1 to 4 inches in diameter**, green to yellow or red, fleshy, sweet or sour, globe-shaped, indented at both ends; seeds small, brown to black.

Leaves: Alternate, simple, 1 to 4 inches long, 3/4 to 3 inches wide, widest at the base or toward the middle; **margin with rounded teeth**, tip pointed; upper surface dark green, thick, smooth; lower surface paler, light to densely hairy; leaf stalk 3/8 to 1 1/4 inches long, stout, hairy, grooved.

Twigs: Stout, densely hairy, light green, becoming smooth and reddish-brown later; some twigs short and stubby.

Trunk: Bark thin to moderately thick with age, dark gray, with numerous flat plates or flaky scales; wood is reddish-brown, hard, close-grained.

Habitat: Commonly planted and occasionally escaping from cultivation along fencerows, stream banks, abandoned home sites and old fields.

Range: A native of Europe and western Asia; known to escape to the wild from southern Canada to the central United States.

Wildlife Uses: At least 15 species of birds are known to eat this fruit. Small rodents, squirrels, raccoon, opossum, cottontail rabbit, foxes, white-tailed deer, and black bear also eat the fruit.

Medicinal Uses: "An apple a day keeps the doctor away."

Remarks: Also known as *Pyrus malus* L. Over 3,000 varieties have been developed by accident, as well as by cultivation, since colonial times. Most of the commercial apple varieties are propagated by budding or grafting onto hardy rootstocks. Seeds from commercial apples that germinate develop into wild apples that are generally coarse and sour and not true to the fruit of the parents. Good fruit crops appear every other year or more. The fruit is usually a little more tart than orchard apples but it is sometimes used to make jelly, cold drinks and is an excellent source for pectin. The wood is used in making tools, bowls, decorative carving, and for fuel.

Although wild apple is not native, it does not appear to be aggressive and usually occupies disturbed or degraded sites.

Malus is the classical Latin name of the apple; *pumila* is Latin and means "small, dwarf," which refers to the small size of the tree.

Malus pumila ❀ a. Growth form with fruit, b. Flower clusters, c. Twig

White mulberry

Morus alba L.

Mulberry family (Moraceae)

Also called silkworm mulberry

Appearance: Medium-sized tree, up to 40 feet tall, with a short trunk, a broad, round crown, and many fine twigs.

Flowers: April–May, male and female flowers develop on new growth on the same tree or on different trees, borne in the axils where the leaves will emerge, yellowish-green; male catkins 1/2 to 1 1/2 inches long, cylindrical, slender, generally drooping, petals absent; stamens 4; female catkins about 1/2 to 3/4 inch long, petals absent.

Fruit: June–August, **white to pink to purple**, globe-shaped to oval, 1/2 to 3/4 inches long, about 1/4 inch wide, **sweet, edible**; fruit a multiple of small fleshy fruits, each surrounding a small single seed.

Leaves: Alternate, simple, broadest at the base or at the middle, 2 to 6 inches long, 1 to 4 inches wide, **often with 1 to 5 lobes**; margin toothed, tip pointed, **3 principal veins arising from the base**; upper surface dark green, shiny, smooth; **lower surface paler, smooth**; leaf stalk 1/2 to 1 inch long, slender, smooth, **exuding a milky juice when cut**; leaves turn yellow in autumn.

Twigs: Reddish-brown, smooth to slightly hairy when young, turning gray and smooth later; flexible, slender; pores prominent; **sap milky**.

Trunk: Bark thin, light to dark brown, sometimes tinged with red or yellow, shallow grooves, ridges long and narrow; wood orange-brown, light, soft, coarse-grained.

Habitat: Escaped from cultivation and found in old fields, pastures, fencerows, and low, wet ground along streams.

Range: Native to China. Naturalized over a large portion of the eastern United States and as far west as Nebraska, Kansas, Oklahoma, and Texas; also in the Pacific Northwest.

Wildlife Uses: The fruit is eaten by a number of species of birds, opossum, and raccoon.

Medicinal Uses: In China, leaf tea was used for headaches, thirst, and coughs. Bark tea was used for lung ailments, asthma, coughs, and edema.

Remarks: White mulberry has few ornamental assets and its fruit is very messy, staining sidewalks and cars. The seed is widely dispersed by birds. It is said to be cultivated in more countries than any other tree, and that more has been written about it than any other tree. In China, it is the favorite food of the silkworm caterpillar. At one time it was introduced into the United States to start the industry but the high cost of labor made the project impractical. White mulberry was apparently present in North America early enough that anthropologists recorded use of the tree for medicine and food by Cherokees. Today the tree is considered a noxious weed and should not be planted.

Mulberry is both from the Latin *morum* for "mulberry," and the Anglo Saxon *berie* for berry.

Morus is from the Celtic word "mor" (black), referring to the color of the fruit of the red mulberry; *alba* refers to the fruit which is sometimes white.

Morus alba ❦ a. Leaf, b. Leaf shapes, c. Male catkins, d. Male flower, e. Female flower clusters, f. Female flower, g. Fruit clusters, h. Twig, i. Leaf scar with bud

Red mulberry

Morus rubra L.

Mulberry family (Moraceae)

Appearance: Medium-sized tree to 60 feet, with a short trunk and a broad, rounded crown.

Flowers: April–May, male and female flowers develop on new growth on the same tree or on different trees, borne in the axils where the leaves are emerging, yellowish-green; male catkins 2 to 3 inches long, cylindrical, slender, generally drooping, petals absent; stamens 4; female catkins about 3/8 inch long, drooping to upright, petals absent.

Fruit: June–August, **red at first, becoming purplish-black, resembling a blackberry**, 3/4 to 1 1/4 inches long, cylindrical, juicy, edible; fruit a multiple of small fleshy fruits, each containing a small single seed.

Leaves: Alternate, simple, broadest at the base or at the middle, 4 to 8 inches long, 3 to 5 inches wide, **mostly entire but sometimes with 1 to 3 lobes**; margin densely toothed, tip pointed; **with 3 principal veins emerging from the base**; upper surface dark green, smooth; **lower surface paler, hairy**; leaf stalk 1/2 to 1 inch long, hairy, **exuding a milky juice when cut**; leaves turn yellow in autumn.

Twigs: Reddish-brown to light greenish-brown, smooth, slender; pores prominent; **sap milky**.

Trunk: Bark thin, dark brown to gray with an orange tint, grooves shallow, ridges narrow, tight, or occasionally with loose scales; wood orange-brown, light, soft, weak, close-grained.

Habitat: Occurs in moist woods in lowland areas or on moist upland slopes.

Range: Texas, Oklahoma, Arkansas, and Louisiana; east to Florida, north to Vermont, and west to Ontario, Wisconsin, Minnesota, Nebraska, and Kansas.

Wildlife Uses: The fruit is known to be eaten by at least 21 species of birds, including wild turkey and ruffed grouse; squirrels, mice, and raccoons.

Medicinal Uses: Native Americans drank root tea for weakness, difficult urination, dysentery, and tapeworms; externally used for ringworms. Large doses can cause vomiting.

Remarks: Red mulberry has been in cultivation since 1629. An attractive, fast growing tree, it is sometimes planted in parks and in large yards which is more conducive to its spreading crown and dark-colored, fleshy fruits. The fruit is made into jams, jellies, pies, drinks, or just eaten fresh. The wood once was used for fence posts and barrel making.

In the 1800s, the tree was cultivated in Europe as a fruit tree and potentially for silkworm food but it was discovered that the silkworm preferred the smoother leaves of the white mulberry. The Choctaw wove blankets using the fibrous inner bark and, in 1540, Desoto's crew made ropes to refit their ships.

Mulberry is both from the Latin *morum* for "mulberry," and the Anglo Saxon *berie* for "berry."

Morus is from the Celtic word "mor" (black), referring to the color of the fruit of the red mulberry; rubra refers to the red immature fruit.

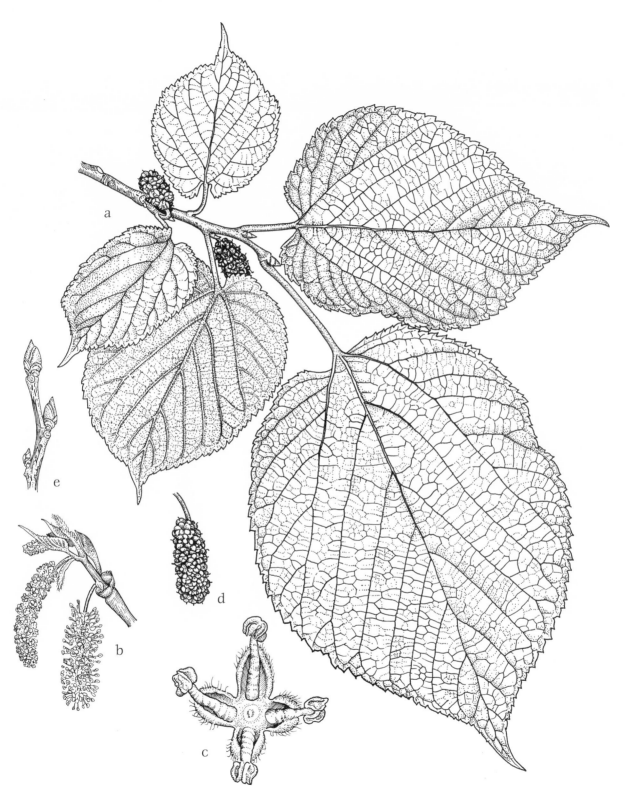

Morus rubra ❀ a. Growth form with fruit, b. Male catkins, c. Male flower, d. Female flower cluster, e. Twig

Water tupelo

Nyssa aquatica L.

Tupelo family (Nyssaceae)

Also called tupelo, swamp tupelo, tupelo gum, cotton gum

Appearance: Large tree, up to 80 feet tall, with a large, **swollen base**, a tapering trunk, and a flattened, spreading crown.

Flowers: April–May, appearing as the leaves unfold, male and female flowers on separate trees; male flowers in rounded clusters on slender, hairy stalks; petals 5, dropping early; female flowers single on a slender, hairy stalk; petals 5 but much reduced.

Fruit: September–October, on drooping stalks 3 to 4 inches long; fruit uniformly wide to widest at the tip, **about 1 inch long, dark purple, skin thick, lightly dotted**, flesh thin, very bitter; seed single, flattened, with long ridges, brown or white.

Leaves: Alternate, simple, widest near the base to almost uniformly wide, 5 to 10 inches long, 2 to 4 inches wide; margin entire or irregularly toothed, **tip abruptly pointed**; upper surface dark green, leathery, shiny, smooth; lower surface paler, finely hairy; leaf stalks thick, hairy, 1 to 3 inches long; leaves turn yellow in autumn.

Twigs: Stout, dark red, hairy when young, becoming brown and smooth later; pith white, with chambers.

Trunk: Bark grayish-brown, thin, grooves small, ridges scaly; wood light brown to white, soft, light, close-grained.

Habitat: Occurs in swamps with bald cypress trees in the southeastern Missouri lowlands, west to two upland sinkhole ponds in the southeastern Ozarks.

Range: East Texas, Oklahoma, Arkansas, and Louisiana; east to the Florida Panhandle, north to Virginia, and west to southern Indiana, southern Illinois, and southeastern Missouri.

Wildlife Uses: The fruit is eaten by at least 10 species of birds, including wood duck; squirrels, raccoon, and white-tailed deer.

Remarks: Water tupelo and bald cypress trees rank as the most flood-tolerant large trees in temperate North America. Both once were commonly found throughout the Bootheel of Missouri but land clearing and draining of swamps in the early 1900s have resulted in only scattered populations of these trees and other swamp related species. The best example of a remnant swamp can be found at Allred Lake Natural Area in Butler County.

Swamp tupelo trees are long lived and begin flowering and fruiting when they are about 30 years old. Mature trees produce heavy seed crops every year that are mostly distributed by water. Seeds germinate on moist soil when water recedes in mid- to late summer.

Water tupelo is known for its honey nectar. Tupelo honey is sold by beekeepers throughout the South. The light wood is made into boxes, broom handles, paneling, and fruit crates.

Tupelo is from the Algonquian (Creek) *ito opilwa*, which translates "swamp tree."

Nyssa is from Mount Nyssa in Asia Minor, the legendary mythical home of the naiads, or water nymphs, who brought fruitfulness to plants, herbs, and mortals; *aquatica* refers to the habitat.

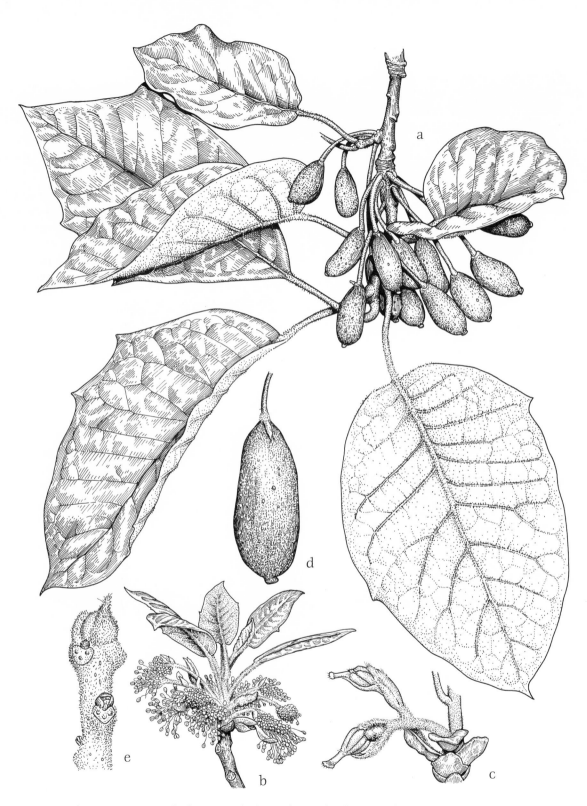

Nyssa aquatica ❧ a. Growth form with fruit, b. Male flower clusters, c. Female flowers, d. Fruit, e. Twig

Black gum

Nyssa sylvatica Marshall

Tupelo family (Nyssaceae)

Also called sour gum, black tupelo, tupelo

Appearance: Large trees, up to 100 feet tall, with horizontal branches and a flat-topped crown.

Flowers: April–June, appearing as the leaves unfold, male and female flowers on separate trees; male flowers in rounded clusters, greenish; flower stalks hairy; petals 5, small; stamens 5 to 10; female flowers 2 to several flowers per cluster, stalk hairy; petals 5, small.

Fruit: September–October, 1 to 3 on a long stalk; **bluish-black, with a whitish coating**, about 1/2 inch long, egg-shaped, bitter, flesh thin; seed solitary, light brown, egg-shaped, with long ridges.

Leaves: Alternate, simple, often crowded towards the tip of the branches; broadest near the base to near the tip, 2 to 6 inches long, 1 to 3 inches wide, thick, firm; margin entire or with a few, coarse, scattered teeth, wavy, **tip abruptly pointed**; upper surface dark green, shiny, smooth; lower surface paler, hairy; leaf stalk about 1 inch long; **leaves turning a brilliant scarlet, orange, purple, or yellow in autumn**.

Twigs: Slender, reddish-brown, slightly hairy at first, becoming gray and smooth later; some twigs short, pointed; pith white, with chambers.

Trunk: Bark gray to brown or black, deeply grooved, **ridges broken into irregularly shaped blocks with an "alligator hide" appearance**; wood light brown, heavy, tough, hard, grain close and twisted, hard to work, warping easily, not durable in contact with the soil.

Habitat: Occurs in acid soils overlying sandstone, chert, or igneous substrate of dry, rocky wooded slopes, ridges, ravines, borders of sinkhole ponds in the Ozarks, and lowland forests in the southeastern part of the state.

Range: Texas, Oklahoma, Arkansas, and Louisiana; east to Florida, north to Maine, and west to Michigan, Wisconsin, Illinois, and Missouri.

Wildlife Uses: The fruit is eaten by at least 32 species of birds, small rodents, opossum, raccoon, foxes, white-tailed deer, and black bear. The latter two also browse the foliage.

Remarks: Black gum has been in cultivation since 1750. It is often used as an ornamental for its brilliant foliage even though it is a slow grower and difficult to transplant. Container-grown trees are preferred. **Black gum is the first tree to turn color, typically beginning in August, and one of the first to drop its leaves**.

The wood is used for veneer, plywood, boxes, pulp, tool handles, gunstocks. The nonsplitting wood has been used in docks and wharves. Beekeepers know the value of its nectar for making quality honey.

Nyssa is from Mount Nyssa in Asia Minor, the legendary mythical home of the naiads, or water nymphs, who brought fruitfulness to plants, herbs, and mortals; *sylvatica* is from the Latin *sylva* (a forest) referring to where black gum is found.

Nyssa sylvatica ❧ a. Growth form with fruit, b. Male flower clusters, c. Male flower,
d. Female flowers, e. Fruit, f. Twig, g. Leaf scar with end bud

Hop hornbeam

Ostrya virginiana (Miller) K. Koch

Birch family (Betulaceae)

Also called ironwood

Appearance: A small tree to 24 feet with wide, spreading branches.

Flowers: April–May, before the leaves; male and female flowers in clusters (catkins) on previous year's growth on the same plant; male catkins 1 to 3 at ends of branches, 1 1/2 to 3 inches long; catkin scales triangular, hairy, reddish-brown, drooping; stamens 3 to 14, attached beneath the scale; female catkins small, single, slender, about 1/4 inch long; scales lance-shaped, hairy, red.

Fruit: June–July, **in conelike clusters resembling hops**, 1 1/2 to 2 inches long; stalk hairy, about 1 inch long; each papery sac about 3/4 inch long and wide, hairy; nut single, enclosed in the sac, small, egg-shaped, brown, shiny, faintly ribbed, about 1/4 inch long.

Leaves: Alternate, simple, blades 2 1/2 to 4 1/2 inches long, 1 1/2 to 2 1/2 inches wide, egg-shaped to broadly lance-shaped, tip pointed, base rounded to heart-shaped, often unequal; margin sharply and densely toothed; **some of the side veins forked near the tips;** upper surface yellowish green to dark green, dull, smooth; **lower surface paler, hairy with veins and vein axils hairiest**; leaf blade usually with 9 to 15 veins on each side of central vein; leaves turning yellow in autumn; leaf stalk about 1/4 inch long, hairy.

Twigs: Usually slightly zigzag, hairy toward the tip, reddish-brown to dark brown, pores small, not obvious.

Trunk: Bark thin, reddish-gray, with narrow, platelike, tight scales; some trees with loose, shreddy scales; wood light to reddish brown, heavy, tough, hard, strong, close-grained, durable; sapwood wide, white.

Habitat: Occurs in fairly dry soil on rocky slopes, along bluffs, in upland woods, and rarely along streams.

Range: East Texas, Oklahoma, Arkansas, and Louisiana, east to Florida, north to Nova Scotia, and west Manitoba, the Dakotas, Nebraska, and Kansas.

Wildlife Uses: The fruit is eaten by at least five species of birds, including bobwhite quail and wild turkey. The catkins and buds rank as the most important ruffed grouse food by volume consumed during late autumn, winter and early spring.

Medicinal Uses: The bark has been used both as a laxative and as a tonic. In colonial times, a fluid extract was used to treat malaria. Both bark and inner bark have been used to treat indigestion and fever.

Remarks: The wood of hop hornbeam ranks among the hardest and strongest of woods; harder than oak, hickory, locust, osage orange and persimmon, surpassed only by flowering dogwood. Because of its size, its use is limited to tool and ax handles, mallets and fence posts. The small tree is slow-growing, but has possibilities as an ornamental; it has been cultivated since 1690.

Ostrya is the ancient Greek name; *virginiana* refers to the state of Virginia where it probably was first described.

Ostrya virginiana ❀ a. Growth form with fruit, b. Male catkins, c. Female catkins,
d. Male catkins in winter, e. Seed, f. Stem with bark

Princess tree

Paulownia tomentosa (Thunb.) Steudel

Figwort family (Scrophulariaceae)

Also called empress tree, royal paulownia, paulownia

Appearance: Medium-sized tree, up to 50 feet tall, with stout spreading branches developed into a flattened or rounded, open crown.

Flowers: April–May, **borne before the leaves in branching, pyramid-shaped clusters, up to 10 inches long with densely hairy flower stalks; flowers pale violet to purple, vanilla-like fragrance, showy**, 1 1/2 to 2 1/2 inches long, petals fused to form a funnel or bell shape, upper two lobes curved back, lower three lobes spreading, throat broad, with dark spots and yellow stripes; stamens 4.

Fruit: September, persisting through winter, capsule, brown, egg-shaped, woody, 1 1/2 to 2 1/2 inches long, tip beaked, densely glandular hairy, splitting open at maturity to release many small, winged seeds.

Leaves: Opposite, simple, **large, 5 to 12 inches long, 3 to 8 inches wide**, broadest near the base, heart-shaped; margin entire or shallowly 3-lobed, tip pointed; upper surface green, hairy; **lower surface paler, densely hairy**; leaf stalk stout, 3 to 8 inches long, hairy; leaves remain mostly green in autumn, dropping one week after the first frost.

Twigs: Stout, brittle, hairy when young, becoming smooth with age, brownish-green, round; pores elongated; **flower buds very conspicuous in the winter, rounded, curved downward, clustered**.

Trunk: Bark gray to dark brown, thin, smooth or with shallow grooves and interlacing ridges; wood purplish-brown, light, soft, with a satin-like surface.

Habitat: Grown as an ornamental in yards and parks and escaping onto disturbed sites.

Also grown in plantations in the South for its valuable wood and planted on strip-mined lands.

Range: Native of central China; introduced to the United States in 1834 and naturalized from Texas, Oklahoma, Arkansas, and Louisiana; east to Florida, north to Maine, and west to Ohio, Indiana, Illinois, and Missouri; also found along the West Coast.

Wildlife Uses: Of little value to wildlife.

Remarks: Princess tree is an aggressive ornamental tree that grows rapidly in disturbed parts of forests, stream banks, and steep, rocky slopes. Although the tree is not a serious problem in Missouri yet, it has the potential to become one. It is considered an ecological threat to natural areas, especially in the southeastern United States where it colonizes rocky cliffs and edges of streams.

Princess tree is from the central region of China in a remote habitat that is shared with that of the famous dawn redwood, *Metasequoia glyptostroboides*, and ginko, *Ginko biloba*. Historical records describe princess tree's medicinal, ornamental, and timber uses as early as the third century B.C. Its wood is also highly valued in Japan.

Paulownia is in honor of Anna Paulownia (1795–1865), Princess of the Netherlands; *tomentosa* is Latin for "dense hair," which refers to the trees' hairy nature.

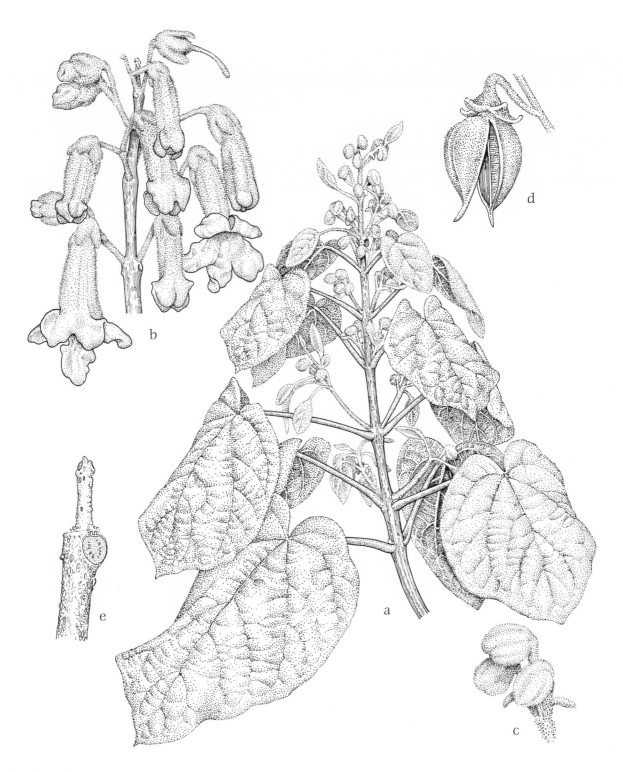

Paulownia tomentosa ❀ a. Growth form with flower buds, b. Flowers, c. Winter flower buds, d. Fruit, e. Twig

Short-leaf pine

Pinus echinata Miller

Pine family (Pinaceae)

Appearance: Large tree, up to 120 feet tall, with a long, clear trunk and broad, open crown.

Flowers: March–April, male and female cones (flowers) found on the same tree; male cones in clusters at the tips of twigs, 2 to 4 times longer than broad, yellowish-brown to purple, 3/4 inch long; female cones in clusters of 1 to 3 along the twig, 2 to 4 times longer than broad, rosy pink, about 1/4 inch long, with stout, short stalks, about 1/4 inch long.

Fruit: September–October, maturing the second year, persistent on the branches, a woody cone in clusters of 1 to 3, hanging, brown, **1 1/2 to 2 1/2 inches long**, narrowly egg-shaped; scales separating at maturity, tips with sharp, curved spines; seeds 2 on each scale, winged, brown mottled with black, triangular, about 3/4 inch long.

Leaves: Needle-like, from persistent sheaths at the base of the needles; **needles in bundles of 2**, sometimes 3, **3 to 5 inches long**, slender, flexible, **not twisted**, sharp-pointed, dark bluish-green, persisting 2 to 4 years.

Twigs: Stiff, stout, rough, brittle, green at first turning gray to reddish-brown with age, usually covered with a whitish coating.

Trunk: Bark thick, reddish-brown to nearly black, broken into large, irregular, scaly plates; wood yellow to yellowish-brown, fairly heavy, medium-hard, coarse-grained.

Habitat: Occurs in moist to dry upland forests and margins of glades on acidic soils derived from sandstone, chert, or igneous substrates; also grown in plantations.

Range: East Texas, Oklahoma, Arkansas, and Louisiana; east to Florida, north to New York, and west to southern Illinois and Missouri.

Wildlife Uses: The seeds are eaten by at least 26 species of birds and small mammals. White-tailed deer browse on the new twigs.

Medicinal Uses: Native Americans used inner bark in tea to induce vomiting. Cold tea of buds was once used as a worm expellant. Tea from the resin was used as a laxative and for tuberculosis; also for kidney ailments causing backaches.

Remarks: Short-leaf pine is the only native pine in Missouri. Pine woodlands were once a major natural community in the Ozarks. Extensive logging of old growth stands from 1890 to 1920 devastated vast pine communities. Oaks then spread into the former pine stands and the community developed into oak/pine forests. Today, some scattered pine populations, mostly on public lands, are being managed with prescribed fire and selective cutting to restore the natural character of pine woodlands, which consists of an uneven pine canopy, an open understory, and a ground layer of grasses and flowering plants. Pine woodlands are being restored not only for their intrinsic value and the plants and animals that are associated with them, but also for future generations to learn about and enjoy what is part of our heritage.

The wood is used for general construction, exterior and interior finishing, and pulpwood.

Pinus is the Latin word, which in turn, comes from the Greek *Pitys*, for pines; *echinata* is from the Greek *echinus*, the name for hedgehog, referring to the hedgehog-like bristly needles.

Pinus echinata ❀ a. Growth form with fruit cones, b. Needles in bundle, c. Male flower cones, d. Female flower cones

Eastern white pine

Pinus strobus L.

Pine family (Pinaceae)

Also called white pine

Appearance: Large tree, over 100 feet tall, with a pyramidal crown when young, becoming flattened or broadly rounded with age.

Flowers: March–May, male and female cones (flowers) found on the same tree; male cones in clusters at the tips of twigs, elongated, about 1/2 inch long, yellowish-green; female cones in clusters of 1 to 3 along the twig, elongated, pink, stalked, 1 to 1 1/2 inches long.

Fruit: September–October, maturing the second year, persistent on the branches, a woody cone in clusters of 1 to 5, hanging, **slightly curved, cylindrical, 4 to 8 inches long**, green turning light brown; scales numerous, **not spine-tipped**, often with sticky resin; seeds 2 on each scale, reddish-brown and mottled, winged, about 3/4 inch long.

Leaves: Needle-like, sheaths at the base of the needles not persistent; **needles in bundles of 5**, 3 to 5 inches long, slender, straight, dark bluish-green, flexible, **soft to touch; under surface of needle lined with white pores**; bundles persisting for about 2 years.

Twigs: Slender, flexible, green becoming brown with age.

Trunk: Bark green, thin, smooth, becoming thick, brown to black, deeply grooved, with broad scaly ridges; wood light brown, soft, light, straight-grained.

Habitat: Introduced to the state and reproducing locally in and around plantings.

Range: Native from Georgia, north to Newfoundland, west to Manitoba, and south to Iowa; also scattered in Mexico and Guatemala; widely introduced elsewhere in North America.

Wildlife Uses: The seeds are eaten by a wide variety of birds and small mammals.

Medicinal Uses: Native Americans used warm pitch (resin) to "draw out" boils and abscesses; also used for rheumatism, broken bones, cuts, bruises, and sores. Twig tea used for kidney and lung ailments. Inner bark formerly used in cough syrups.

Remarks: Eastern white pine is the tallest tree in the eastern United States. The long straight, strong stems were used for masts on sailing ships. Eastern white pine is commonly planted for windbreaks, erosion control, as an ornamental, and as a plantation tree for lumber. The trees are fast-growing and long-lived, producing large seed crops every 3 to 5 years. The wood is used for furniture, cabinets, house framing, and carving.

Early settlers moving west often planted "coffin pines" of eastern white pine at their new homes. The new frontier was often dominated by oaks that could not be fashioned as quickly for coffins as the softer pine. A matched pair of pine trees was often planted for husband and wife. Many of the trees never served their intended purpose and are said to still survive around some old home sites.

Pinus is the Latin word, which in turn, comes from the Greek *Pitys*, for pines; *strobus* is Greek for a "twist, turn, or whirl," referring to the curved, somewhat twisted pinecone.

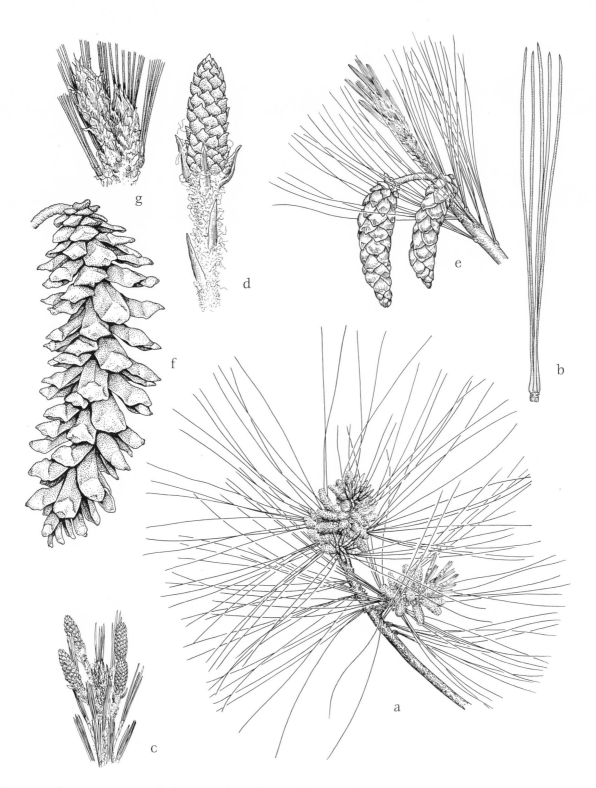

Pinus strobus ❦ a. Growth form with male and female flower cones, b. Needles in bundle, c. Female flower cones, d. Female flower cone, e. Immature cones, f. Mature cone, g. Twig with buds

Loblolly pine

Pinus taeda L.

Pine family (Pinaceae)

Appearance: Large trees, up to 120 feet tall, with a long, straight trunk and a large, open crown.

Flowers: March–April, male and female cones (flowers) found on the same tree; male cones in clusters at the tips of the twigs, elongated, about 2 inches long, yellow-green; female cones in clusters of 1 to 3, about 1/2 inch long, egg-shaped, yellow-green.

Fruit: September–October, maturing the second year, persistent on branches, a woody cone in clusters of 1 to 3, egg-shaped to narrowly cone shaped, **3 to 5 inches long**, reddish-brown, scales thickened at the tip and bearing short incurved or straight spines, sharp to the touch; seeds 4-sided, dark brown and mottled, 2 on each scale, attached to a thin wing about 3/4 inch long.

Leaves: Needle-like, sheaths at the base of the needles persistent; **needles in bundles of 3**, light to dark green, rigid, slender, 3-sided, **5 to 9 inches long**, slightly twisted, fragrant; bundles persisting for two years.

Twigs: Stout, reddish-brown, scaly.

Trunk: Bark rough, thick, reddish-brown, deeply grooved, ridges are large, flat, irregular plates, with papery scales; wood yellow-brown, resinous, soft, brittle, coarse-grained.

Habitat: Grown in plantations for lumber in the southern part of the Ozarks and in the Bootheel; escaping locally.

Range: Native from east Texas, southeastern Oklahoma, southern Arkansas, and Louisiana; east to southern Tennessee, Mississippi, Alabama, and Florida, and north to Virginia, Maryland, and Delaware; widely planted in the eastern United States.

Wildlife Uses: The seeds are eaten by a variety of birds and small mammals.

Remarks: Loblolly pine was first cultivated in 1713. It is a fast-growing pine and may begin to produce seed at 10 years of age. In urban areas throughout the South, loblolly pines are often used as shade trees and for wind and noise barriers. This pine grows well on poor, upland soils that have suffered years of abuse. In the 1930s, when the U.S. Forest Service began purchasing worn out farmsteads in southern Illinois to become part of the newly created Shawnee National Forest, loblolly pine plantations were quickly established to help reclaim the sites.

Commercially, the wood is used in general construction and for pulp.

The name "loblolly" means a thick gruel or a mud puddle and is used in eastern North Carolina's coastal plain region to describe a natural depression, and in such situations grows loblolly pine.

Pinus is the Latin word, which in turn, comes from the Greek *Pitys*, for pines; *taeda* is an ancient name for resinous pine trees.

Pinus taeda ❧ a. Growth form with mature cone and male and female flower cones, b. Needles in bundle, c. Twig with buds

Scrub pine

Pinus virginiana Mill.

Pine family (Pinaceae)

Also called Virginia pine

Appearance: Small to medium sized-trees, up to 50 feet tall, with an open, rounded crown and **scrubby appearance because of persistent lower dead branches**.

Flowers: March–April, male and female cones (flowers) found on the same tree; male cones in clusters at the tips of twigs, elongated, about 1/2 inch long, yellow; female cones in clusters of 2 to 3, stalked, globe-shaped, 1 1/2 to 2 inches long, light green.

Fruit: September–October, maturing the second year, persistent on the branches, a woody cone in clusters of 1 to 3, egg-shaped, **1 1/2 to 2 1/2 inches long**, dark reddish-brown; scales thin, flat, with a slender, curved spine at the tip; seed pale brown, winged, about 1/2 inch long.

Leaves: Needle-like, sheaths at the base of the needles persistent; **needles in bundles of 2**, flexible, **1 1/2 to 3 inches long**, yellow-green, flattened, **twisted**, persistent for 3 to 4 years; sheaths about 1/4 inch long.

Twigs: Slender, tough, light green with waxy bloom, becoming purplish-brown or gray-brown with age, smooth; buds resinous, about 1/2 inch long, sharp pointed.

Trunk: Bark thin, dark brown, becoming grooved with scaly plates, upper trunk and large limbs may be orange-brown; wood orange-brown, weak, brittle, coarse-grained.

Habitat: Introduced and escaped from plantings, mostly in the Ozarks and Ozark border.

Range: Native to Alabama, Tennessee, Georgia, and South Carolina; north to New York, and west to Ohio, southern Indiana, and Kentucky.

Wildlife Uses: The seeds are eaten by a wide variety of birds and small mammals. Because the wood of older trees is frequently softened by fungal decay, scrub pine provides nesting habitat for woodpeckers.

Remarks: Scrub pine is a moderate to slow-growing pine, generally short-lived. It invades old or abandoned fields and is used in reforestation projects aimed at reclaiming exhausted soils. In the Southeast, it is also widely planted for wildlife habitat, and windbreaks, and as an ornamental where it is the most preferred as a Christmas tree. Scrub pine is utilized for pulpwood but larger, older trees on better sites are harvested for lumber and paneling.

Scrub pine is in the yellow pine group. All pines with 2 to 3 needles in a bundle are called yellow pines, while all pines with 5 needles in a bundle are called white pines.

The common name, scrub pine, refers to its tendency to retain its lower dead branches, thus giving the tree a scrubby appearance.

Pinus is the Latin word, which in turn, comes from the Greek *Pitys*, for pines; *virginiana* refers to the state of Virginia.

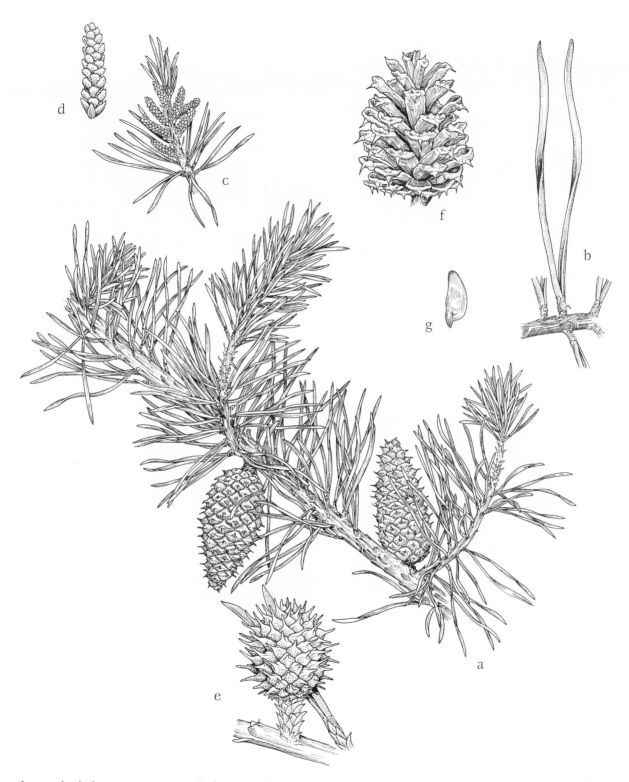

Pinus virginiana ❀ a. Growth form with immature cones, b. Needles in bundle, c. Male flower cones, d. Single male flower cone, e. Female flower cone, f. Mature cone, g. Seed

Water elm

Planera aquatica (Walter) J. Gmelin

Elm family (Ulmaceae)

Also called planer tree

Appearance: A large shrub or small tree to 40 feet, growing in swampy ground.

Flowers: March–April, in separate clusters on the same tree with male, female, and perfect flowers appearing on last year's twigs; male flowers in clusters of 2 to 5; **petals lacking; calyx 4 to 5 lobed, bell-shaped**, greenish-yellow, lobes egg-shaped, tips blunt; stamens 4 to 5, extending beyond the flower; female flowers 1 to 3, greenish-yellow, on short stalks.

Fruit: August–September, about 3/8 inch long, **covered with an irregular warty surface**, leathery, egg-shaped, flattened, ridged, on a short stalk; seed egg-shaped, shiny black.

Leaves: Alternate, simple, **similar to elm leaves, which are lopsided (asymmetrical), with one-half of the leaf longer or broader than the other half**; leaf 2 to 4 inches long, 1/2 to 1 inch wide, egg- to lance-shaped, tip pointed, **base uneven**, heart-shaped or flattened, margin toothed; upper surface dark green, paler beneath; leaf stalk about 1/4 inch long, stout, hairy.

Twigs: Slender, reddish, slightly zigzag, hairy, becoming silvery-gray and smooth with age.

Trunk: Bark on young trunk thin, smooth, light reddish-brown or gray; when older gray, dividing into large shreddy scales, inner bark reddish; wood pale brown, soft, light, not strong, close-grained.

Habitat: Occurs in swamps and low, wet bottomland forests in southeastern Missouri's Bootheel. Base of trunk frequently inundated during wet seasons.

Range: Texas, Oklahoma, Arkansas, and Louisiana; east to Florida, north to North Carolina, and west to Kentucky, Illinois, and Missouri.

Wildlife Uses: The peculiar little warty fruit is considered to be an important food for waterfowl, especially mallards and wood ducks. Squirrels also eat the fruit.

Remarks: Water elm is a small understory tree often found in swamps in association with bald-cypress *(Taxodium distichum)*, water tupelo *(Nyssa aquatica)*, pin oak *(Quercus palustris)*, Nuttall's oak *(Quercus texana* formerly *Q. nuttallii)*, pumpkin ash *(Fraxinus tomentosa)*, and water locust *(Gleditsia aquatica)*.

The wood has been used for fence posts and fuel; it is not commercially important.

Planera is in honor of the German botanist Johann Jakob Planer (1743–1789), a professor at the University of Erfurt in Germany; *aquatica* refers to the swampy habitat in which the small tree occurs.

Planera aquatica ✽ a. Growth form, b. Branch with flowers, c. Male flower, d. Female flower, e. Fruit

Sycamore

Platanus occidentalis L.

Plane tree family (Platanaceae)

Also called American sycamore, plane tree, buttonwood

Appearance: Large tree, up to 120 feet tall, with a massive trunk, a broad open, irregular crown, and **large, crooked, spreading, white branches**.

Flowers: April–June, male and female flowers on the same tree with **numerous flowers in dense, globe-shaped clusters on long, drooping stalks**, both appearing as the leaves emerge on previous year's growth; male flower cluster red or yellow, about 3/8 inch in diameter; female flower cluster red, about 1/2 inch in diameter.

Fruit: September–October, **persisting through the winter, solitary, rounded, dry, 1 to 1 1/2 inches in diameter, drooping on a stalk 3 to 6 inches long; ball composed of numerous, closely packed, long, narrow fruits called achenes**; each achene contains a single seed.

Leaves: Alternate, simple, broadly egg-shaped, 4 to 8 inches long and broad, sometimes larger; **margin with 3 to 5 broad, shallow lobes with coarse teeth**, each lobe tip pointed; upper surface bright green, smooth; lower surface whitish, hairy; leaf stalk stout, hairy, 3 to 5 inches long, with a large leafy appendage at the base; leaves turn a dull tan in autumn.

Twigs: Slender, shiny, zigzag, hairy and orange-brown at first, smooth and gray with age; **buds covered by the enlarged base of the leaf stalk**.

Trunk: Bark reddish-brown to gray, **bark on upper limbs, scaling off in thin plates to reveal the conspicuous white new bark**; wood light brown, heavy, tough, hard, close-grained.

Habitat: Occurs in valleys either on gravel bars or in low or wet bottomland.

Range: Texas, Oklahoma, Arkansas, and Louisiana; east to Florida, north to Maine, and west to Ontario, Michigan, and Minnesota; and south to Missouri and Kansas.

Wildlife Uses: Purple finch and goldfinch eat the seeds, especially in late winter when other seeds are scarce. The seeds were once the favorite food of the now extinct Carolina parakeet. The large cavities are used by nesting chimney swifts and tree swallows and mammals seeking shelter. About 98 percent of the great blue heron rookeries in Missouri are found in the huge, open, horizontal limbs of sycamore.

Medicinal Uses: Native Americans used inner-bark tea for dysentery, colds, lung ailments, coughs; also as a "blood purifier" and laxative.

Remarks: Sycamore was first cultivated in 1640. It attains the largest size of any deciduous tree in the United States and is often planted in urban areas as an ornamental for its fast growth, imposing stature, and unusual bark. In cold, wet early springs, it is susceptible to anthracnose disease, a fungus infection, which kills the young leaves.

The wood is used for crates, interior finishing, and furniture. Difficult to split, it is used for butcher blocks and buttons, hence the common name buttonwood.

Platanus is from the Greek *platanos*, which is associated with the Latin *platys* "broad," in reference to its leaves; *occidentalis* means "western" in reference to its New World location.

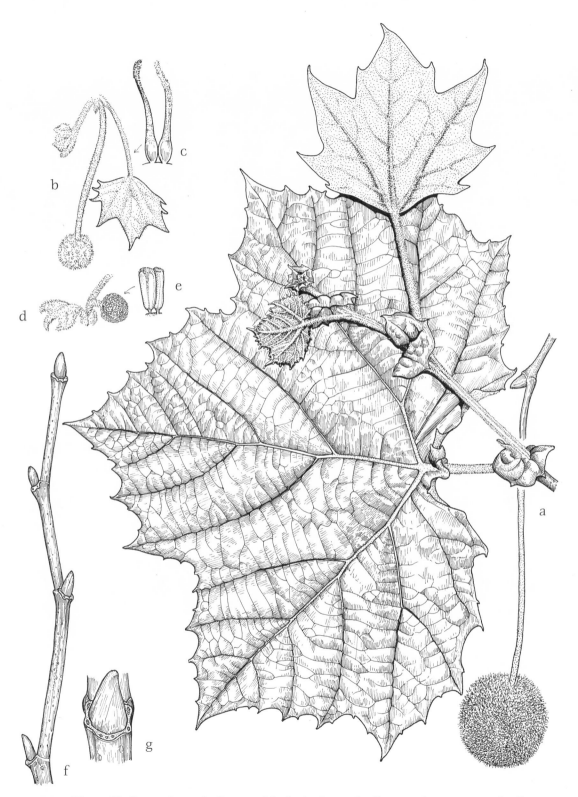

Platanus occidentalis ❦ a. Growth form with fruit, b. Male flower cluster, c. Male flowers, d. Female flower cluster, e. Female flowers, f. Twig, g. Leaf scar with bud

Silver poplar

Populus alba L.

Willow family (Salicaceae)

Also called white poplar

Appearance: Medium-sized tree, up to 70 feet tall, with a short trunk, forming a large, spreading, rounded or irregular crown; **lateral roots send up suckers to form thickets; recognized by the silver-white undersurface of the leaves**.

Flowers: March–May, male and female flowers borne in catkins on separate trees before the leaves emerge, both lacking petals; male catkins hanging, cylindrical, 2 to 4 inches long; stamens 6 to 10; female catkins hanging, cylindrical, 1 1/2 to 3 inches long.

Fruit: May–June, in drooping catkins, 1 1/2 to 3 inches long; capsules narrowly egg-shaped, about 1/4 inch long, splitting into two parts; seeds light brown, minute, numerous, each with a tuft of long silky, white hairs at the base.

Leaves: Alternate, simple, broadly egg-shaped, 2 to 4 inches long, **maple-like with 3 to 5 lobes**, leathery; margin coarsely toothed, tip blunt or rounded; upper surface dark green, shiny, some hairs on the veins; lower surface silvery-white, with thick, matted white hairs; **leaf stalk covered with flattened white hairs**, 3/4 to 1 1/2 inches long; leaves turn yellow in autumn.

Twigs: Slender, greenish-gray, covered with short, white hairs

Trunk: Bark greenish-white, smooth on young trees, with age becoming dark gray-brown, roughened into firm dark ridges and shallow grooves; pores enlarging and becoming corky.

Habitat: Introduced and spreading into the wild from homesites; establishing along streams, fence rows, and roadsides.

Range: Native to central and southern Europe to western Siberia and central Asia; naturalizing in 43 states throughout the contiguous United States.

Wildlife Uses: Very little value.

Remarks: Silver poplar was first introduced into the United States in 1748. It is chiefly planted as an ornamental for its attractive leaves of contrasting color, i.e., green above, white below. Silver poplar's ornamental value is low due to its susceptibility to pest insects and diseases and its vulnerability to storm and wind damage. Its roots are prone to clog sewers and other drainage systems. Silver poplar can produce thick clones due to its ability to sucker from its roots. If both sexes occur sufficiently close together for pollination, female trees produce large amounts of small seeds, adorned with cottony fluff that are easily blown by the wind to new sites. These develop into dense stands that prevent other plants from coexisting by reducing the amount of sunlight, nutrients, water, and space available. There are over 100 native trees and shrubs that can be planted in place of silver poplar. Sources for these native plants can be found in the appendix.

The word "poplar" first appeared in writings in 1356, taken from the Anglo-French popler.

Populus is the Latin name for "poplar;" *alba* is Latin for "white" referring to the color of the lower surface of the leaves.

Populus alba ❧ a. Growth form, b. Fruit cluster, c. Fruit opening with seeds, d. Twig

Cottonwood

Populus deltoides Bartram ex Marshall

Willow family (Salicaceae)

Also called eastern cottonwood, southern cottonwood

Appearance: Large tree, up to 100 feet or more tall, **with a long, straight trunk and massive branches forming a rounded top**.

Flowers: March–May, male and female flowers borne in catkins on separate trees before the leaves emerge, both lacking petals; male catkins densely flowered, hanging, cylindrical, 3 to 5 inches long, reddish; stamens 30 to 60; female catkins loosely flowered, hanging, cylindrical, 1 to 2 1/2 inches long, greenish-yellow; female flower with a 3-parted, distinctive fan-shaped stigma (the portion that is receptive to pollen).

Fruit: May–June, in drooping catkins, 5 to 10 inches long; capsules broadest near the base, about 1/4 inch long, splitting into 2 to 4 parts; seeds brown, small, numerous, each with a tuft of long cottony hairs at the base.

Leaves: Alternate, simple, **broadly triangular-shaped**, 3 to 7 inches long, and as about as wide; **margin coarsely toothed with tiny hairs**, tip abruptly pointed, **base flat to heart-shaped, with glands (small projections) at the base of the leaf blade**; upper surface green, shiny, smooth; lower surface paler, smooth; **leaf stalk slender, flattened, allowing the leaf to flutter in the wind**, 1 1/2 to 3 inches long; leaves turn yellow in autumn.

Twigs: Stout, angular, yellowish to brown, smooth; pores prominent; bud at tip about 1/2 inch long, brown, with sticky bud scales.

Trunk: Bark thin, smooth, yellow-green when young, thick, corky, brown to gray, with deep, straight grooves and wide, flat ridges with age; wood dark brown, light, soft, weak, close-grained, easily warping.

Habitat: Occurs in moist lowlands near streams and rivers.

Range: From Texas, Oklahoma, Arkansas, and Louisiana; east to Florida, north to Quebec, west to Ontario, Wisconsin, Minnesota, the Dakotas, and Kansas.

Wildlife Uses: Some songbirds, especially rose-breasted grosbeak and evening grosbeak, eat the seeds. Beaver eat the bark, leaves, and buds. White-tailed deer eat the small twigs and leaves.

Medicinal Uses: Native Americans gave inner-bark tea to women about to give birth and it was also taken for scurvy, heartburn, and for general discomfort.

Remarks: Cottonwood has been cultivated since 1750. It is the fastest growing native tree in Missouri; reaching a height of 50 feet and 8 inches in diameter in as little as 6 years under good conditions. Cottonwood trees do not live long. At 75 years of age, it is already old and a cottonwood at 125 years old is probably exceptional. The wood is used for veneer, kite and ice cream sticks, baskets, pulpwood, and fuel. Having the ability to sprout from woody stem cuttings, 3-foot sections can be pounded into eroding banks and be left alone to grow and stabilize the stream or river's edge.

Cottonwood is so named for the cottony fluffs of hairs attached to the seeds.

Populus is the Latin name for "poplar;" *deltoides* is Latin for "triangular," for the shape of the leaf.

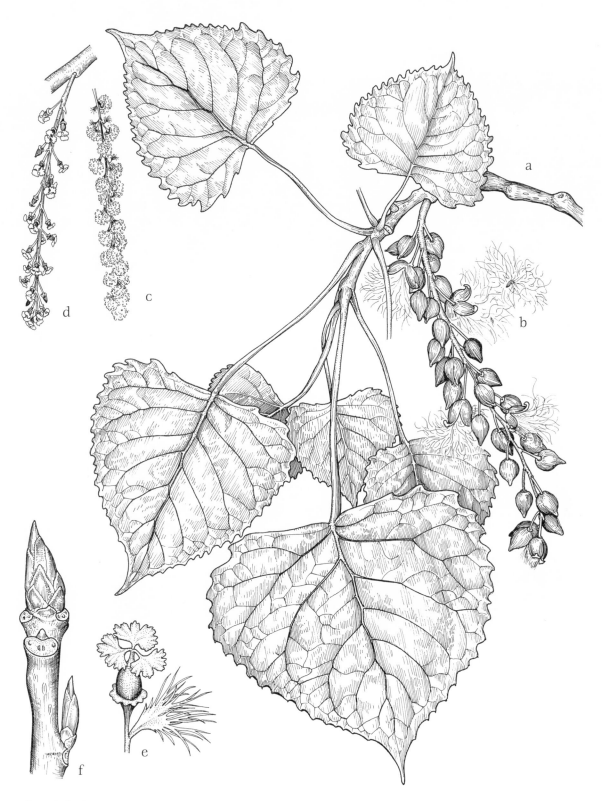

Populus deltoides ❧ a. Growth form with fruit, b. Seed, c. Male catkin, d. Female catkin, e. Female flower, f. Twig

Bigtooth aspen

Populus grandidentata Michaux

Willow family (Salicaceae)

Also called large-toothed aspen

Appearance: Medium-sized tree, up to 60 feet tall, with a long, clear trunk, ascending branches, and a taller than broad, irregular crown.

Flowers: March–May, male and female flowers borne in catkins on separate trees before the leaves emerge, both lacking petals; male catkins densely flowered, hanging, cylindrical, 1 to 1 1/2 inches long; stamens 6 to 12; female catkins 2 to 4 inches long, loosely-flowered, cylindrical, hanging.

Fruit: May–June, in drooping catkins, 3 to 6 inches long; capsules narrowly egg-shaped, about 1/4 inch long, splitting into two parts; seeds light brown, minute, numerous, each with a tuft of long silky, white hairs at the base.

Leaves: Alternate, simple, broadest near the base, 2 1/2 to 5 inches long, 1 1/2 to 3 1/2 inches wide; margin with **large teeth somewhat triangular and short-pointed**, tip pointed; upper surface dark green, smooth; lower surface grayish-green, smooth; leaf stalk slender, flattened, allowing the leaf to flutter in the wind, 1 1/2 to 3 1/2 inches long; leaves turn pale yellow in autumn.

Twigs: Slender to moderately stout, brown, hairy on new growth becoming smooth with age; pores orange.

Trunk: Bark smooth, thin, gray, tight when young, becoming dark, grooved with dark, flat-topped ridges on older trunks; wood light brown, light, soft, close-grained.

Habitat: Occurs in upland sites along the edge of woods.

Range: Missouri, Illinois, Indiana, and Kentucky; east to Delaware, north to Maine and Nova Scotia, and west to Quebec, Ontario, Manitoba, and Minnesota.

Wildlife Uses: Ruffed grouse, and quail eat the buds and catkins; cottontail rabbit and white-tailed deer browse the leaves; beaver eat the bark.

Remarks: In Missouri, bigtooth aspen has either been planted or is a relict of previously cooler climate conditions. Colonies occur in a few isolated populations, forming relatively dense clones from root suckers that can grow as much as 6 feet in the first year. In northern states and Canada, it is a pioneer tree species, rapidly entering sites disturbed by fires and logging. Pioneer species help build soils and protect seedlings of slower growing species until they get established and eventually out-compete the short-lived aspens, which rarely exceed 120 years of age. The wood is used for paper pulp, pallets, boxes, and composite wood products. The bark is pelletized for supplemental cattle feed and fuel.

Native Americans used the bark as a food source. They cut the inner bark into strips, dried and ground it into meal to be mixed with other starches to make bread or mush. The catkins were eaten raw in early spring.

Bigtooth refers to the size of the teeth on the leaves, and aspen is from the Old English *aespe*.

Populus is the Latin name for "poplar;" *grandidentata* is from the Latin *grand*, "large or great," and *dentat* is "toothed."

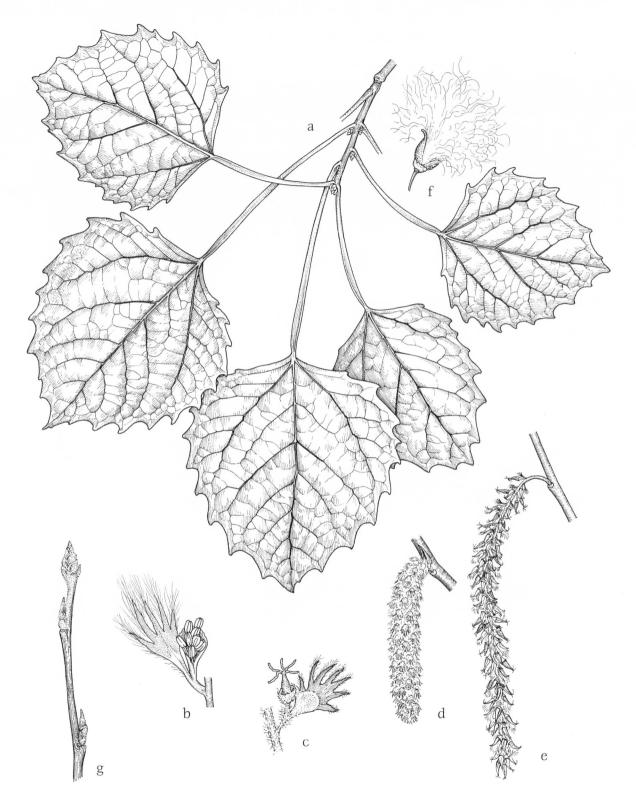

Populus grandidentata ❧ a. Growth form, b. Male flower, c. Female flower, d. Male catkin, e. Fruit cluster, f. Fruit capsule with seeds, g. Twig

Swamp cottonwood

Populus heterophylla L.

Willow family (Salicaceae)

Appearance: Medium to large-sized tree, up to 100 feet tall, with a long, straight trunk and a narrow, round-topped crown.

Flowers: March–April, male and female flowers borne in catkins on separate trees before the leaves emerge, both lacking petals; male catkins densely flowered, hanging, cylindrical, 1 1/2 to 2 inches long, reddish; stamens 30 to 60; female catkins loosely flowered, cylindrical, hanging, 3 to 3 1/2 long; female flower with 3 distinctive fan-shaped stigmas (the portion that is receptive to pollen).

Fruit: May, in drooping catkins, 3 to 6 inches long, cylindrical; capsules 1/4 to 1/2 inches long, broadest at the base, splitting into 2 to 3 parts; seeds brown, small, numerous, each with a tuft of long cottony hairs at the base.

Leaves: Alternate, simple, broadest near the base to nearly round, 3 to 7 inches long, 3 to 6 inches wide; margin with small, rounded teeth, **tip blunt, base triangular to heart-shaped**; upper surface dark green, smooth or with hairs along the veins; **lower surface paler, coated with whitish hairs, especially when young; leaf stalk slender, rounded**, hairy to smooth, 2 1/2 to 3 1/2 inches long; leaves turn yellow in autumn.

Twigs: Stout, gray to brown, densely hairy when young, smooth with age; pores small, elongated; **pith orange**.

Trunk: Bark brown, deeply grooved with broad, flat ridges separating into long, loose, scaly plates; wood dull brown, light, soft, close-grained.

Habitat: Occurs in swamps and seasonally inundated bottomland forests throughout the lowlands of southeastern Missouri; occasionally found in sinkhole ponds of southeastern Ozarks.

Range: Arkansas and Louisiana, east to Florida, north along the Atlantic coastal plain to Connecticut, west to Ohio, Indiana, Illinois, and Missouri.

Wildlife Uses: Some songbirds eat the seeds. Beaver eat the bark, leaves, and buds. White-tailed deer eat the small twigs and leaves.

Remarks: Swamp cottonwood grows fairly rapidly and is relatively short-lived. It tolerates even wetter conditions than cottonwood. Swamp cottonwood is sparse throughout its range and is not a major part of any forest cover. In southeast Missouri, it grows with bald cypress, water tupelo, pumpkin ash, water locust, overcup oak, water hickory, black willow, water elm, swamp privet, buttonbush, and possum haw among others.

The wood is used for boxes, crates, and interior parts for furniture. Pulpwood is used in high-grade book and magazine paper.

Cottonwood is so named for the cottony fluffs of hairs attached to the seeds, which are widely scattered in the wind but sometimes accumulate in drifts.

Populus is the Latin name for "poplar;" *heterophylla* combines the Greek *hetero* (other or different) with *phyla* (leaf), which refers to the variable leaf shape of swamp cottonwood.

Populus heterophylla ❧ a. Growth form, b. Male catkin, c. Male flower, d. Female flower, e. Fruit with capsules opening to release seeds, f. Twig

Lombardy poplar

Populus nigra L. var. *italica* Muenchh.

Willow family (Salicaceae)

Appearance: Medium-sized tree, up to 60 feet tall, **with a straight, slender trunk and numerous short, ascending branches forming a narrow column to a tapered point**.

Flowers: March–May, before the leaves emerge, male flowers are produced in catkins about 3 inches long; stamens 8 to 10; no female flowers are produced.

Fruit: None is produced.

Leaves: Alternate, simple, triangular-shaped, 2 to 4 inches long, 1 1/2 to 3 inches wide; **margin with small teeth, tip abruptly pointed, base flattened**; upper surface dark green, shiny, smooth; lower surface lighter, somewhat shiny, smooth; leaf stalk slender, flattened, allowing the leaves to flutter in the wind, 1 to 2 inches long; leaves turn yellow to golden yellow in autumn.

Twigs: Slender, smooth, shiny, yellowish-brown, becoming gray with age.

Trunk: Bark thin and smooth on young stems, becoming thick, grooved with ridges, and grayish-brown with age; wood light, soft, weak, not durable.

Habitat: Native to Europe. Commonly planted throughout Missouri.

Range: Planted as ornamentals and windbreaks throughout North America.

Wildlife Uses: Of little wildlife value. Some songbirds such as orioles and grosbeaks nest on the branches.

Medicinal Uses: Leaf buds are covered with a resinous sap that contains salicin, that decomposes into salicylic acid (aspirin) in the body. The buds are taken internally in the treatment of bronchitis and upper respiratory tract infections, and stomach and kidney disorders. Externally, the buds are used to treat colds, arthritis, rheumatism, muscular pain, and dry skin conditions. The stem bark is used internally to treat rheumatism, arthritis, gout, lower back pains, anorexia, also to reduce fevers.

Remarks: Lombardy poplar is thought to be a freak or atypical variety of a male Italian or Black Poplar, *Populus nigra* L., originating in the Lombardy province of Italy. It is unusual among poplars because of its columnar shape instead of the typical rounded crown of other poplars. This unusual shape has been repeatedly propagated from stem cuttings for more than 300 years because all Lombardy poplars are male, hence no seeds. Lombardy poplars are planted across the United States as an ornamental and windbreak. They are fast growing but short-lived, rarely lasting over 20 years after planting. A canker disease almost always infects the tree by the time it is 10 to 15 years old so trees rarely reach 30 feet tall. The thin stems are easily damaged by wind, ice, and snow.

The wood has no commercial value. The bark on older trees has been used as a substitute for fishing floats or bobbers.

The word "Lombardy" is for a province in Italy and "poplar" first appeared in writings in 1356, taken from the Anglo-French *popler*.

Populus is the Latin name for "poplar;" *nigra* is Latin for "black" referring to the bark, and *italica* refers to its country of origin.

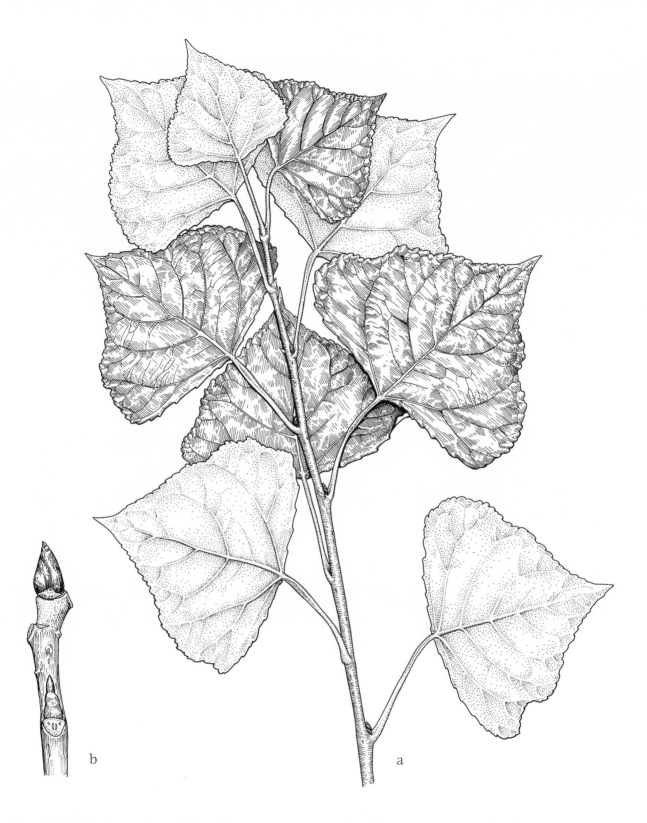

Populus nigra ❀ a. Growth form, b. Twig

Quaking aspen

Populus tremuloides Michaux

Willow family (Salicaceae)

Also called trembling aspen

Appearance: Medium-sized tree, up to 60 feet tall, with a long slender trunk and a narrow, rounded crown; **bark is conspicuously whitened**.

Flowers: March–April, male and female flowers borne in catkins on separate trees before the leaves emerge, both lacking petals; male catkins drooping, cylindrical, slender, 1 to 2 inches long; stamens 6 to 12; female catkins 2 to 4 inches long.

Fruit: May–June, in drooping catkins, 2 to 4 inches long; capsules narrow, widest towards the bottom, 1/4 to 1/2 inch long, splitting into 2 parts; seeds yellow-green, small, numerous, each with a tuft of long cottony hairs at the base.

Leaves: Alternate, simple, those on young shoots much larger than leaves on older trees, 1 to 4 inches long, **nearly round**; margin with fine teeth, tip with a short point; upper surface dark green, smooth, shiny; lower surface paler, smooth; leaf stalk slender, flattened, allowing the leaf to flutter in the slightest wind, 1 to 3 inches long; leaves turn bright yellow to golden in autumn.

Twigs: Slender, reddish-brown to gray, shiny, smooth; pores scattered, orange to yellow.

Trunk: Bark thin, smooth, light gray to white, becoming grooved with ridges that become dark brown to black with age; black limb scars persist; wood light brown, soft, weak, straight-grained.

Habitat: Occurs in thickets and borders of upland woods in a few northern Missouri locations.

Range: One of the most widely distributed trees in North America; occurring from sea level to an altitude of 10,000 feet. From Texas west to California, east to West Virginia and Pennsylvania, and north to Canada and Alaska. Extending southward in the mountains of Mexico.

Wildlife Uses: The seeds are eaten by a number of species of birds. The buds, twigs, and bark are browsed by beaver and white-tailed deer.

Medicinal Uses: Native Americans used inner-bark tea for stomach pain, urinary ailments, worms, colds, fevers, and as an appetite stimulant. A salve from leaf buds was used for colds, coughs, and irritated nostrils. All of the *Populus* species contain varying amounts of salicin and populin, the precursors to aspirin.

Remarks: Quaking aspen was first cultivated in 1811. It is an attractive ornamental with its golden leaves in autumn, its white bark, and its quaking leaves in summer. The wood is used for fences, railings, crates, boxes, and paper products.

The European aspen, *Populus tremula* L., native to Europe, Asia, and North Africa, rarely escapes from cultivation but is similar to quaking aspen in general appearance. Refer to the key on page 31 for the differences.

Quaking refers to the movement of the leaves and aspen is from the Old English *aespe*.

Populus is the Latin name for "poplar;" *tremuloides* is from the Latin word meaning "like a tremula," referring to its similarity to the European aspen.

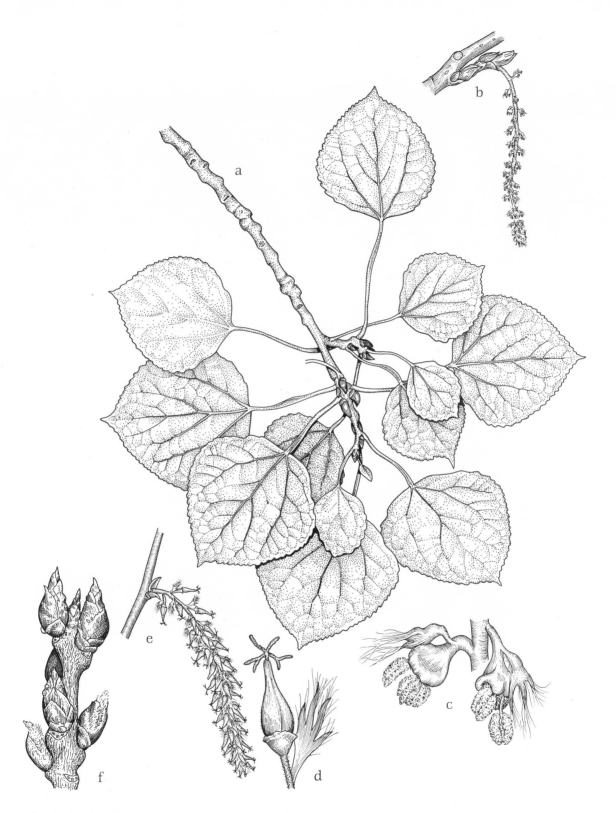

Populus tremuloides ❧ a. Growth form, b. Male catkin, c. Male flowers, d. Female flower, e. Fruit, f. Twig

Wild plum

Prunus americana Marshall

Rose family (Rosaceae)

Also called American plum

Appearance: Shrub propagates by root sprouts to form thickets or a small tree to 20 feet with spreading, more or less hanging, branches.

Flowers: April–May, in clusters of 2 to 5, stalks 1/4 to 3/4 inch long, smooth; flowers 3/4 to 1 1/4 inches broad, white, fragrant; petals 5, broadest at the middle, rounded at the tip, and narrow at the base; stamens about 20.

Fruit: July–September, in clusters with 15 to 30 fruits; fruit variable in size, usually 3/4 to 1 inch long, globe-shaped, **red or sometimes yellow, conspicuously marked with pale dots**; skin tough; flesh yellow and juicy, varying in flavor; stone oval, rounded at the tip, grooved on one side.

Leaves: Simple, alternate, 2 1/2 to 4 inches long, 1 1/2 to 2 inches wide, egg-shaped to broadest at the middle and narrowing at both ends, tip pointed, base rounded or wedge-shaped, margin sharply toothed, leaf thick, firm; dark green, smooth above; paler and net-veined beneath; **leaf stalk smooth** 1/2 to 3/4 inch long, slender, sometimes with glands at the tip where it meets the leaf blade.

Twigs: Slender, **smooth**, green to orange to reddish-brown; lateral branches spurlike, or sometimes thorny; pores circular, raised, minute buds smooth (without hairs).

Trunk: Bark dark brown to reddish, breaking into thin, long, scaly plates, pores horizontal and prominent; wood dark brown, with lighter colored sapwood, close-grained, strong, hard.

Habitat: Occurs in woodlands, pastures and thickets throughout Missouri.

Range: New Mexico, Texas, Oklahoma, Arkansas, and Louisiana; east to Florida, north to New York and Massachusetts; west to Ontario, Minnesota, Montana, Wyoming, and Utah.

Wildlife Uses: The fruit is eaten by many species of birds, including bobwhite quail. White-tailed deer, raccoons and squirrels also eat the fruits.

Remarks: This fast-growing, short-lived small tree has been planted in parks and orchards for its attractive, fragrant flowers and edible fruits. There are many horticultural forms and hybrids of this popular shrub; one source lists 76 hybrids. The fruit makes excellent jellies and preserves, or may be eaten raw or cooked. It is rated as the best fruit plum in the Midwest and North regions.

Wild plum is one of the first shrubs to bloom in woodlands. Its showy white flowers appear before the leaves have unfolded and while the woods are mostly bare of foliage.

The word plum is from the Old English *plume*, which is derived from an Asiatic word meaning "something desirable." The name was first recorded in 1780.

Prunus is the classical name for a European plum; *americana* refers to the country in which it was discovered.

Prunus americana ❀ a. Growth form, b. Branch with flowers, c. Flower, d. Fruit

Chickasaw plum

Prunus angustifolia Marshall

Rose family (Rosaceae)

Appearance: A twiggy shrub forming dense thickets, or a short-trunked, irregularly branched small tree to 25 feet.

Flowers: March–April, in 2- to 4-flowered clusters along the stem before the leaves emerge, flower stalks smooth, 1/4 to 1/2 inch long; petals 5, about 1/4 inch across, white, broadest at the middle, tip rounded; stamens usually 15 to 20.

Fruit: June–July, globe-shaped, 1/2 to 3/4 inch in diameter, **red or yellow with yellow dots**, shiny, skin thin with juicy, edible pulp; stone (hard seed casing) egg-shaped to longer than broad, about 1/2 inch long.

Leaves: Simple, alternate, **3/4 to 2 inches long, 1/4 to 3/4 inch wide,** mostly lance-shaped, tip pointed, **base rounded, base narrow; to wedge-shaped and folded, margin sharply toothed and bearing a gland between the two teeth**; upper surface bright yellowish-green, smooth, shiny; lower surface paler, smooth; **blade usually slightly folded lengthwise and the tip curled down**; leaf stalk slender, smooth to slightly hairy, 1/4 to 1/2 inch long, sometimes reddish, often with two red glands near the base of leaf.

Twigs: Reddish-brown, shiny, hairy at first but smooth later, slender, zigzag, often with thornlike spurs; pores horizontal and prominent.

Trunk: Bark reddish-brown to dark gray, scales thin and flattened; pores horizontal and prominent; wood reddish-brown, sapwood lighter, rather soft, not strong, fairly heavy.

Habitat: Occurs in thickets, pastures, fields, along fence rows, roadsides and prairie streams.

Range: Texas, Oklahoma, Arkansas, and Louisiana; east to Florida, north to New Jersey, and west to Indiana, Illinois, Missouri, and Kansas.

Wildlife Uses: Dense thickets of this shrub provide excellent cover for small birds and also produce a quantity of fruit for a variety of birds and mammals. Rodents often open the hard stones by gnawing and then eating the kernel inside.

Remarks: Chickasaw plum was first introduced into cultivation in 1750. It is sometimes used in shelter-belt plantings. There have been several ornamental varieties developed including big chickasaw, transparent, Emerson, Coletta, Clark, and Caddo Chief plum. The Comanche Indians ate the fresh fruits or they pitted and dried them for winter use. Early European settlers in the prairie region of western Missouri and Kansas made extensive use of the Chickasaw plum. They gathered the fruit by the bushel and wagonload, and used it for sauces, pies, puddings, jellies and preserves.

The word plum is from the Old English *plume*, which is derived from an Asiatic word meaning "something desirable." The name was first recorded in 1780. Chickasaw is named after the Chickasaw Indians who occupied what is now northern Mississippi and were closely related in language and culture to the Choctaw.

Prunus is the classical name for a European plum; *angustifolia* refers to the narrow leaves.

Prunus angustifolia ❧ a. Growth form with fruit, b. Stem with flowers, c. Gland-tipped leaf margin

Sour cherry

Prunus cerasus L.

Rose family (Rosaceae)

Appearance: Small to medium-sized tree, up to 30 feet tall, with short trunk and a spreading round-topped canopy.

Flowers: April–May, in clusters of 2 to 5 along the sides of the branches before or as the leaves unfold; **leaf-like bracts conspicuous at the base of the flower clusters**; flowers about 1 inch across; petals 5, white, broadest near the rounded tip; stamens 20 to 30.

Fruit: June–August, in clusters with **leaf-like bracts at the base of the fruit stalk**; fruit rounded, red to reddish-black cherry, 3/4 to 1/2 inch across, with a wax-like coating, juicy, sour flesh that encloses a small, round stone which contains the seed.

Leaves: Alternate, simple, broadest at or above the middle, 2 to 4 inches long; margin with coarse, prominent teeth, tip pointed; upper surface dark green, smooth; lower surface paler, hairy; leaf stalk smooth, with poorly developed glands at the tip.

Twigs: Slender, flexible, reddish-brown, shiny, smooth, becoming gray with age.

Trunk: Bark gray to brown, shiny, thinly scaled becoming almost black with age.

Habitat: Commonly planted and escaped from cultivation to fence rows, thickets, borders of woods and prairies, and along roadsides.

Range: Introduced into the United States; native to southeastern Europe and Asia.

Wildlife Uses: The fruit is eaten by birds, which distribute the seeds to fence rows, roadsides, and edges of woods. White-tailed deer and cottontail rabbits browse on the young twigs and leaves.

Medicinal Uses: Bark tea has been used in the treatment of fevers, coughs, and colds. The root bark has been used as a wash for open sores. The leaves, bark, and seeds of all members of the genus *Prunus* contain amygdalin and prunasin, substances that break down in water to form hydrocyanic acid (cyanide or prussic acid). In small amounts this exceedingly poisonous compound stimulates respiration, improves digestion, and gives a sense of well-being. In larger amounts, children have been poisoned by chewing twigs, eating seeds, and making tea from leaves of the wild and domestic cherries.

Remarks: There is good evidence that sour cherry arose from a cross between sweet cherry, *Prunus avium* L., and ground cherry, *Prunus fruticosa* L., both of which occur in the area between the Black and Caspian seas of Asia Minor. In 1629, English colonists brought both sour cherry and sweet cherry to the United States. Sour cherry is considerably more tart than sweet cherry so it is mainly used in pie fillings.

The gum obtained from the stem has been used as an adhesive and for chewing, while a drying oil obtained from the seed is used in cosmetics.

Cherry is from the Anglo-French *cherise*, a word that originated in the 13th Century.

Prunus is the Latin name of a European plum; *cerasus* is Latin for "wax," referring to the wax-like coating on the fruit.

Prunus cerasus ❀ a. Growth form with fruit, b. Flower clusters, c. Flower, d. Twig

Hortulan plum

Prunus hortulana Bailey

Rose family (Rosaceae)

Also called wild goose plum

Appearance: Many-stemmed shrub or small tree to 30 feet, with a broad, round-topped crown.

Flowers: March–May, in clusters of 2 to 4 flowers on slender, smooth to slightly hairy stalks about 1/2 inch long, flowers white, 3/4 to 1 inch across; petals 5, broadest in the middle and narrowing at both ends, tip rounded; stamens numerous.

Fruit: July–October, globe-shaped, 3/4 to 1 inch long, red or yellow-red, white-dotted, shiny, thin-skinned; stone net-veined, about 3/4 inch long, tip round or short-pointed, grooved on one edge.

Leaves: Simple, alternate, blades 4 to 6 inches long, 1 to 1 1/2 inches wide, egg-shaped to somewhat lance-shaped, tip pointed, base heart-shaped or rounded, **margin finely toothed with a gland arising from the very tip of each tooth, teeth conspicuous, spreading away from the margin**; upper surface smooth, dark green, shiny; lower surface paler, smooth or slightly hairy; leaf stalk slender, 1 to 1 1/2 inches long, orange to reddish-colored, grooved, usually two glands just below the base of leaf.

Twigs: Dark reddish-brown, stout, rigid, smooth or hairy, occasionally with thorns.

Trunk: Bark dark or light brown, separating into large, thin plates; wood reddish-brown, hard, heavy, with a wide, white sapwood.

Habitat: Occurs in open woodlands, borders of woods, along streams and thickets. Scattered in Missouri.

Range: Texas, Oklahoma, Arkansas, and Louisiana; north to Tennessee, Kentucky, Ohio, Indiana, Missouri, Kansas, and Iowa.

Wildlife Uses: The fruit is eaten by many species of birds, including bobwhite quail. White-tailed deer, raccoons, opossum, fox, squirrels and other mammals also eat the fruit.

Remarks: Hortulan plum is considered by some to be the most beautiful American plum. It is known mostly in horticultural forms, being rather rare in a wild state. About 34 forms are known, including Miner Hortulan plum and Missouri Hortuland plum.

In Missouri, hortulan plum is often a small tree and rarely forms thickets. When thickets are present they are created from seedlings, since this plum does not form sucker sprouts from the roots. The fruit is hard and firm until fully ripe, then becomes soft, juicy and edible. It may be eaten raw or cooked in pies or made into jams or jellies.

Although also called wild goose plum, this name is more appropriate for wild goose plum, *Prunus munsoniana*. See remarks for that species. The word plum is from the Old English *plume*, which is derived from an Asiatic word meaning "something desirable." The name was first recorded in 1780.

Prunus is the classical name for a European plum; *hortulana* means "of gardens" and refers to its value in horticulture, hence the common name hortulan.

Prunus hortulana ❀ a. Growth form, b. Twig with flower clusters, c. Flower, d. Fruit
e. Gland-tipped leaf margin

Perfumed cherry

Prunus mahaleb L.

Rose family (Rosaceae)

Also called Mahaleb cherry

Appearance: A large shrub to small tree up to 26 feet, with low branches, often forming small thickets around the parent plant.

Flowers: April–May, fragrant, opening with the leaves on short lateral branches of the current year's growth; clusters with 4 to 10 flowers; flowers white, about 3/4 inch across; petals 5, oval to broadest above the middle, about 3/8 inch long, narrowed to the base, tip rounded; stamens 20, extending beyond the flower.

Fruit: July, about 3/8 inch long, about 1/4 inch across, globe- to egg-shaped, dark reddish-purple, flesh thin, bitter; stone egg-shaped, slightly flattened, pinkish, smooth, tip pointed, a ridge on one side, a groove on the other.

Leaves: Alternate, simple, 1 to 3 inches long, 3/4 to 1 inch wide, **egg-shaped to broadly heart-shaped or circular, tip abruptly pointed to blunt**, base rounded or slightly heart-shaped, margin with rounded teeth; **upper surface dark green, shiny, smooth;** lower surface paler, with a few hairs on the central vein; leaf stalk 1/4 to 3/4 inch long, hairy at first, smooth later, flattened or grooved on the upper side, with 1 to 2 greenish or red glands at the upper summit.

Twigs: Reddish- to grayish-brown, hairy at first, smooth later, covered with a white, waxy coating; pores prominent.

Trunk: Bark on young trees not grooved, grayish-brown, with large crosswise pores; on old trees, dark gray and scaly; wood aromatic, hard, light, reddish-brown, with a light sapwood.

Habitat: Escapes from cultivation and forms thickets along roadsides, fence rows, and into wooded areas and borders of limestone glades.

Range: Native of Europe; introduced and naturalized in North America from Arkansas, Kansas, and Missouri; east to Indiana, Pennsylvania, and Delaware; north to New England and Ontario.

Wildlife Uses: Several species of birds readily eat the bitter fruits.

Remarks: Perfumed cherry has the potential to become aggressive; it has been found invading at least one natural area and other sites where it is unwelcomed. Its planting is discouraged.

Because of its hardiness, perfumed cherry has been used as a root base for grafting other cherries. It is used for making cabinets, smoking pipes and walking sticks. Oil from the seeds has been used in making perfume and by the Arabs as a remedy for bladder disorders. The fruit yields a violet dye and also a fermented liquor which is used in Eurasia.

Cherry is from the Anglo-French *cherise*, a word that originated in the 13th century.

Prunus is the ancient Latin name of a European plum; *mahaleb* is a Persian name.

Prunus mahaleb ❀ a. Growth form with flower clusters, b. Flower, c. Twig with fruit

Big tree plum

Prunus mexicana S. Watson

Rose family (Rosaceae)

Also called wild plum, Mexican plum

Appearance: Shrub or small tree to 25 feet, with an irregular open crown.

Flowers: April–May, in clusters of 2 to 4 flowers on slender, smooth stalks; flowers white, 3/4 to 1 inch in diameter; petals 5, broadest at or above the middle, narrowed to the base, tip rounded, hairy; stamens 15 to 20.

Fruit: July–September, globe-shaped, **eventually turning grayish-blue or grayish-lavender with a whitish coating,** 1 1/4 to 1 1/2 inches across; flesh thick, juicy with a tendency to stick to the stone; stone oval to egg-shaped, one edge grooved, the other ridged.

Leaves: Simple, alternate, thickish, blades 1 3/4 to 3 1/2 inches long, 1 to 2 inches wide, egg-shaped to broad in the middle and tapering at both ends, tip pointed, base heart-shaped or rounded, margin toothed; upper surface yellowish-green, smooth, shiny; **lower surface hairy,** especially on the veins; prominently net-veined both above and below; **leaf stalk stout, hairy,** about 3/4 inch long, with glands near the base of leaf.

Twigs: Slender, stiff, smooth or pubescent early, shiny, grayish-brown.

Trunk: Bark gray to black, separating into plate-like scales when young, when older rough and deeply grooved; upper branches tight and with large pores; wood hard, heavy, brown, with a narrow, light sapwood.

Habitat: Occurs in rocky or open woodlands and thickets throughout Missouri.

Range: Texas, Oklahoma, Arkansas, and Louisiana; east to Alabama, north to Kentucky and Ohio; and west to Indiana, Illinois, Nebraska, and Kansas; also in northeastern Mexico.

Wildlife Uses: The fruit is eaten by many species of birds, including wild turkey and bobwhite quail. White-tailed deer, raccoons, opossum, fox, squirrels and other mammals also eat the fruit.

Remarks: The common name refers to its tendency to form small trees, since it does not usually form sucker sprouts from the roots, like most other plums. Big tree plum is somewhat drought resistent and it has been used as grafting stock. Several varieties have been described across its range. Horticultural varieties include Quaker, Van Buren and Wolf.

The fruit is sweet and juicy, but, too often, is assumed to be ripe when it turns red. At that time it is still somewhat bitter and not really edible.

The word plum is from the Old English *plume*, which is derived from an Asiatic word meaning "something desirable." The name was first recorded in 1780.

Prunus is the classical name for a European plum; *mexicana* refers to this species' Southwestern distribution. Some authors consider this species to be a variety of *Prunus american*, i.e. *Prunus americana* var. *lanata*.

Prunus mexicana ❧ a. Growth form with fruit, b. Twig with flowers, c. Flower

Wild goose plum

Prunus munsoniana Wight & Hedrick

Rose family (Rosaceae)

Appearance: Shrub or small tree to 25 feet, with an irregular open crown.

Flowers: March-May, in clusters of 2 to 4 flowers, white, about 1/2 to 3/4 inch across, appearing before the leaves expand; flower stalks slender, smooth, 3/4 to 1 inch long; petals 5, about 1/4 inch long, egg-shaped, base narrow, tip pointed or blunt, with glands on the margins, smooth or hairy; stamens usually 15 to 20.

Fruit: June-August, globe-shaped to oval, about 3/4 inch long, **red or yellow, white-dotted, with thin whitish coating**, skin thin, flesh yellow and juicy; stone oval, tip pointed, a wide groove on one side, narrow on the other.

Leaves: Simple, alternate, blades 2 1/2 to 4 inches long, 3/4 to 1 1/4 inches wide, lance-shaped, tip pointed, base heart-shaped or rounded, **margin finely toothed to rounded with a gland on the incurved face;** bright shiny green above; sparingly hairy, especially along the veins beneath; **fully grown leaves more or less folded lengthwise, troughlike;** leaf stalk slender, smooth or hairy, with two glands near the base of the leaves.

Twigs: Flexible, reddish-brown, shiny, smooth becoming gray in the second year, pores pale and numerous.

Trunk: Bark reddish- or chestnut-brown, thin, smooth, usually with horizontal white patches; the pores horizontal; old trunks gray to gray-brown, flaky; wood hard, heavy, pale red-brown, with a light sapwood.

Habitat: Occurs in thickets, prairies, borders of streams and woodlands, and idle ground. Scattered throughout Missouri except for the extreme northwestern and southeastern parts of the state.

Range: Texas, Oklahoma, Arkansas, and Louisiana; north to Kentucky and Ohio, and west to Missouri and southeastern Kansas; also in northeastern Mexico.

Wildlife Uses: The fruit is eaten by many species of birds, including wild turkey and bobwhite quail. White-tailed deer, raccoons, opossum, fox, squirrels and other mammals also eat the fruit. The dense thickets provide cover for small birds.

Remarks: This is a shrub to small tree that sends up sucker sprouts from the roots, forming rather dense thickets. The name wild goose plum comes from the discovery of a seed of this species in the craw of a wild goose, which had been shot by a Captain Means of Nashville, Tenn. From this seed, which was planted, grew a plum which was later developed by nurserymen into a superior strain.

The fruit is somewhat bitter and firm even after falling to the ground, but because of its abundance is often gathered in quantities to be made into jelly. Most wild plums have a tendency to be infected by insects and should be carefully examined before using.

Prunus comes from the classical name of a European plum; *munsoniana* refers to T. V. Munson (1823–1913), an American botanist.

Prunus munsoniana ❀ a. Growth form, b. Twig with flower clusters, c. Flowers, d. Fruit, e. Gland-tipped leaf margin

Peach

Prunus persica (L.) Batsch

Rose family (Rosaceae)

Appearance: A small tree to a height of 24 feet, with a rounded crown and spreading branches.

Flowers: March-April, opening before the leaves on the previous year's growth; flowers single or 2 together, fragrant, pink to rose-colored, 1 to 2 inches across; petals 5, spreading, rounded; stamens 20 to 30, extending beyond the flower.

Fruit: July-October, 2 to 3 1/4 inches across, globe-shaped, grooved on one side, **velvety to densely hairy with matted wool,** fleshy, separating in halves along a groove; stone rounded in the middle and rounded toward the end, deeply pitted, very hard; fruit of escaped trees usually harder and smaller.

Leaves: Alternate, simple, some appearing clustered, sometimes more than one leaf emerging from the same bud, almond-scented, impregnated with prussic acid; blades 3 to 6 inches long, lance-shaped, the edges often turned upward, tip pointed, base tapering to broadly wedge-shaped, margin finely toothed; both surfaces bright green, smooth, shiny, thin; **leaves troughlike, the halves more or less folded lengthwise, conspicuously drooping;** leaf stalk about 1/2 inch long, with 1 or 2 glands at the upper summit.

Twigs: Upper portion often reddish, while the lower part is greenish, smooth; **buds strongly hairy.**

Trunk: Bark rough, scaly, grayish-brown, pores prominent.

Habitat: Commonly planted and escaped from cultivation to thickets, fence rows and along roadsides.

Range: Native of China; introduced and naturalized in the United States from Texas, east to Florida, north to New York, and west to Ontario, Michigan, Illinois, Iowa, and Missouri.

Wildlife Uses: The fruit is eaten by several species of birds and small mammals.

Remarks: Although it escapes from cultivation, peach does not seem to be aggressive, and appears to limit its naturalizing to disturbed areas. There are many forms, varieties and hybrids that have been developed for ornamental and fruit-bearing qualities. Peaches are notoriously susceptible to insect and disease pests. The flower buds and flowers are often injured in cold winters or by late frosts.

Prunus is the ancient Latin name of a plum of Europe; *persica* means "Persian," and is also an old name for peach.

Prunus persica ✿ a. Growth form, b. Twig with flowers, c. Fruit

Black cherry

Prunus serotina Ehrh.

Rose family (Rosaceae)

Also called wild cherry, wild black cherry, rum cherry

Appearance: Medium to large trees, up to 60 feet tall, with a straight trunk, somewhat hanging branches, and a rather spreading, rounded crown.

Flowers: April–May, after the leaves have emerged, in dense, elongated, cylinder-shape clusters, 2 to 4 inches long; flowers white, about 1/4 inch across; petals 5, broadest near the tip; stamens 15 to 20.

Fruit: August–September, **in clusters with 15 to 30 fruits**; fruits round, dark purple to black, 1/4 to 1/2 inch in diameter, shiny, skin thin, flesh juicy, bittersweet, edible; stone broadest at the base, about 1/3 long, thin, smooth, broadly ridged on one margin.

Leaves: Alternate, simple, broadest near the middle and lance-shaped or uniformly wide, 2 to 6 inches long, 1 to 2 inches wide; **margin finely toothed, teeth turned inward, tip long, gradually tapering**; upper surface dark green, shiny, smooth; lower surface paler with hairs along the central vein; leaf stalk with glands near the leaf base; leaves turn yellow or reddish in autumn.

Twigs: Slender, flexible, smooth, reddish- or olive brown with a grayish coating; pores small, numerous, extremely bitter almond taste and smell upon scratching.

Trunk: Bark dark reddish-brown, smooth when young, black, broken into small scaly plates with age, bitter to the taste; pores narrow, horizontal, prominent; wood reddish-brown, heavy, moderately hard, strong, close-grained.

Habitat: Occurs in low or upland woods and along streams.

Range: Texas, Oklahoma, Arkansas, and Louisiana; east to Florida, north to Nova Scotia, west to North Dakota, Nebraska, and Kansas, and southward into Mexico to Guatemala; it is naturalized in several South American countries.

Wildlife Uses: The fruit is eaten by at least 33 species of birds, raccoon, opossum, squirrels, cottontail rabbit, and others.

Medicinal Uses: Rum cherry was widely used by Native Americans who used it to treat a variety of complaints. Bark tea was used in small amounts to treat fever, colds, sore throats, laryngitis, diarrhea, etc. The leaves, buds, twigs, and bark contain glycoside prunasin, which is converted in the stomach to the highly toxic hydrocyanic acid (cyanide). See discussion under sour cherry for more information.

Remarks: Black cherry has been in cultivation as an ornamental since 1629. In Missouri, black cherry is second in demand to walnut for quality wood products. The wood is used for furniture, cabinetmaking, veneer, panels, interior trim, and handles. The fruit is used for making jelly and wine. The eastern tent caterpillar is a common pest on black cherry. The "tents" or "bags" are formed between branches from which the caterpillars venture out to feed on leaves, often defoliating smaller trees. Trees weakened by these insects are prone to attacks by borers.

Prunus is the Latin name of a European plum; *serotina* is Latin for "late-flowering."

Prunus serotina ❀ a. Growth form with flower clusters, b. Flower, c. Fruit, d. Twig

Choke cherry

Prunus virginiana L.

Rose family (Rosaceae)

Appearance: Large shrub or small tree to 30 feet, with erect or horizontal branches, sometimes forming thickets from root sprouts.

Flowers: April-May, in short, dense cylinderlike clusters 3 to 6 inches long, many-flowered; flowers white, 1/4 to 1/2 inch in diameter, on slender, smooth stalks; petals 5, small, rounded; stamens 15 to 20.

Fruit: August-September, **in clusters with 15 to 30 fruit; fruit a cherry** 1/4 to 3/8 inch across, dark red, scarlet or nearly black, globe-shaped, shiny; skin thick, flesh juicy, bitter, barely edible; stone egg-shaped to oval, one edge ridged, the other with a sharp angle. Good crops are produced almost annually.

Leaves: Simple, alternate, **thin,** blades 3/4 to 4 inches long, 1/2 to 2 inches wide, oval to longer than broad and tapering at both ends, **tip abrupt and sharp-pointed,** base rounded to wedge-shaped or heart-shaped, margin sharply toothed; dark green and shiny above; paler on the lower surface, sometimes hairy on the veins, turning yellow in autumn, strong odor when crushed; leaf stalk slender, 1/2 to 1 inches, smooth, grooved above, 2 glands near the base of leaf.

Twigs: Shiny reddish-brown to orange-brown, smooth, slender, flexible, pores prominent, pale.

Trunk: Bark thin, reddish-brown; pores prominent on young trees; grooved and scaly on old trees; wood heavy, hard, reddish-brown, with a wide, light sapwood.

Habitat: Occurs on moist, mostly north-facing wooded slopes and bluffs, and ravines, rarely on borders of woods, thickets, fence rows, ditches or roadsides. More frequent north of the Missouri River.

Range: New Mexico, Texas, Oklahoma, Arkansas, and Louisiana; east to Georgia, north to Maine and Newfoundland; and west to the Dakotas, Saskatchewan, and British Columbia; south to Washington, Oregon, and California.

Wildlife Uses: There are about 14 native species of wild cherries widely distributed throughout the country. They are considered to be some of the most important wildlife food plants. The wild cherries are eaten by a wide variety of songbirds, game birds, and mammals from black bear to white-footed mouse.

Medicinal Uses: Native Americans used a warm drink made from the bark to ease the pains of childbirth, and a tea made of the root bark as a sedative and stomach remedy. Early settlers used root bark tea to treat malaria, worms, tuberculosis, indigestion and fever.

Remarks: The small tree is sometimes planted for ornament and for erosion control. It has been in cultivation since 1724. The fruit is used to make jellies and jams.

The name choke refers to the fruits bitter taste. Cherry is from the Anglo-French *cherise*, a word that originated in the 13th century.

Prunus is the classical name for a European plum; *virginiana* refers to the state of Virginia.

Prunus virginiana ✿ a. Growth form with fruit, b. Twig with flower cluster

Hop tree

Ptelea trifoliata L.

Citrus family (Rutaceae)

Also called common hop tree, wafer ash, stinking ash

Appearance: Usually a rounded shrub, but occasionally a small tree to 25 feet. Leaves are divided into 3 leaflets that are unpleasantly scented.

Flowers: April-June, arising from the leaf axils with male, female, and perfect flowers in clusters on the same plant, on slender stalks 1/4 to 1 1/2 inches long; flowers small, greenish-white; petals 4 to 5, longer than broad, somewhat hairy; stamens 4 to 5, alternating with the petals; female flowers with a raised central pistil and stamens absent.

Fruit: August-September, **samaras (winged fruits) in drooping clusters on slender stalks;** yellowish-green, later turning brown when dry; net-veined, compressed, thin, wafer-like or somewhat circular, 3/4 to 1 inch across, persistent into winter, unpleasantly scented; seeds 2 to 3, oval, leathery, reddish-brown, about 1/4 inch long.

Leaves: Alternate, **compound with 3 leaflets; leaflets stalkless**, blades 4 to 6 inches long, 2 to 4 inches wide, longer than broad and tapering at both ends, tip pointed, base wedge-shaped, **margin entire or finely toothed;** upper surface dark green, shiny; lower surface paler, slightly hairy; **unpleasantly scented**; leaf stalk stout, base slightly swollen, 2 to 3 inches long, hairy.

Twigs: Slender, green to yellow or reddish-brown, hairy, unpleasantly scented when bruised.

Trunk: Bark thin, smooth except for the prominent pores, light to dark gray or brown, older bark slightly cracked, bitter to the taste; wood heavy, hard, yellowish-brown, with a narrow light sapwood.

Habitat: Occurs on limestone and dolomite glades, prairies, rocky open woods and edge of woods, low woods in ravines, and valleys, thickets and along fence rows.

Range: New Mexico, Texas, Oklahoma, Arkansas, and Louisiana; east to Florida, north to New York and Quebec; and west to Ontario, Minnesota, Kansas, and Colorado; also in Mexico.

Medicinal Uses: Early European settlers used the root as a tonic or invigorating drink. It also was thought that it might be a substitute for quinine because of its bitter flavor. The name hop tree came about not because the fruits looked like hops, but because they were thought to be a possible replacement for the hops that were put into beer. Most of these promises of medicinal or economic value faded throughout the years.

Remarks: Hop tree is occasionally planted for ornament. It was first introduced into cultivation in 1724, and eventually became widespread in European gardens. All parts of the plant emit a disagreeable odor, with some comparing the smell to that of a bobcat.

Ptelea is the classical Greek name for the elm, here applied to a plant with similar fruit; *trifoliata* (three-leaved) refers to the three leaflets.

Ptelea trifoliata ✽ a. Growth form with flower cluster, b. Flower, c. Fruit

Pear

Pyrus communis L.

Rose family (Rosaceae)

Appearance: Medium-sized tree, up to 60 feet tall, with a straight trunk, stiff, upright branches and a generally pyramidal shape leading to a narrow crown.

Flowers: April–May, before or as the leaves are emerging in clusters of 4 to 12 flowers, along a central stock, **usually on short, compressed twigs**; flowers 1 to 2 inches across; petals 5, **white**, broad, rounded at the tip; stamens 20 to 30.

Fruit: August–October, **pear-shaped**, 2 to 4 inches long, skin green to brown, hard, becoming fleshy at maturity, juicy, sweet, edible; **flesh containing gritty stone cells with several large, seeds at the core**; seeds brown, smooth.

Leaves: Alternate, simple, **usually on short, compressed twigs**; leaves 1 1/2 to 4 inches long, variable shape, broadest below, at, or above the middle, thick, leathery; margin finely toothed, tip pointed; upper surface dark green, shiny, smooth; lower surface paler, smooth; leaf stalk slender, 1 1/4 to 3 inches as long or longer than the leaf; leaves turning yellow in autumn.

Twigs: Stout, smooth, reddish-brown, **some twigs compressed into spur shoots with some spur shoots bearing a spine at the end**.

Trunk: Bark dark brown to gray, with shallow grooves and flat-topped, scaly ridges; wood reddish-brown, hard, fine-grained.

Habitat: Commonly planted and sometimes escaping to old fields and along fence rows, and persisting in abandoned farm lots.

Range: Native to Europe and Asia; widely planted and escaping cultivation in North America.

Wildlife Uses: The fruit is eaten by some birds, small mammals, coyote, foxes, cottontail rabbits, and white-tailed deer.

Remarks: Although not native to Missouri, it is not considered to be aggressive nor a threat to natural communities in the state. There are at least 8 varieties and 90 horticultural forms of the common pear. Under cultivation, the trees are heavily pruned for greater production and ease of harvesting, so they seldom reach full size. A light crop usually follows a season of heavy fruit production.

The fruit is eaten raw or cooked. Wild pears often remain very hard unless allowed to over ripen. They are more suitable for use in pies, etc.

The wood is used for carving, and to make rulers, drawing and musical instruments, and cabinets. When covered with black varnish, it is an excellent ebony substitute.

The name pear is from the Old English (450 to 1100) *pere*.

Pyrus is the Latin name for the pear-tree; *communis* means "common."

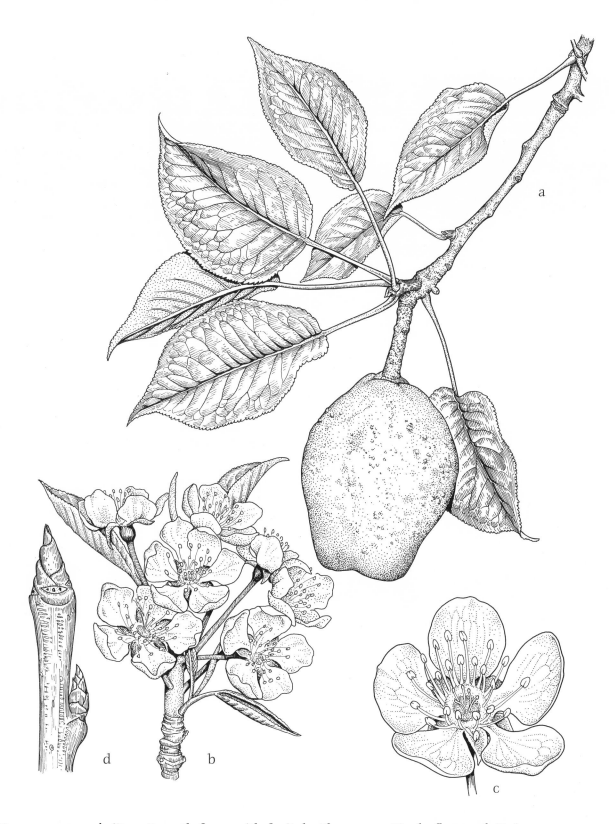

Pyrus communis ❀ a. Growth form with fruit, b. Flowers, c. Single flower, d. Twig

Sawtooth oak

Quercus acutissima Carruthers

Oak family (Fagaceae)

Also called gobbler oak

Appearance: Medium-sized tree, up to 40 feet tall, with a broad pyramidal shape and rounded crown.

Flowers: April–May, see p. 380 for oak reproductive cycle.

Fruit: September–October, nut brown, shiny, oval, about 1 inch long; cup covering 1/2 to 2/3 of the nut; **scales fringed or shaggy; unlike other oaks in the red/black oak group, the acorns ripen in the fall of the first year**.

Leaves: Alternate, simple, 4 to 8 inches long, 2 to 4 inches wide, broadest at the base or middle, 3 to 4 times longer than broad; **margin toothed ending in bristle tips**, tip pointed; upper surface dark green, shiny, smooth; lower surface paler, smooth with tufts of hairs in the axils of the veins; leaf stalk 3/4 to 1 inch long; leaves turn clear yellow to golden brown in autumn.

Twigs: Slender, gray to brown, smooth with more than one bud at the tip.

Trunk: Bark grayish-brown, slight grooves and ridges when young, becoming more pronounced and even corky with age.

Habitat: Planted in yards and escaping into the wild.

Range: Native to Japan, China, Korea, and the Himalayas; widely planted in the United States.

Wildlife Uses: Acorns are eaten by squirrels and wild turkeys.

Medicinal Uses: As in other oaks, parts of sawtooth oak have astringent (causes tissue to contract) properties. The stem bark is used to clean sores. The seeds are used in the treatment of diarrhea.

Remarks: Sawtooth oak is being promoted commercially as the "ideal" food for wild turkeys because of the size of the nut. There are, however, native oaks such as pin oak, shingle oak, post oak and black jack oak that can fill this purpose. Because sawtooth or gobbler oak escapes and naturalizes, native oaks are recommended for ornamental and wildlife plantings.

The wood is used for boat building, construction, charcoal, and fuel. A black dye is obtained from the acorn cups.

Oak is from the Old English *ac*, beyond that its origin is uncertain.

Quercus is the Latin name for oak; *acutissima* for "sharp," referring to the bristle-tipped teeth along the leaf margin, hence, the common name of sawtooth.

Quercus acutissima ❀ a. Growth form, b. Acorn, c. Twig

White oak

Quercus alba L.

Oak family (Fagaceae)

Appearance: Large tree, up to 120 feet tall, with a long, straight trunk, and broad, rounded crown.

Flowers: April–May, see p. 380 for oak reproductive cycle.

Fruit: September–October, acorn solitary or in pairs; nut light brown, shiny, widest near the base or middle, tapering to a round tip, 3/4 to 1 inch long; **cup covering up to 1/4 of the nut, bowl-shaped to saucer-shaped, light brown; scales numerous, surface warty or corky**, flattened, knobby; seeds somewhat sweet, edible; acorns ripen in autumn of the first year.

Leaves: Alternate, simple, 5 to 9 inches long, 2 to 4 inches wide, usually widest above the middle to almost uniformly wide along the sides; **margin entire, with 6 to 10 lobes; lobes rounded at the tip**; upper surface bright green, smooth, often shiny; **lower surface whitened, smooth (without hairs)**; leaf stalk short, stout, about 1 inch long; leaves turn a dark red to purple wine color in autumn.

Twigs: Slender to stout, green to reddish-green, and hairy when young, turning red-brown to ash gray and smooth with age.

Trunk: Bark light gray, with shallow grooves and flat, loose ridges; **large limbs and branches scaly**; wood light brown, strong, hard, heavy, durable, close-grained.

Habitat: Occurs on dry upland slopes and ridges; also low ground of valleys and ravine bottoms.

Range: East Texas, Oklahoma, Arkansas, and Louisiana; east to Florida, north to Maine, and west to Ontario, and Minnesota; and south to Iowa, Missouri, and eastern Kansas.

Wildlife Uses: Acorns are eaten by blue jay, woodpeckers, wood duck, wild turkey, ruffed grouse, bobwhite quail, mice, squirrels, raccoons, and white-tailed deer.

Medicinal Uses: As in other oaks, the bark, especially, has astringent (causes tissue to contract) properties. Native Americans used inner-bark tea to treat diarrhea, mouth sores, chapped skin, asthma, and coughs.

Remarks: White oak has been in cultivation since 1724. It is one of the most attractive, long-lived (over 300 years) shade trees in Missouri. White oak is one of Missouri's most ubiquitous trees, found in a wide variety of forest, woodland, and savanna natural communities throughout the state.

The wood is second only to walnut in unit value. Once used extensively in ship construction, white oak is now used for interior finishing, veneer, cabinets, general construction, fence posts, railroad ties, fuel, and tight cooperage (e.g., whiskey and wine barrels).

Native Americans ground the acorns into meal and poured water through it to leach out the tannin before baking into a type of pasty bread.

Oak is from the Old English *ac*, beyond that its origin is uncertain.

Quercus is the Latin name for oak; *alba* is Latin for "white," referring to the bark.

Quercus alba ✤ a. Leaves with female flowers, b. Female flowers, c. Acorn, d. Twig

Swamp white oak

Quercus bicolor Willd.

Oak family (Fagaceae)

Appearance: Medium-sized tree, up to 80 feet tall, with an open, irregular, rounded crown, ascending upper branches, and somewhat pendulous lower branches.

Flowers: April–May, see p. 380 for oak reproductive cycle.

Fruit: September–October, acorn in clusters of 1 to 3, **on slender, dark brown stalks, 2 to 3 times longer than the leaf stalks, 3/4 to 2 1/2 inches long**; nut light brown, uniformly wide to slightly broadest at the base, about 1 inch long, tip pointed and hairy; cup covering 1/3 to 1/2 of the nut, bowl-shaped, light brown, hairy; scales flattened, sometimes forming a short fringe on the border; seeds sweet, edible; acorns ripen in autumn of the first year.

Leaves: Alternate, simple, 4 to 7 inches long, 3 1/2 to 4 1/2 inches wide, broadest above the middle; **margin sometimes with variable lobes or large, rounded teeth, or both, some of the side veins not ending in the teeth, especially near the notch and tip of the leaf blade**; upper surface dark green, shiny, smooth; **lower surface dense whitish, hairy**; leaf stalk stout, hairy at first, smooth later, 1/2 to 3/4 inches long; leaves turn yellowish-brown to red-purple in autumn.

Twigs: Stout, short, reddish-brown, smooth; older twigs with peeling bark.

Trunk: Bark brownish on young trunks, turning gray to dark brown on older trunks, grooves deep, ridges broad, flattened and loosely curling back at the ends to give a rough appearance; bark on larger branches often scaly, peeling away; wood light to dark brown, strong, hard, tough, heavy, close-grained.

Habitat: Occurs in bottomland forests in valleys and on rich, lower slopes, in wet ground bordering swamps and oxbow lakes of floodplain and stream meanders, and along streams.

Range: Oklahoma, Arkansas, Tennessee, and North Carolina; north to Maine and Quebec, west to Ontario and Minnesota, and south to Missouri.

Wildlife Uses: Acorns are eaten by blue jay, woodpeckers, wood duck, wild turkey, ruffed grouse, bobwhite quail, mice, squirrels, raccoon, and white-tailed deer.

Remarks: Swamp white oak was first used in cultivation in about 1800. A handsome shade tree, swamp white oak grows relatively fast and can live up to 350 years old. The tree begins flowering at 25 to 30 years of age. Although it grows in low, wet areas in the wild, it does very well in urban areas and can withstand drought conditions once it is established. Alkaline soils will cause leaf yellowing and growth problems.

The wood of this oak is not distinguished commercially from that of white oak. It is used for general construction, furniture, cabinets, veneer, interior finishes, fence posts, and fuel.

Swamp white oak does not grow in swamps as the name implies, but rather, is found in low, wet, sometimes poorly drained soils.

Oak is from the Old English *ac*, beyond that its origin is uncertain.

Quercus is the Latin name for oak; *bicolor* is Latin for "two-colored" and refers to the contrasting upper and lower leaf surfaces.

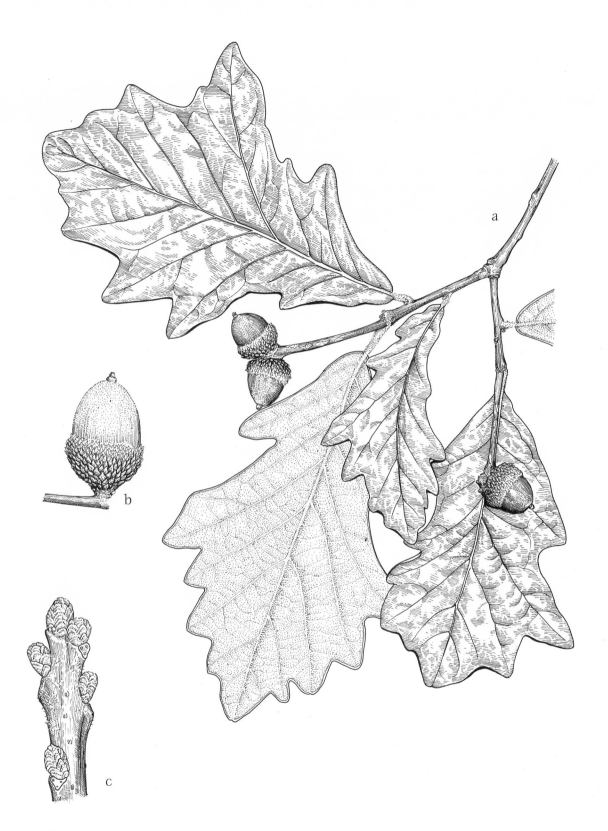

Quercus bicolor ❦ a. Growth form with acorns, b. Acorn, c. Twig

Scarlet oak

Quercus coccinea Muenchh

Oak family (Fagaceae)

Appearance: Medium-sized tree, up to 80 feet tall, with a long, straight trunk, an open, narrow crown, and sometimes persistent dead branches on the lower trunk.

Flowers: April–May, see p. 380 for the oak reproductive cycle.

Fruit: September–October, acorns solitary or paired, stalkless or nearly so; nut brown, broadest near the base, 1/2 to 1 inch long, **tip sometimes with concentric rings**; cup covering 1/3 to 1/2 of the nut, bowl-shaped, over 1/4 inch long, over 5/8 across; **cup scales thick, flattened, sometimes warty, shiny, smooth**; seed bitter; acorns ripen in autumn of the second year.

Leaves: Alternate, simple, 3 to 7 inches long, 2 to 5 inches wide, broadest near or above the middle; margin with 7 to 9 lobes extending more than halfway to the central vein, **the lobes are rounded and C-shaped at their notches**, the tips have large teeth, each ending in a bristle; upper surface bright green, shiny, smooth; lower surface paler, occasionally with tufts of rusty hairs at the axis of main veins; leaf stalk slender 1 to 3 inches long; leaves turn scarlet in autumn.

Twigs: Slender, greenish at first, orange-red or brown with age, smooth or hairy; bud scales with whitish-gray hairs near the tip.

Trunk: Bark brownish-black, with shallow grooves and irregular ridges becoming scaly with age; wood light to reddish-brown, heavy, hard, strong, coarse-grained.

Habitat: Occurs in acid soils associated with sandstone, chert, or igneous rocks on narrow ridges, slopes, and upland woods bordering headwaters of tributary streams.

Range: Eastern Oklahoma, Arkansas, and northern Mississippi; east to Georgia and South Carolina, north to Massachusetts and Maine, west to southern Ontario and Michigan, and south to Illinois and Missouri.

Wildlife Uses: Acorns are eaten by blue jay, woodpeckers, wild turkey, ruffed grouse, bobwhite quail, mice, squirrels, raccoon, and white-tailed deer.

Remarks: Scarlet oak has been in cultivation since 1691. It is a desirable ornamental for its relatively fast growth, attractive form, and scarlet foliage in autumn. In urban areas, scarlet oak is a good substitute for pin oak on drier sites, but not as tolerant as northern red oak to air pollution.

The wood is used for general construction, flooring, pallets, and fuel.

Scarlet oak and black oak both are relatively short-lived (less than 120 years). As old-growth short-leaf pine was removed from the Ozarks from 1890 to 1920, scarlet and black oak moved in to fill the gaps. In the last decade or so these oaks have been declining, and there are efforts by public agencies to replace them with the original occupants in the form of pine woodlands, one of the rarest forest communities today.

Oak is from the Old English *ac*, beyond that its origin is uncertain.

Quercus is the Latin name for oak; *coccinea* is Latin for "scarlet," referring to the color of the leaves in autumn.

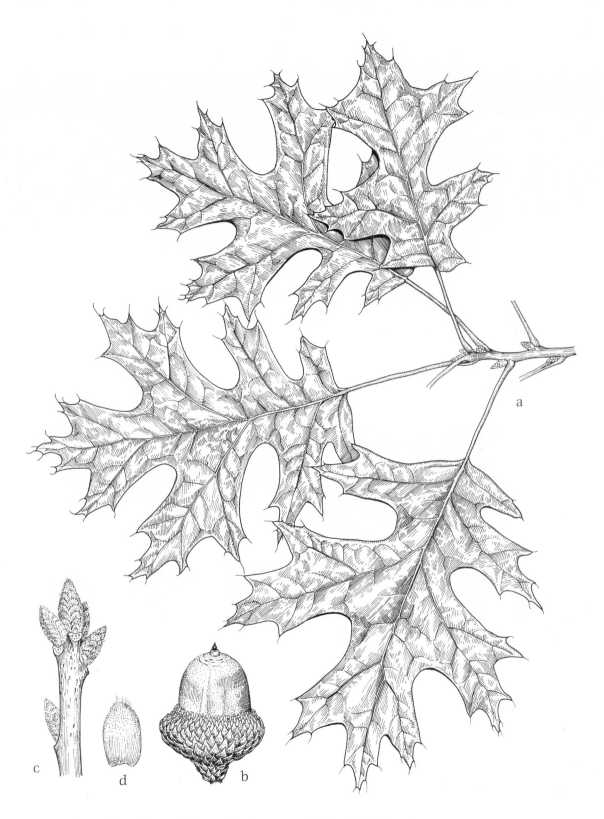

Quercus coccinea ❧ a. Growth form, b. Acorn, c. Twig, d. Bud scale

Southern red oak

Quercus falcata Michaux

Oak family (Fagaceae)

Also called Spanish oak

Appearance: Large-sized tree, up to 90 feet tall, with a long, straight trunk, open, rounded crown, and spreading branches.

Flowers: April–May, see p. 380 for the oak reproductive cycle.

Fruit: September–October, acorns solitary or in pairs on a short stalk; nut brown and faintly striped with light brown, globe-shaped, about 1/2 inch long; cup covering about 1/3 of the nut, saucer-shaped, red-brown; **scales flattened, with a reddish-brown dark border**, hairy; seed yellowish, bitter; acorns ripen in autumn of the second year.

Leaves: Alternate, simple, 6 to 7 inches long, 4 to 5 inches wide, very variable in shape and lobing, **broadest near the notch; margin with 3 to 5 bristle-tipped lobes, first pair of lobes typically the largest and longest, often curved or sickle-shaped, notch of the lobes wide and nearly to the central vein**; upper surface dark green, shiny, smooth; **lower surface paler with light brown to grayish-white matted hairs**; leaf stalk slender, flattened, 1 to 2 inches long, hairy; **leaf often has drooping appearance**; leaves turn reddish-brown in autumn.

Twigs: Stout, reddish-brown, hairy at first, smooth later.

Trunk: Bark grayish-black, broken into deep grooves, becoming ridged and rough-plated near the base, not scaly; wood light red, durable, heavy, hard, strong, coarse-grained.

Habitat: Occurs on acid soils of chert, or sandstone on upland ridges and hills, or on sand and gravel hills of Crowley's Ridge in the Bootheel, or in valley or river bottom woods.

Range: East Texas, Oklahoma, Arkansas, and Louisiana; east to Florida, north to New York, and west to Ohio, Indiana, Illinois, and Missouri.

Wildlife Uses: Acorns are eaten by woodpeckers, wild turkey, mice, squirrels, raccoon, and white-tailed deer.

Medicinal Uses: The bark is used as an astringent (causes tissues to contract).

Remarks: Southern red oak is also called *Quercus falcata* var. *falcata*. In open-grown situations, southern red oak is an excellent, durable shade tree and is widely planted in southern towns. Considered a moderately fast-growing tree, it can live up to 150 years of age.

The wood is used for construction, flooring, furniture, panels and doors, veneer, railroad ties, and fuel. It is considered more "limby" and of lower quality than cherrybark oak.

In the red oak complex, northern red oak is the common name given to *Quercus rubra* and southern red oak is used for *Quercus falcata*. The other name, Spanish oak, comes from the suggestion that the form of the leaf looks like a Spanish dagger.

Oak is from the Old English *ac*, beyond that its origin is uncertain.

Quercus is the Latin name for oak; *falcata* is Latin for "falcate or sickle-shaped," referring to the shape of the leaf lobes.

Quercus falcata ❧ a. Growth form, b. Female flower, c. Acorns, d. Twig

Shingle oak

Quercus imbricaria Michaux

Oak family (Fagaceae)

Also called laurel oak

Appearance: Medium-sized tree, up to 80 feet tall, with a straight trunk and an open, broadly rounded crown.

Flowers: April–May, see p. 380 for the oak reproductive cycle.

Fruit: September–October, acorn solitary or in pairs, on short, stout stalks up to 1/2 inch long; nut light to dark brown, **often with pale stripes**, shiny, broadest at the base and rounded at the tip, about 1/2 inch long; cup covering 1/3 to 1/2 of the nut, thin, bowl-shaped, red-brown to dark brown; scales thin, flattened, hairy; seeds bitter; acorns ripen in autumn of the second year.

Leaves: Alternate, simple, 4 to 6 inches long, **1 to 2 inches wide**, uniformly wide, or widest at or above the middle; margin entire, often slightly wavy, tip rounded or abruptly pointed, **not tipped by a bristle**; upper surface dark green, shiny, smooth; **lower surface paler, hairy; leaf stalk stout, hairy**, 1/4 to 1/2 inch long; leaves turn yellow or reddish-brown, **many persisting through winter and dropping as the sap begins to flow in early spring**.

Twigs: Slender, dark green to reddish-brown to gray brown, smooth at maturity, shiny, dead twigs and branches often remaining on the middle portion of the trunk.

Trunk: Bark on young trees and branches smooth, brownish-gray, on older trunks grayish-brown, with grooves and long, flat, scaly ridges, dead branches often persistent; wood brownish-red, hard, heavy, strong, coarse-grained.

Habitat: Occurs in upland ridges, slopes, and ravines; lowland areas in valleys and along streams; and borders of prairies.

Range: Eastern Oklahoma, Arkansas, Tennessee, and North Carolina; north to New Jersey and Virginia, west to Wisconsin, Iowa, Missouri, and eastern Kansas.

Wildlife Uses: Acorns are eaten by blue jay, woodpeckers, wood duck, wild turkey, ruffed grouse, bobwhite quail, mice, squirrels, raccoon, and white-tailed deer.

Medicinal Uses: The bark is used as an astringent (causes tissues to contract).

Remarks: Shingle oak has been in cultivation since 1724. The tree is moderately fast growing with a medium life span. The wood is reported to still be in use for roof shingles in Tennessee and some other states. Of lower quality than other oaks, the wood is used for some construction and for fuel.

Shingle oak is a pioneer species, often invading newly disturbed sites and pastures with the help of blue jays. It has been documented that the birds can carry an acorn up to a mile away from the tree, tucking the nut into grassy litter only to be eaten later. Of course, many acorns are not relocated and are left to grow into new trees.

Quercus is the Latin name for oak; *imbricaria* is Latin for "overlapping," as with the shingles. Michaux gave the name to the plant when he found early settlers making hand-hewn shingles from the tree.

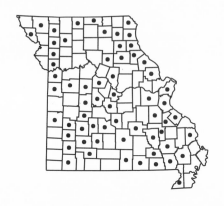

Quercus imbricaria ❧ a. Growth form, b. Male catkins, c. Acorn, d. Twig

Overcup oak

Quercus lyrata Walter

Oak family (Fagaceae)

Appearance: Medium-sized tree, up to 80 feet tall, with an irregular crown, twisted branches, and a swollen base when growing along the edges of swamps.

Flowers: April–May, see p. 380 for the oak reproductive cycle.

Fruit: September–October, acorn solitary or in pairs, with or without a short stalk; **nut light brown, globe-shaped, 1/2 to 1 inch tall, over 1/2 inch wide; cup enclosing from 2/3 to nearly all of the nut**, globe-shaped, reddish-brown, hairy, thin, sometimes splitting at the tip, thicker towards the base; **scales sometimes warty and ragged towards the tip, otherwise flattened**; seeds edible; acorns ripen in autumn of the first year.

Leaves: Alternate, simple, 3 to 10 inches long, 1 to 4 inches wide, narrow but broadest above the middle; margin with 5 to 9 rounded lobes, **middle lobes usually widest, often squarrish**, notch of lobes with various shapes, tip rounded to pointed; upper surface dark green, shiny, smooth; lower surface white, hairy, smooth later; leaf stalk stout, hairy to smooth, 1/3 to 1 inch long; leaves turn yellow, brown, or reddish in autumn.

Twigs: Slender, **angled**, green, hairy at first, becoming grayish-brown, smooth with age.

Trunk: Bark similar to white oak but thinner, less scaly plates, ridges irregular, broad, gray to brown; wood dark brown, durable, hard, strong, tough, close-grained.

Habitat: Occurs in wet bottomland forests bordering swamps and in valleys with floodplain forests bordering the Mississippi and Meramec Rivers.

Range: East Texas, Oklahoma, Arkansas, and Louisiana; east to Florida, north to New Jersey, and west to Kentucky, Illinois, and Missouri.

Wildlife Uses: Acorns are eaten by woodpeckers, wood duck, mice, squirrels, raccoon, and white-tailed deer.

Medicinal Uses: The bark is used as an astringent (causes tissues to contract).

Remarks: Overcup oak has been in cultivation since 1786. Although native to flooded sites, it can tolerate somewhat drier conditions. The slow growing, long-lived trees are very attractive and make excellent shade trees in low-lying areas.

The wood is so similar to white oak that it is usually cut, sold, and used for the same purposes as white oak.

Forest clearing and ditching of floodplains and swamps has greatly reduced the distribution and abundance of overcup oak in southeastern Missouri. This oak depends on seasonal overflow or floodwaters to float the acorns to new sites for establishment; however, these conditions are much less frequent today because of the changes in hydrology.

The name "overcup" refers to the acorn cup covering much of the nut. Oak is from the Old English *ac*, beyond that its origin is uncertain.

Quercus is the Latin name for oak; *lyrata* is Latin for "lyre," a small stringed instrument of the harp family, used by ancient Greeks to accompany singers and reciters; here, the name is in reference to the shape of the leaves.

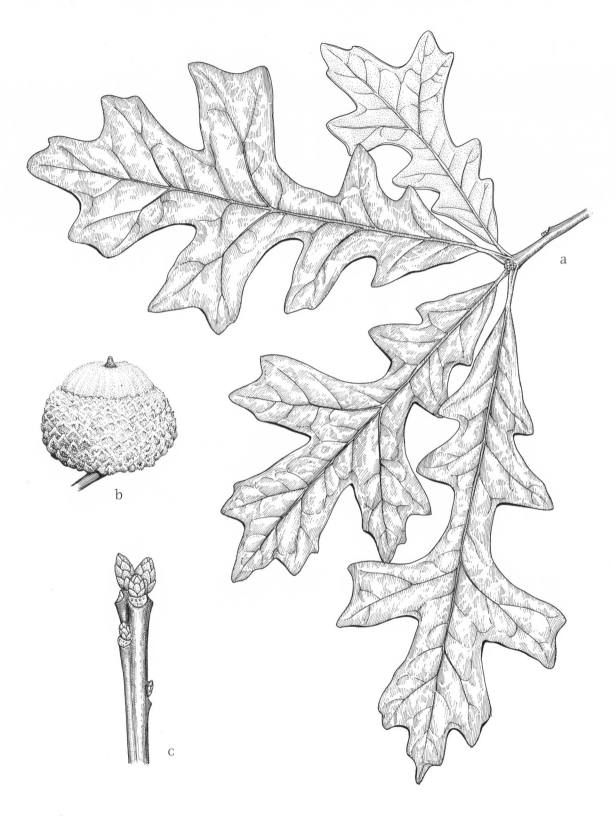

Quercus lyrata ❀ a. Leaves, b. Acorn, c. Twig

Bur oak

Quercus macrocarpa Michaux

Oak family (Fagaceae)

Also called mossy cup oak

Appearance: Medium to large tree, up to 80 feet tall, with a broad, spreading, rounded crown, a massive trunk, and low, large spreading branches.

Flowers: April–May, see p. 380 for the oak reproductive cycle.

Fruit: September–October, acorn solitary or in pairs, stalk short or absent; nut brown, nearly globe-shaped to broadest near the base, **3/4 to 2 inches long, largest of the oaks**; cup deep, hairy, enclosing 1/2 to 3/4 of the nut, nearly globe-shaped, brown; **scales along the tip producing a fringed or ragged border, giving a mossy appearance**; seeds edible, relatively sweet; acorns ripen in autumn of the first year.

Leaves: Alternate, simple, 6 to 12 inches long, 3 to 6 inches wide, broadest near the middle; margin with 5 to 9 lobes, **notch of the two largest lobes extending almost to the central vein, tips of lobes rounded and similar in appearance**; upper surface dark green, shiny, smooth; lower surface paler, hairy; leaf stalks stout, hairy to smooth, 1/4 to 1 inch long; leaves turn yellow or brown in autumn.

Twigs: Light brown, hairy, becoming dark brown and smooth with age, **sometimes developing corky ridges after the first year**.

Trunk: Bark thick, gray-brown, **deeply grooved**, ridges long, flat-topped; wood light or dark brown, heavy, strong, tough, durable, close-grained.

Habitat: Occurs in low woods in valleys or on lower slopes and along streams in the Ozarks; but in glaciated northern Missouri often in upland woods as well as in valleys and in degraded or former savannas.

Range: Texas, Oklahoma, Missouri, Arkansas, and Louisiana; east to Alabama, northeast to Maine, New Brunswick, and Quebec; west to Minnesota and Manitoba; and south to the Dakotas, Nebraska, and Kansas.

Wildlife Uses: Acorns are eaten by woodpeckers, mice, squirrels, raccoon, and white-tailed deer.

Medicinal Uses: The bark is used as an astringent (causes tissues to contract).

Remarks: Bur oak has been cultivated since 1811. The tree is slow growing, but long lived, and may reach ages approaching 600 years. Often too large for the average lawn, it makes an excellent ornamental for parks where it has room to grow. It is also very tolerant of air pollution in urban areas.

The wood is similar to that of white oak and is used for baskets, lumber, ties, fences, cabinets, flooring, furniture, boat decks, and fuel.

The thick, fire-resistant bark made this tree a common site in savannas and oak groves in prairies that once covered much of the north-central states.

The common name, bur, is used to reference the shaggy, fringed acorn. Oak is from the Old English *ac*, beyond that its origin is uncertain.

Quercus is the Latin name for oak; *macrocarpa* means "large fruited," referring to the large acorn.

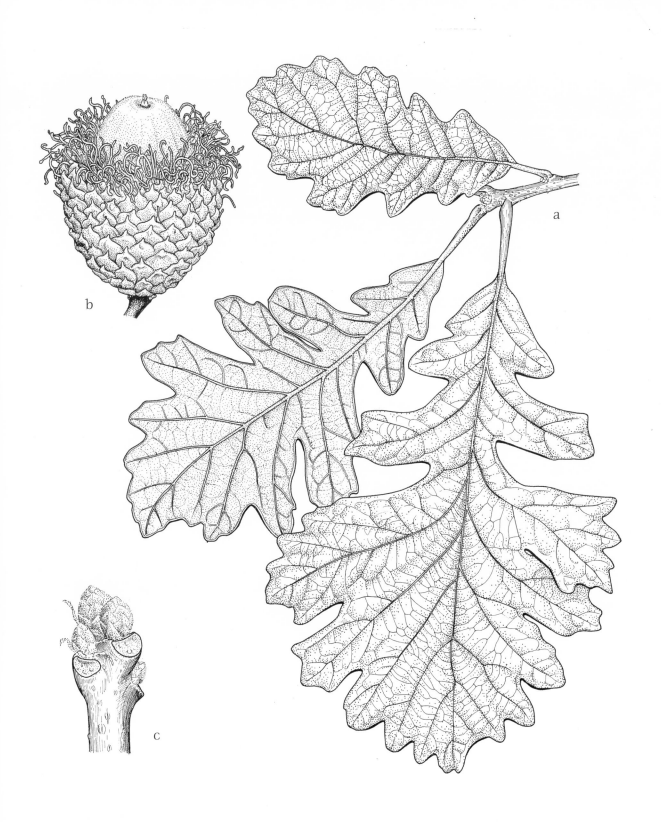

Quercus macrocarpa ❧ a. Leaves, b. Acorn, c. Twig

Black jack oak

Quercus marilandica Muenchh.

Oak family (Fagaceae)

Appearance: Small to medium-sized tree, up to 60 feet tall, with a rounded, irregular crown, bark with nearly black blocky plates, and a tendency to retain dead branches on the mid to lower part of the trunk.

Flowers: April–May, see p. 380 for the oak reproductive cycle.

Fruit: September–October, solitary or in pairs; nut on a very short stalk, light brown, oval, 1/2 to 1 inches long; cup covering 1/3 to 1/2 of the nut, **turban-shaped**, red-brown; **scales loose, hairy**; seed yellow, bitter; acorns ripen in autumn of the second year.

Leaves: Alternate, simple, 3 to 7 inches long, 2 to 5 inches wide, **abruptly broadest near the end, fan-shaped, firm, leathery; margin with three lobes of variable lengths or rounded, entire or with small bristle-tipped teeth at the tips**; notch rounded; upper surface dark green, shiny, smooth; **lower surface yellow-brown or yellow-green, with tan to brown hairs**; leaf stalk stout, smooth or hairy, 1/2 to 3/4 inch long; leaves turn burnt orange to crimson to reddish-brown in autumn with **several leaves persisting through winter**.

Twigs: Stout, stiff, grayish-brown, densely hairy at first, smooth with age; buds reddish-brown, hairy.

Trunk: Bark nearly black, thick, broken into irregular, rough, blocky plates similar to persimmon; the inner bark is mustard yellow; wood dark brown, heavy, hard, strong.

Habitat: Occurs in acid soils over sandstone, chert, or igneous bedrock, on dry, often level uplands, slopes, and glades.

Range: Central Texas, Oklahoma, Arkansas, and Louisiana; east to Florida, north to New York, and west to Ohio, Indiana, Illinois, Missouri, and Kansas.

Wildlife Uses: Acorns are eaten by blue jay, woodpeckers, wild turkey, mice, squirrels, raccoon, and white-tailed deer.

Medicinal Uses: As in other oaks, the bark, especially, has astringent (causes tissue to contract) properties. Native Americans used inner-bark tea to treat diarrhea, mouth sores, chapped skin, asthma, and coughs.

Remarks: Black jack oak is a slow-growing tree and relatively short lived. It often occupies rocky, very low-nutrient soils. A pioneer species, it invades newly burned sites and can form nearly pure stands. The tree also can withstand fires due to its thick, insulating bark and ability to sprout from its base. Black jack oak has been found to hybridize with at least 8 other species of oaks throughout its range.

The wood has been used for railroad ties, fence posts, charcoal, and fuel.

Oak is from the Old English *ac*, beyond that its origin is uncertain. Black jack is so named for the color of the bark and the latter, an Old English term for a drinking vessel, sometimes made of wood.

Quercus is the Latin name for oak; *marilandica* refers to the state of Maryland.

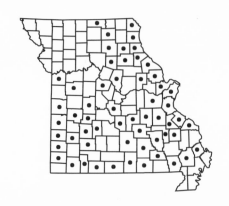

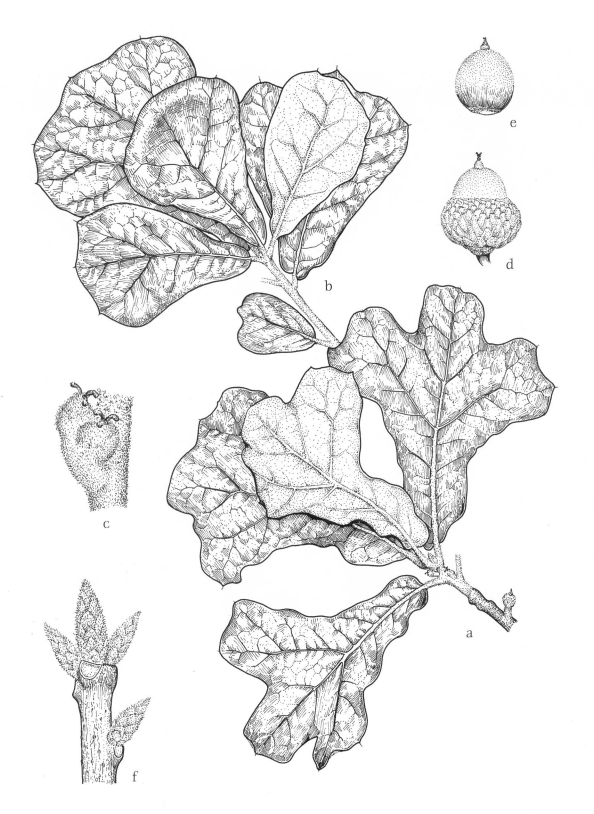

Quercus marilandica ❦ a. & b. Leaf variation, c. Female flowers, d. Acorn, e. Nut, f. Twig

Swamp chestnut oak

Quercus michauxii Nutt.

Oak family (Fagaceae)

Also called basket oak, cow oak

Appearance: Medium to large-sized tree, up to 100 feet tall, with a wide, rounded crown and bark resembling that of white oak.

Flowers: April–May, see p. 380 for the oak reproductive cycle.

Fruit: September–October, acorn solitary or in pairs; nut brown, shiny, broadest near the base, gradually tapering to a rounded tip, **large**, 3/4 **to 1 1/2 inches long**; cup covering 1/3 to 1/2 of the nut, bowl-shaped, reddish-brown; **scales wedge-shaped hard, stout, hairy, attached only at the base and overlapping, giving a somewhat fringed appearance**; nut sweet, edible; acorns ripen in autumn of the first year.

Leaves: Alternate, simple, 4 to 8 inches long, 1 1/2 to 4 inches wide, broadest above the middle; **margin with large, rounded or sometimes sharp teeth**, tip pointed; upper surface dark green, shiny, smooth; lower surface whitish, **velvety to the touch**; leaf stalk about 3/4 inches long; leaves turn reddish- or yellowish-brown in autumn.

Twigs: Moderately stout, smooth, reddish-brown.

Trunk: Bark light gray, with scaly plates on mature trees; inner bark reddish; wood light brown, heavy, tough, hard, strong, durable, close-grained.

Habitat: Occurs in bottomland forests in large valleys and depressions, bordering slow moving streams, sloughs, and swamps; found principally in the southeastern Missouri lowlands.

Range: East Texas, Arkansas, and Louisiana; east to Florida, north to Delaware, and west to southern Indiana, southern Illinois, and southeastern Missouri.

Wildlife Uses: Acorns are eaten by woodpeckers, mice, squirrels, raccoon, and white-tailed deer.

Medicinal Uses: As in other oaks, the bark, especially, has astringent (causes tissue to contract) properties. Native Americans used inner-bark tea to treat diarrhea, mouth sores, chapped skin, asthma, and coughs.

Remarks: Swamp chestnut oak, formerly called *Quercus prinus* L. by some authors, has been in cultivation since 1737. It makes an attractive shade tree in low-lying areas. The wood is used for posts, tools, splints, boards, veneer, and fuel. Because the wood splits easily into long strips, it was woven into baskets in the South to carry cotton, hence the name basket oak. The acorn, second only to bur oak in size, can be eaten raw because of its low tannin level; they are considered the sweetest tasting of all the oaks. Also called cow oak for their preference for this sweet tasting acorn.

The common name is for the habitat and its similarity in appearance to chestnut oak. Oak is from the Old English *ac*, beyond that its origin is uncertain.

Quercus is the Latin name for oak; *michauxii* honors Francois André Michaux, (1770–1855), a French botanist, who was the first to collect and make record of the tree.

Quercus michauxii ❧ a. Growth form with acorn, b. Acorn, c. Twig

Chinkapin oak

Quercus muehlenbergii Englem.

Oak family (Fagaceae)

Also called chinquapin oak, yellow chestnut oak

Appearance: Medium-sized tree, up to 60 feet tall, often with large, low branches and a narrow, irregular crown.

Flowers: April–May, see p. 380 for the oak reproductive cycle.

Fruit: September–October, acorns mostly solitary or in pairs; nut brown, shiny, broadest near the base and tapering slightly to the tip, 1/2 to 3/4 inches long; **cup covering about 1/2 of the nut**, bowl-shaped, thin, brown, hairy; scales small, flattened; seed sweet, edible; acorns ripen in autumn of the first year.

Leaves: Alternate, simple, 4 to 8 inches long, 1 to 3 1/2 inches wide, broadest near the base or above the middle; **margin with coarse teeth, 8 to 13 on each side, slightly curved inwards**, tip pointed; upper surface dark yellow-green, shiny, smooth; **lower surface paler with gray hairs, veins conspicuous**; leaf stalk slender, 3/4 to 1 1/4 inches long; leaves turn yellow to yellowish-brown in autumn.

Twigs: Slender, yellowish- to reddish-brown, initially hairy becoming smooth with age.

Trunk: Bark light gray, with shallow grooves and short, flaky ridges; wood reddish-brown, hard, heavy, strong, durable, close-grained.

Habitat: Occurs most frequently in alkaline, rocky soils derived from limestone or dolomite on bluffs, borders of glades, and upland woods; also in floodplain forests and lower slopes along streams.

Range: Texas, Oklahoma, Arkansas, and Louisiana; east to Florida, north to Maine, and west to Illinois, Iowa, Missouri, and Kansas; also on the mountains of Mexico.

Wildlife Uses: Acorns are eaten by blue jay, woodpeckers, wood duck, wild turkey, ruffed grouse, bobwhite quail, mice, squirrels, raccoon, and white-tailed deer.

Medicinal Uses: As in other oaks, the bark, especially, has astringent (causes tissue to contract) properties. Native Americans used inner-bark tea to treat diarrhea, mouth sores, chapped skin, asthma, and coughs.

Remarks: Chinkapin oak was first cultivated in 1822. It is an attractive shade tree and relatively resistant to insects and disease. The acorns are sweet and edible when roasted.

The wood is used for cabinets, furniture, pallets, fence posts, fuel, and traditionally for railroad ties.

Chinkapin oak, in its younger stages, looks similar to the shrubby dwarf chinkapin oak, *Quercus prinoides* Willd. While chinkapin oak has leaves 4 to 8 inches long, with 8 to 13 teeth on each side; dwarf chinkapin oak has leaves 1 1/2 to 4 inches long, with 4 to 8 teeth on a side.

Chinkapin or sometimes spelled "chinquapin," is from *chinkomen*, an Algonquin (Native American) term for chestnuts. Oak is from the Old English *ac*, beyond that its origin is uncertain.

Quercus is the Latin name for oak; *muehlenbergii* is in honor of G. H. E. Muhlenberg (1753–1815), botanist and minister in Pennsylvania.

Quercus muehlenbergii ❀ a. Growth form, b. Acorns, c. Twig

Water oak

Quercus nigra L.

Oak family (Fagaceae)

Appearance: Medium to large-sized tree, up to 80 feet tall, with a tall straight trunk, a rounded, symmetrical crown, and ascending branches.

Flowers: April–May, see p. 380 for the oak reproductive cycle.

Fruit: September–October, acorn solitary or in pairs, brown, broadest at the base and broadly rounded at the tip, about 1/2 inches long; cup covering 1/3 to 1/2 of the nut, cup shallow, *saucer-shaped*, thin, reddish-brown; scales small, thin, flattened, hairy; seeds bitter; acorns ripen in autumn of the second year.

Leaves: Alternate, simple, 2 to 4 inches long, 1 to 2 inches wide, **broadest near the tip, fan-shaped, tapering to a long, narrow base**; margin variable, occasionally entire with a rounded tip, but **usually with three broad lobes at the tip**; lobes sometimes with bristle tips; upper surface dark green, shiny, smooth; lower surface paler, smooth or hairy in the vein axils; leaf stalk stout, **less than 1/4 inch long**; leaves turn yellow in autumn with brown leaves persisiting into winter.

Twigs: Slender, reddish-gray, smooth.

Trunk: Bark grayish-black, smooth and tight on young trees becoming shallowly grooved with flat, scaly ridges when older.

Habitat: Occurs in wet bottomland forests and edges of swamps in the southeastern Missouri lowlands. Also used as an ornamental in lawns of southeast Missouri.

Range: East Texas, Oklahoma, Arkansas, and Louisiana; east to Florida, north to New Jersey, and west to Tennessee and southeastern Missouri.

Wildlife Uses: Acorns are eaten by songbirds, woodpeckers, ducks (especially mallards and wood ducks), wild turkey, mice, squirrels, raccoon, and white-tailed deer.

Medicinal Uses: As in other oaks, the bark, especially, has astringent (causes tissue to contract) properties. Native Americans used inner-bark tea to treat diarrhea, mouth sores, chapped skin, asthma, and coughs.

Remarks: Water oak was first cultivated in 1723. In southern states, it is extensively planted as a street shade tree. Water oak has a tendency to retain dead branches so the wood is considered of poorer quality because of the knots. The wood is used mainly for fuel.

In Missouri, water oak is a species of conservation concern. It is classified as rare due to a loss of habitat from extensive clearing, rowcropping, ditching, and draining of the Bootheel. One place to view this interesting species is at Allred Lake Natural Area, Butler County, where it can easily be seen along the woods edge while walking the path from the parking lot to the boardwalk at the swamp. The willow oak, uncommon also due to loss of habitat, can also be viewed along the path.

Oak is from the Old English *ac*, beyond that its origin is uncertain.

Quercus is the Latin name for oak; *nigra* is Latin for black and refers to the black bark.

Quercus nigra ❀ a. Growth form, b. Leaves, c. Acorn, d. Twig

Cherrybark oak

Quercus pagoda Raf.

Oak family (Fagaceae)

Appearance: Medium to large-sized tree, up to 100 feet tall, with a straight branch-free trunk and an open, rounded crown.

Flowers: April–May, see p. 380 for the oak reproductive cycle.

Fruit: September–October, acorns single or in pairs; nut light brown, broadest at the base and rounded at the top, 1/2 inch long; cup covering 1/3 of the nut, shallow; **scales reddish-brown with a dark border**, flattened, hairy; seed bitter; acorns ripen in autumn of the second year.

Leaves: Alternate, simple, 6 to 7 inches long, 4 to 5 inches wide, broadest at or above the middle; **margin with 5 to 11 lobes; lobes at right angle to the central vein, fairly evenly spaced and uniform in size**, bristle-tipped, notches between lobes shallow; upper surface dark green, shiny, smooth; **lower surface paler, with a yellowish, grayish, or whitish hairiness**; leaf stalk slender, flattened, 1 to 2 inches long, hairy; **leaf often has a drooping appearance**; leaves turn reddish-brown in autumn.

Twigs: Moderately stout, slightly grooved, dark red and smooth.

Trunk: Bark gray to black with scaly, narrow ridges similar to the bark of black cherry, hence the common name of cherrybark oak; wood reddish-brown, hard, heavy, coarse-grained.

Habitat: Occurs in bottomland forests in the southeastern Missouri lowlands.

Range: East Texas, Arkansas, Missouri, southern Illinois, and Louisiana; east to Florida, and north along the coastal plain of Georgia, the Carolinas, and Virginia.

Wildlife Uses: Acorns are eaten by blue jay, woodpeckers, wood duck, wild turkey, mice, squirrels, raccoon, and white-tailed deer.

Medicinal Uses: As in other oaks, the bark, especially, has astringent (causes tissue to contract) properties. Native Americans used inner-bark tea to treat diarrhea, mouth sores, chapped skin, asthma, and coughs

Remarks: Cherrybark oak is also known as *Quercus falcata* var. *pagodaefolia* Elliott. It is closely related to southern red oak but cherrybark oak typically grows in wetter sites. This large, fast-growing tree is one of the most valuable oaks for timber production in the Southern states. The wood is used for pulp, fuel, veneer, cabinets, furniture, crates, and boxes.

Cherrybark oak can be found growing with sweet gum, tulip tree, shellbark hickory, Shumard oak, swamp chestnut oak, Nuttall oak, red buckeye, red mulberry, and giant cane.

Oak is from the Old English *ac*, beyond that its origin is uncertain.

Quercus is the Latin name for oak; *pagoda* refers to the appearance of the leaf when it is viewed with the leaf pointed down. From this perspective, the angle of the lobes resembles the overlapping roofs of an oriental pagoda.

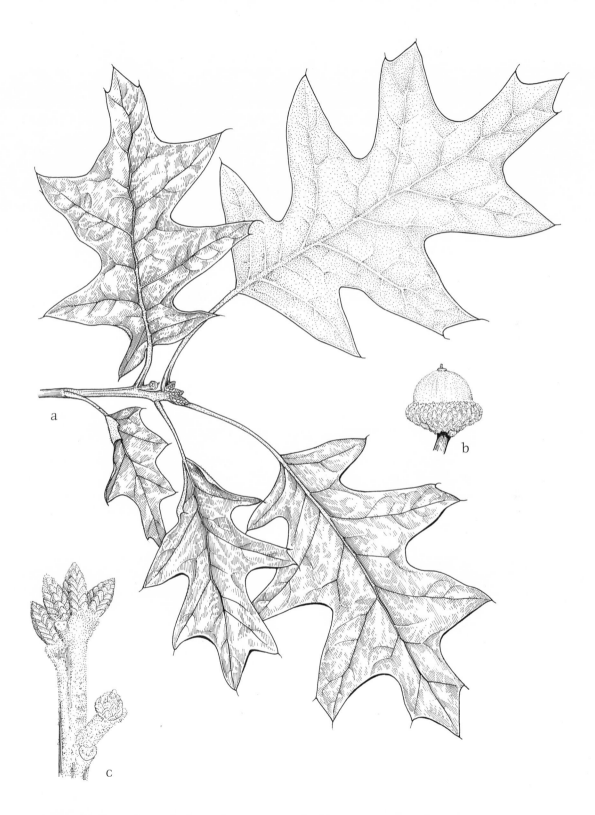

Quercus pagoda ❧ a. Growth form, b. Acorn, c. Twig

Pin oak

Quercus palustris Muenchh

Oak family (Fagaceae)

Appearance: Large tree, up to 100 feet tall, with a tall, straight trunk, a pyramid-shaped crown, and **drooping branches on the lower 1/3 of young to mature trees**.

Flowers: April–May, see p. 380 for the oak reproductive cycle.

Fruit: September–October, acorn solitary or in clusters of 2 to 3; nut light brown, **small, 3/8 to 1/2 inch long, often striped, shaped like 1/2 of a sphere**, about 1/2 inch in diameter; **cup short, less than 1/4 inch long**, 3/8 to 5/8 inch across, covering 1/4 to 1/3 of the nut, saucer-shaped reddish-brown; scales small, flattened; seeds bitter; acorns ripen in autumn of the second year.

Leaves: Alternate, simple, 4 to 6 inches long, 2 to 5 inches wide, usually broadest at the middle; margin with 5 to 9 lobes, notches between lobes rounded, cut 2/3 or more to the central vein, each lobe with 2 to 4 teeth, bristle-tipped; upper surface dark green, shiny, smooth; lower surface paler, smooth except for tufts of hairs in the axils of the veins; leaf stalk slender, yellow, hairy or smooth, 1/2 to 2 1/2 inches long; leaves turn scarlet, red, or brown in autumn.

Twigs: Slender, reddish- to grayish-brown, smooth, shiny, numerous; **older dead twigs and branches retained on the tree, resembling pins thrust into the trunk, hence the name pin oak; buds very small, less than 1/4 long**.

Trunk: Bark light brown, smooth, shiny on young trees, later becoming grayish-brown, developing shallow grooves and slightly roughened, closely flattened scales; wood light brown, heavy, hard, strong, often knotty due to persistence of many small limbs, close-grained.

Habitat: Occurs in bottomland forests in floodplains along streams, rivers, sloughs, and edges of swamps, and around margins of upland sinkhole ponds and flatwoods.

Range: Oklahoma, Arkansas, and Tennessee; east to North Carolina, north to Massachusetts, and west to Michigan, Indiana, Illinois, Iowa, Missouri, and eastern Kansas.

Wildlife Uses: Acorns are eaten by songbirds, blue jay, woodpeckers, ducks (especially mallard and wood duck), wild turkey, bobwhite quail, mice, squirrels, raccoon, and white-tailed deer.

Medicinal Uses: As in other oaks, the bark, especially, has astringent (causes tissue to contract) properties. Native Americans used innerbark tea to treat diarrhea, mouth sores, chapped skin, asthma, and coughs.

Remarks: Pin oak was first cultivated in 1770. It was used extensively for street and yard planting in the Northeastern states and in Europe. It grows rapidly but is relatively short-lived, often not beyond 150 years. Trees planted in alkaline soils develop iron chlorosis, which leads to poor health and yellow to yellowish-green leaves.

The wood is used for fuel, interior finish, shingles, and general construction.

Oak is from the Old English *ac*, beyond that its origin is uncertain.

Quercus is the Latin name for oak; *palustris* means "of low grounds," referring to the tree's habitat.

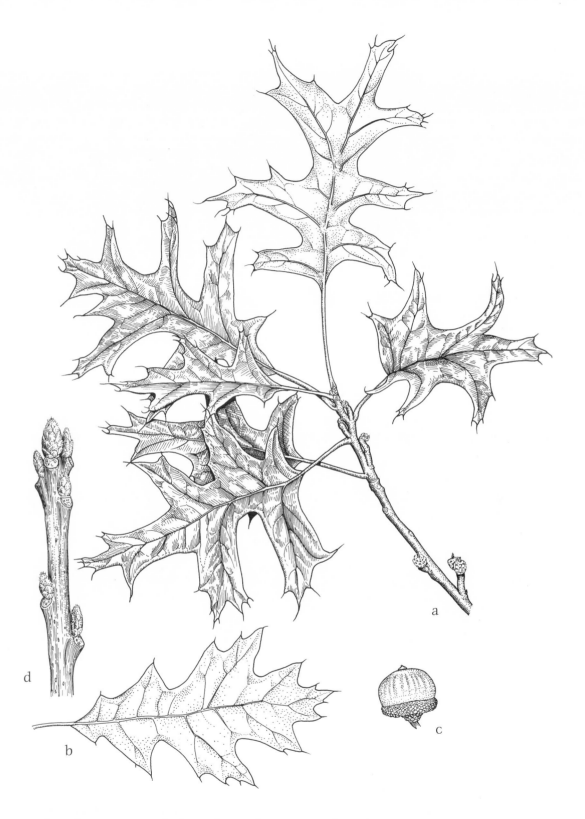

Quercus palustris ❧ a. Growth form, b. Leaf, c. Acorn, d. Twig

Willow oak

Quercus phellos L.

Oak family (Fagaceae)

Appearance: Medium to large-sized tree, up to 80 feet tall, with a dense, pyramid-shaped crown, becoming more rounded with age; a straight, clear trunk; and willow-like leaves.

Flowers: April–May, see p. 380 for the oak reproductive cycle.

Fruit: September–October, acorn solitary or in pairs; **nut brown with dark stripes**, broadly rounded, about 1/2 inch long; **cup covering about 1/4 of the nut, saucer-shaped, shallow**; scales small, flattened, greenish- to reddish-brown, finely hairy; seed bitter; acorns ripen in autumn of the second year.

Leaves: Alternate, simple, 2 to 5 inches long, 1/3 to 1 inch wide, **willow-like in shape**, narrow, gradually tapering at both ends, thick; **margin entire, bristle-tipped**; upper surface dark green, shiny, smooth; lower surface paler, smooth, sometimes hairy along the central vein; leaf stalk stout, about 1/4 inches long, hairy at first, smooth later; leaves turn pale yellow in autumn.

Twigs: Slender, reddish-brown and hairy at first, gray and smooth with age.

Trunk: Bark smooth, light reddish-brown on young trees, becoming dark gray with roughened irregular scale-covered plates and shallow grooves when older; wood pale reddish-brown, soft, moderately strong, not durable and coarse-grained.

Habitat: Occurs in wet bottomland forests bordering swamps and slow streams in the southeastern Missouri lowlands.

Range: Eastern Texas, southeastern Oklahoma, Arkansas, and Louisiana; east to Florida, north to New York, and west to Kentucky, southern Illinois, and southeastern Missouri.

Wildlife Uses: Acorns are eaten by songbirds, blue jay, woodpeckers, ducks (especially mallard and wood duck), wild turkey, bobwhite quail, mice, squirrels, raccoon, and white-tailed deer.

Medicinal Uses: As in other oaks, the bark, especially, has astringent (causes tissue to contract) properties. Native Americans used inner-bark tea to treat diarrhea, mouth sores, chapped skin, asthma, and coughs.

Remarks: Willow oak has been in cultivation since 1723. It is a popular ornamental tree in the South; known for its rapid growth, long life, and handsome shape. The wood is used for interior finishes, railings, stairs, furniture, general construction, and fuel.

Willow oak is uncommon in Missouri due to loss of habitat in the southeastern lowlands. Allred Lake Natural Area, Butler County, provides a good opportunity to see this tree as well as other more Southern species. Watch for the tree along the trail from the parking lot to the viewing deck over the water.

Oak is from the Old English *ac*, beyond that its origin is uncertain.

Quercus is the classical Latin name for the oaks; *phellos* is Latin for "cork," which is the Greek name for cork oak, *Quercus suber* L., a tree from the Mediterranean region with similar looking leaves.

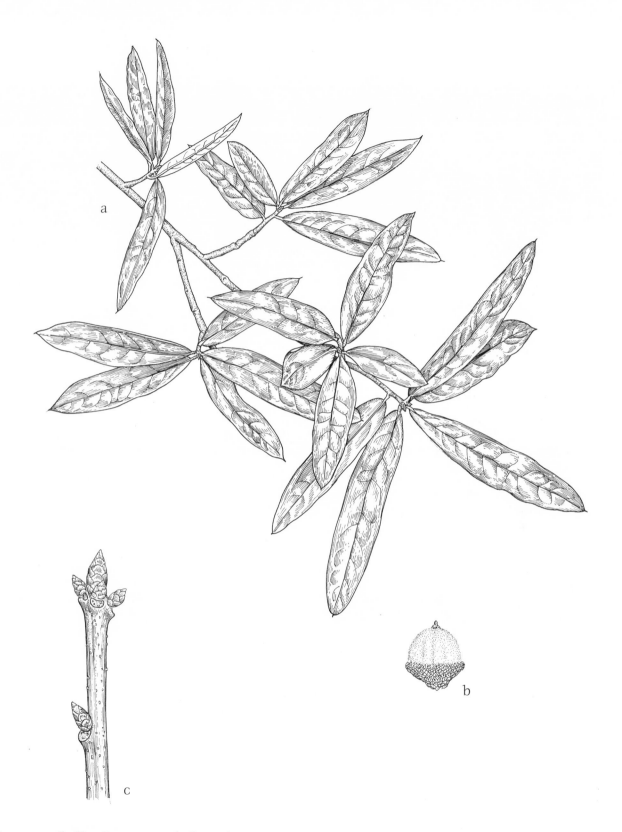

Quercus phellos ❀ a. Growth form, b. Acorn, c. Twig

Dwarf chinkapin oak

Quercus prinoides Willd.

Oak family (Fagaceae)

Also called dwarf chinquapin oak, dwarf chestnut oak, scrub oak

Appearance: A shrub or small tree, up to 15 to 8 feet high, usually growing in clumps or thickets.

Flowers: April–May, with male and female flowers in separate clusters (catkins) on the same plant; male catkins near the base of new growth, 1 to 2 1/2 inches long, drooping, cylindrical-shaped, loosely flowered; flowers small, green, densely hairy; stamens 4 to 6; female catkins near the tip of new growth, short, 1 to 4 flowered in axils of leaves; flowers small, green, densely hairy; see p. 380 for oak reproductive cycle.

Fruit: September–October, **fruit an acorn, maturing the first season**, cap enclosing 1/3 of the acorn; cup 3/8 to 1/2 inch high, about 3/4 inch wide, grayish-brown; scales on the cup small, densely hairy; acorn about 1/2 to 3/4 inch long, about 3/4 inch thick, egg-shaped, dark reddish-brown; nut sweet, edible.

Leaves: Alternate, simple, leaves leathery, 1 1/2 to 4 inches long, 1 to 2 1/2 inches wide, broadest at or above the middle and narrowing at both ends, tip pointed, base wedge-shaped, margin wavy, widely toothed, **teeth 4 to 8 on each side**, a vein running to each tooth; upper surface olive-green to bright green, shiny, smooth; lower surface much paler, velvety hairy; leaf stalk slender, grooved, 1/4 to 3/4 inches long, hairy; leaves red in autumn.

Twigs: Young reddish-brown and hairy, older ones gray and smooth.

Trunk: Bark on young trunks gray, smooth, except for noticeable, horizontal pores; old trunks gray with flat, scaly, checkered ridges and shallow furrows; wood hard, yellowish.

Habitat: Occurs in dry soils in open woods, glades, prairies, along bluffs and thickets.

Range: Northeast Texas, Oklahoma, Arkansas, and Louisiana; east to Georgia, north to Maine, and west to Minnesota, southeast Nebraska, and east Kansas.

Wildlife Uses: The acorns are eaten by several birds and mammals.

Remarks: Dwarf chinkapin oak easily can be confused with the taller chinquapin oak. The former has leaves 1 1/2 to 4 inches long, with 4 to 8 teeth on each side; the latter with leaves 4 to 8 inches long and 8 to 13 teeth on each side.

Dwarf chinkapin oak can sometimes be difficult to manage in prairies, having a tendency to form thickets. Periodic burning (a natural process) or haying helps to keep it and other woody plants from dominating prairies. The dwarf nature of this oak makes for an interesting planting for borders. It was introduced into cultivation about 1730.

Chinkapin, or sometimes spelled "chinquapin," is from *chinkomen*, an Algonquin (Native American) term for chestnuts. Oak is from the Old English *ac*, and its origin is uncertain.

Quercus is the classical name; *prinoides* refers to its resemblance, especially in the leaves, to rock chestnut oak, *Quercus prinus.*

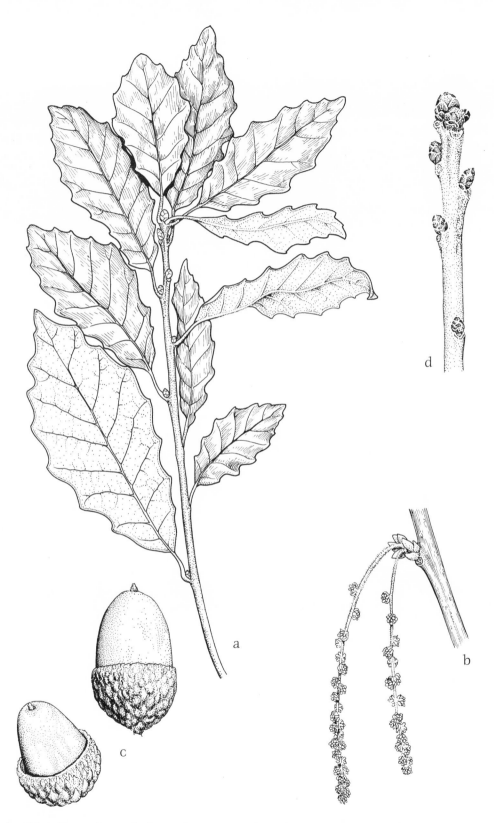

Quercus prinoides ❧ a. Growth form, b. Twig with catkins, c. Acorns, d. Winter twig

Northern red oak

Quercus rubra L.

Oak family (Fagaceae)

Also called red oak

Appearance: Large tree, up to 100 feet tall, with a tall, straight, columnar trunk and large, spreading branches forming a round-topped crown.

Flowers: April–May, see p. 380 for the oak reproductive cycle.

Fruit: September–October, acorns solitary or in pairs; **nut reddish-brown, shiny, large, barrel-shaped, 1 to 1 1/4 inches long, 1/2 to 3/4 inches wide; cup enclosing the base to 1/4 of the nut**, saucer-shaped; scales reddish-brown, shiny; seed bitter; acorns ripen in autumn of the second year.

Leaves: Alternate, simple, 5 to 9 inches long; 4 to 6 inches wide, widest at or above the middle; margin with 7 to 11 lobes, **lobes uneven in size and length with lobes along the upper half of leaf short and broad**, ends of lobes with 1 to 3 bristle-tipped teeth; notches between lobes rounded; upper surface dark green, dull, smooth; lower surface paler, smooth with occasional tufts of hairs at the vein axils; leaf stalk stout, red to yellow, smooth, 1 1/2 to 2 inches long; leaves turn dark red, crimson, or golden orange in autumn.

Twigs: Moderately stout, reddish-brown, shiny, smooth.

Trunk: Bark greenish-brown to gray when young, becoming brown to black with age, **grooves shallow, ridges wide, flat-topped with grayish bark appearing as stripes**; wood reddish-brown, heavy, hard, strong, close-grained.

Habitat: Occurs in well-drained soils of moist ravines, north and east facing slopes, and on slopes at the base of bluffs.

Range: East Oklahoma and Arkansas; east through northern Mississippi and Alabama to Florida; north along the Appalachian Mountains to Delaware, then continuing along the coast to New England and Quebec; west to Ontario, Wisconsin, and Minnesota; and south eastern Nebraska, eastern Kansas, and Missouri.

Wildlife Uses: Acorns are eaten by blue jay, woodpeckers, wild turkey, mice, squirrels, raccoon, and white-tailed deer.

Medicinal Uses: As in other oaks, the bark, especially, has astringent (causes tissue to contract) properties. Native Americans used inner-bark tea to treat diarrhea, mouth sores, chapped skin, asthma, and coughs.

Remarks: Northern red oak is also known as *Quercus borealis* Michaux. This long-lived, fast growing tree was first introduced into cultivation in the late 1600s. It is a popular shade tree in the Northeastern states and, in Europe, where it is the most popular of exotic oaks planted there. The relatively smooth, striped bark is a primary ornamental feature. The wood is used for furniture, flooring, veneer, interior finishing, railroad ties, posts, general construction, and fuel.

Oak is from the Old English *ac*, beyond that its origin is uncertain.

Quercus is the Latin name for oak; *rubra* is Latin for "red," and refers to the reddish wood.

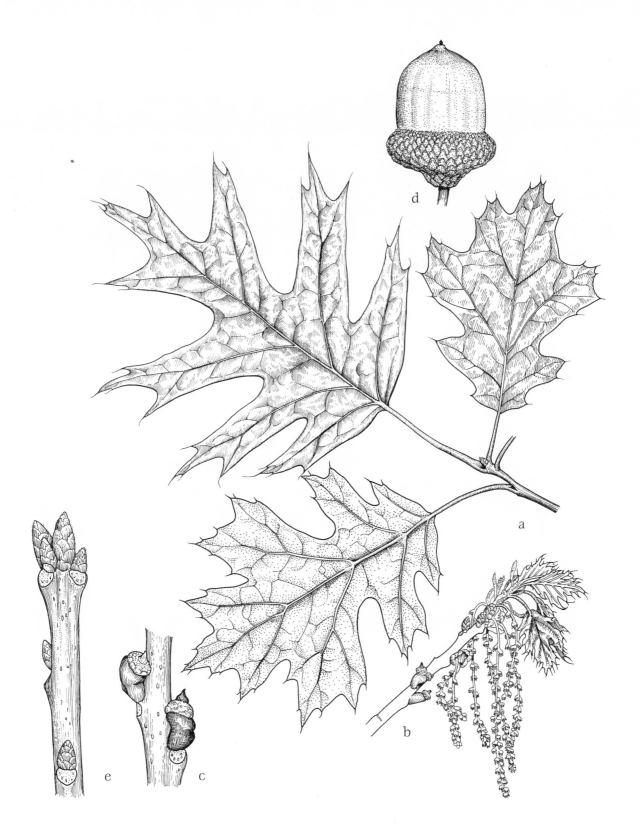

Quercus rubra ❧ a. Growth form, b. Male and female flowers, c. Young fruit, d. Acorn, e. Twig

Shumard oak

Quercus shumardii Buckley

Oak family (Fagaceae)

Appearance: Medium to large-sized tree, up to 100 feet tall, with a tall, straight trunk, stout branches, and a large, open crown.

Flowers: April–May, see p. 380 for the oak reproductive cycle.

Fruit: September–October, acorn solitary or paired; nut reddish-brown, egg-shaped to 2 to 4 times longer than broad, rounded or flattened at the base, 1/2 to 1 inch long, 1/2 to 3/4 inch wide; cup covering 1/4 to 1/3 of the nut, shallow, thick, saucer-shaped to top-shaped; scales reddish-brown, flattened, hairy or smooth; seed bitter; acorns ripen in autumn of the second year.

Leaves: Alternate, simple, 6 to 8 inches long, 3 to 4 inches wide, broadest above the middle; margin with 7 to 9 lobes; **lobes wider at their tip than at base**, with 2 to 6 bristle-tipped teeth, **notches between lobes rounded, over halfway to central vein**; upper surface dark green, shiny, smooth; lower surface paler, smooth with tufts of hairs in the vein axils; leaf stalk moderately slender, grayish-brown, smooth, about 1 1/2 to 2 1/2 inches long; **leaves turn red in autumn and are usually the first of the oaks to turn color**.

Twigs: Moderately stout, reddish- or grayish-brown, smooth, shiny; mature buds smooth.

Trunk: Bark dark gray to reddish-brown, smooth when young breaking into thick, flat, scaly ridges with shallow grooves; wood light reddish-brown, hard, strong, durable, close-grained.

Habitat: Occurs in dry, rocky upland woods and borders of glades; also in valleys and along banks of larger Ozark streams.

Range: Texas, Oklahoma, Arkansas, and Louisiana; east to Florida, north to Pennsylvania, and west to southern Illinois, Missouri, and eastern Kansas.

Wildlife Uses: Acorns are eaten by blue jay, woodpeckers, wood duck, wild turkey, mice, squirrels, raccoon, and white-tailed deer.

Medicinal Uses: As in other oaks, the bark, especially, has astringent (causes tissue to contract) properties. Native Americans used inner-bark tea to treat diarrhea, mouth sores, chapped skin, asthma, and coughs.

Remarks: Shumard oak is a moderately fast growing, long-lived tree but it is not used much as an ornamental. The tree would make a good alternative to northern red oak because it seems to tolerate wetter and drier sites while having otherwise similar features. The wood is used for veneer, cabinets, furniture, flooring, interior trim, lumber, and for fuel.

There are two varieties of Shumard oak, both found in central and southern counties in Missouri. *Quercus shumardii* var. *schneckii* occurs in dry rocky upland woods, glades, and edges of bluffs; it has a deeper bowl-shaped cup, 3/4 inches wide or less, covering about 1/2 of the nut. *Quercus shumardii* var. *shumardii* occurs in valleys and along banks of large Ozark streams in addition to drier upland areas; it has a shallow, saucer-shaped cup, 3/4 to 1 1/2 inches wide, and covering 1/4 of the nut.

Quercus is the Latin name for oak; *shumardii* honoring Benjamin Franklin Shumard (1820–1869), state geologist of Texas.

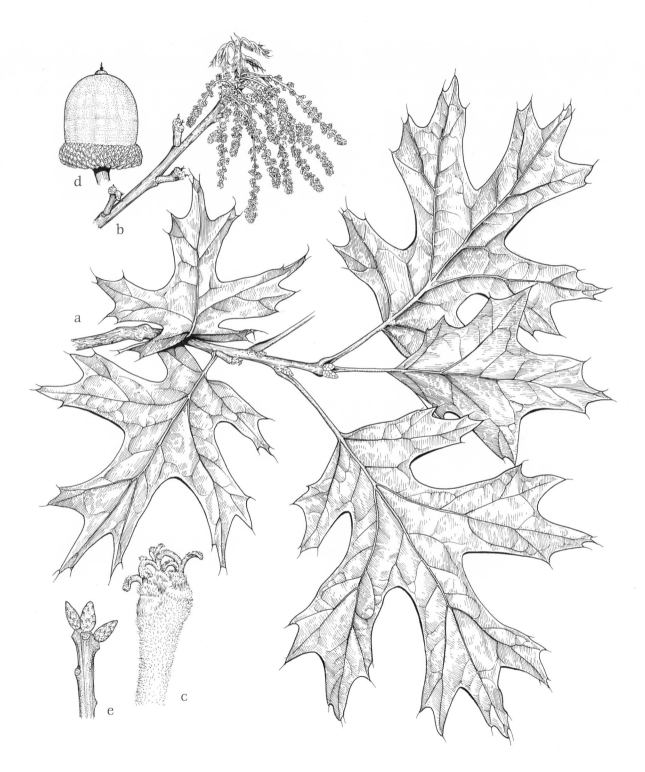

Quercus shumardii 🌿 a. Growth form, b. Male and female flowers, c. Female flowers, d. Acorn, e. Twig

Post oak

Quercus stellata Wangenh.

Oak family (Fagaceae)

Appearance: Small to medium-sized tree, up to 70 feet tall, with a broad, rounded crown and stout branches that are sometimes contorted.

Flowers: April–May, see p. 380 for the oak reproductive cycle.

Fruit: September–October, acorn solitary or in pairs; nut brown, broadest at the base and tapering to a rounded tip, 1/2 to 3/4 inches long, less than 1/2 inch in diameter, often with small, fine hairs; cup covering 1/3 to 1/2 of the nut, bowl-shaped, pale and often hairy within, hairy on the outside; **scales thick, flattened, or somewhat indented, hairy**; seed bitter; acorns ripen in autumn of the first year.

Leaves: Alternate, simple, 4 to 7 inches long, 3 to 4 inches wide, usually widest above the middle, leathery, thick; margin with 3 to 5 lobes, **middle lobes almost square, giving the appearance of a cross, end lobe often 3-notched**, notches between lobes deep, rounded; upper surface dark green, rough, smooth; lower surface paler, **with small star-shaped hairs; leaf stalk stout, 1/2 to 1 inch long, with small star-shaped hairs**; leaves turn golden-brown in autumn.

Twigs: Stout, brown, **densely hairy throughout most of the season**.

Trunk: Bark gray, divided into irregular grooves, ridges narrow, rough with plate-like scales; wood light to dark brown, heavy, hard, durable, close-grained.

Habitat: Occurs in mostly dry to rocky upland woodlands and glades; also in flatwoods on broad ridges and lowland terraces where it is typically the dominant tree.

Range: Texas, Oklahoma, Arkansas, and Louisiana; east to Florida, north to New York and Massachusetts; and west to Iowa and Kansas.

Wildlife Uses: Acorns are eaten by blue jay, woodpeckers, wood duck, wild turkey, ruffed grouse, bobwhite quail, mice, squirrels, raccoon, and white-tailed deer.

Medicinal Uses: As in other oaks, the bark, especially, has astringent (causes tissue to contract) properties. Native Americans used inner-bark tea to treat diarrhea, mouth sores, chapped skin, asthma, and coughs.

Remarks: Post oak has been cultivated since 1819. A slow growing, drought resistant tree, it is difficult to transplant, and does better on sites where it is already found growing. A long-lived tree, post oaks can live to 300 years or more. They are also found in flatwoods where a somewhat impermeable clay pan layer typically about 20 inches down in the soil keeps the soil above it soggy in the spring and droughty in the summer. An upland flatwoods can be seen at Quercus Flatwoods Natural Area, Texas County; a lowland flatwoods is located at Bradyville Natural Area, Stoddard County.

The wood is used for railroad ties, fence posts, furniture, general construction, and fuel.

The limbs are sturdy and durable, which were favored by pioneers for use as fence posts and thus gave it a name. Oak is from the Old English *ac*, beyond that its origin is uncertain.

Quercus is the Latin name for oak; *stellata* is Latin for "star," referring to the star-shaped hairs on the undersurface of the leaves and the leaf stalk.

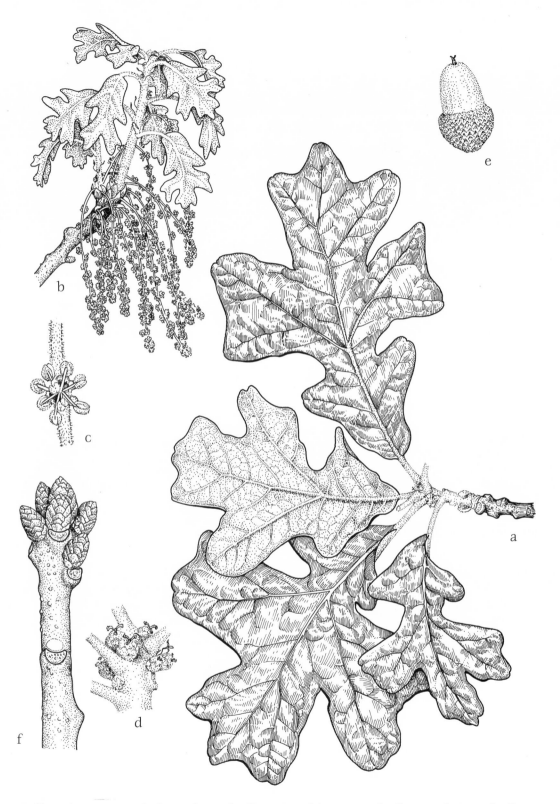

Quercus stellata ❧ a. Growth form, b. Male flower catkins, c. Male flower, d. Female flowers, e. Acorn, f. Twig

Nuttall oak

Quercus texana Buckley

Oak family (Fagaceae)

Appearance: Medium to large-sized tree, up to 80 feet tall, with a rounded, open crown of spreading branches.

Flowers: April–May, see p. 380 for the oak reproductive cycle.

Fruit: September–October, acorn solitary or in pairs; nut dark brown, 2 to 4 times longer than broad, 1 inch long, with a rounded tip and brownish stripes the length of the nut; **cup covering 1/3 to 5/8 of the nut**, saucer to bowl-shaped, 1/3 to 3/4 inch across, thin, hairy, **sloping or stalked at the base**; scales small, flattened; seed bitter; acorns ripen in autumn of the second year.

Leaves: Alternate, simple, 3 to 6 inches long, 3 to 6 inches wide, widest above the middle; margin usually with 7 lobes; tip of lobes with 1 to 5 bristle-tipped teeth, notches between lobes rounded and wide; upper surface dull green, smooth; lower surface paler with tufts of hairs in the axils of the veins; **leaf stalk moderately slender, smooth, 3/4 to 2 inches long**; leaves turn reddish-brown in autumn.

Twigs: Slender, smooth, green to reddish-brown, turning gray with age.

Trunk: Bark gray-brown, smooth, becoming blackish, shallow grooved, and scaly ridged with age; wood light brown, strong, heavy, durable.

Habitat: Occurs in wet bottomland forests in the southeastern Missouri Bootheel.

Range: From the Gulf Coastal Plain of southeast Texas, Louisiana, Mississippi, Alabama, and Florida; north along the Mississippi River and its tributaries in southeastern Oklahoma, Arkansas, western Tennessee, and southeastern Missouri.

Medicinal Uses: As in other oaks, the bark, especially, has astringent (causes tissue to contract) properties. Native Americans used inner-bark tea to treat diarrhea, mouth sores, chapped skin, asthma, and coughs.

Wildlife Uses: Acorns are eaten by blue jay, woodpeckers, mallard, wood duck, wild turkey, mice, squirrels, raccoon, and white-tailed deer.

Remarks: Nuttall oak, also known as *Quercus nuttallii* Palmer, was not distinguished as a species until 1927. Nuttall oak closely resembles pin oak and may hybridize with the latter species where their ranges overlap in the southeastern Missouri lowlands.

Nuttall oak is one of the few commercially important tree species found on poorly drained clay flats and floodplains of the Gulf Coastal Plain and the lower Mississippi River and its tributaries. The lumber is often cut and sold as red oak. It is a heavy mast producer, providing food for a variety of wildlife.

Nuttall oak is a species of concern in Missouri and is classified as rare. Habitat destruction in the Bootheel is the principal reason for its limited numbers.

Nuttall oak is named for Thomas Nuttall (1786–1859), who traveled extensively in the United States and had several plants that he discovered named after him. Oak is from the Old English ac, beyond that its origin is uncertain.

Quercus is the Latin name for oak; *texana* refers to the state of Texas.

Quercus texana ❧ a. Leaves, b. Acorn, c. Twig

Black oak

Quercus velutina Lam.

Oak family (Fagaceae)

Appearance: Medium-sized tree, up to 70 feet tall, with a wide spreading, open crown and tall, straight trunk.

Flowers: April–May, see p. 380 for the oak reproductive cycle.

Fruit: September–October, acorn solitary or in pairs; nut reddish-brown, striped, 2 to 4 times longer than broad to egg-shaped, with a rounded tip, 1/2 to 1 inch long; cup covering 1/3 to 1/2 of the nut, bowl-shaped, **inner surface hairy**; scales light brown, **with a tiny fringe of hairs along the edges**, close, flattened near base of cup, **loose and spreading, forming a fringe towards the rim**; seed bitter; acorns ripen in autumn of the second year.

Leaves: Alternate, simple, 4 to 10 inches long; 3 to 7 inches wide, uniformly wide or broadest near or above the middle, leathery texture; **margin with 5 to 9 lobes, separated by prominent spaces, lobes with 1 to 3 bristle-tipped teeth, notches between lobes rounded; upper surface dark green, shiny**, smooth; lower surface paler, either hairy or smooth with tufts of hairs in the leaf axils; leaf stalk stout, red or yellow, hairy or smooth, 1 to 3 inches long; leaves turn yellow-brown or dull red in autumn.

Twigs: Stout, reddish-brown, hairy at first, smooth with age; **end buds sharp-pointed, distinctly angled, covered with gray hairs**.

Trunk: Bark black with deep grooves and flattened, scaly ridges; **inner bark mustard yellow to orange**; wood reddish-brown, strong, heavy, hard, coarse-grained.

Habitat: Occurs on rocky, sandy, or dry upland ridges and slopes; also on sandstone, chert, or igneous glades, and borders of woods and fields.

Range: East Texas, Oklahoma, Arkansas, and Louisiana; east to Florida, north to Maine, west to Ontario, Wisconsin, and Iowa; and south to southeast Nebraska and Kansas.

Wildlife Uses: Acorns are eaten by blue jay, woodpeckers, wild turkey, ruffed grouse, bobwhite quail, mice, squirrels, raccoon, and white-tailed deer.

Medicinal Uses: As in other oaks, the bark, especially, has astringent (causes tissue to contract) properties. Native Americans used inner-bark tea to treat diarrhea, mouth sores, chapped skin, asthma, and coughs.

Remarks: Black oak has been in cultivation since 1802 but it is seldom used for ornamental planting because it is slow growing and lacks the brilliant autumn coloring compared to some of the other oaks.

Black oak and scarlet oak are both relatively short-lived (less than 120 years). As old-growth short-leaf pine was removed from the Ozarks from 1890 to 1920, scarlet and black oak moved in to fill the gaps. In the last decade or so these oaks have been declining, and there are efforts by public agencies to replace them with the original occupants in the form of pine woodlands, one of the rarest forest communities today.

Quercus is the Latin name for oak; *velutina* is Latin for "velvety," referring to the velvety hairs on the lower surface of the young leaves.

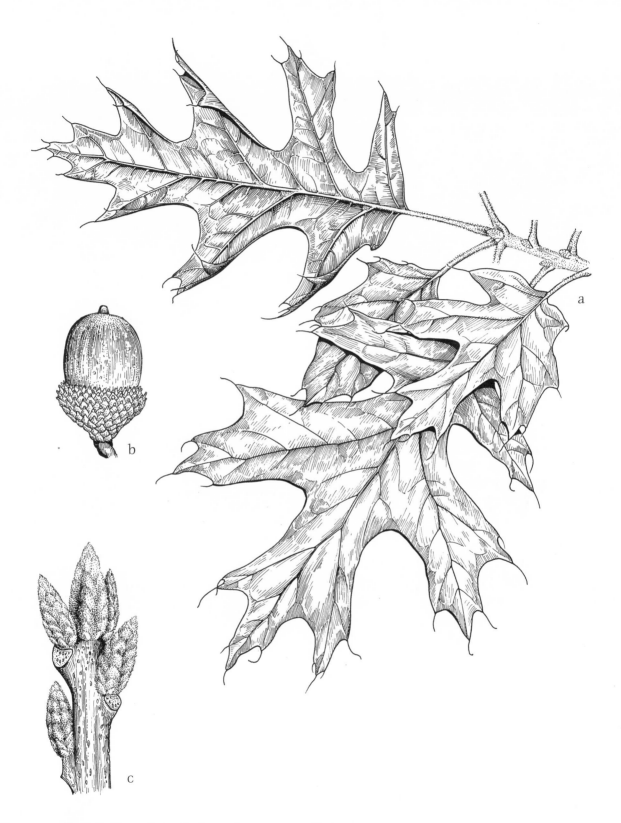

Quercus velutina ❧ a. Growth form, b. acorn, c. Twig

Carolina buckthorn

Rhamnus caroliniana Walter

Buckthorn family (Rhamnaceae)

Also called Indian cherry

Appearance: Shrub or small tree attaining a height of 35 feet, with a diameter of up to 8 inches.

Flowers: May–June, single or in clusters of 2 to 10, arising from leaf axils; flowers small, greenish-yellow; petals 5, minute, tip pointed; stamens 5, alternating with the petals.

Fruit: August–October, berry persistent into winter, sweet, round, about 1/4 inch in diameter, red at first, turning black and shiny, at maturity usually 3-seeded; seeds reddish-brown.

Leaves: Simple, alternate, scattered along the branches; blade 2 to 6 inches long, 1 to 2 inches wide, narrow at the ends and broadest in the middle, tip pointed, base wedge-shaped to rounded, **margin slightly toothed**, rather thin; **upper surface bright green, smooth, shiny**, sometimes hairy; lower surface velvety hairy to only slightly hairy or smooth; leaf blades usually 4 to 10 veins on each side of the central vein; leaves turning yellow in autumn; leaf stalk slender, about 1/4 to 1/2 inch long, widened at base, smooth or hairy.

Twigs: Slender, young ones green to reddish, later gray; hairy at first, smooth later; sometimes terminating in a cluster of very small folded leaves; **buds naked, not covered by scales, densely hairy, slender and elongated.**

Trunk: Bark gray to brown, sometimes blotched, smooth, grooves shallow; wood light brown, sapwood yellow, close-grained, fairly hard, rather weak.

Habitat: Occurs in low woodlands in valleys along streams, rocky open wooded slopes, upland ridges, thickets and glades.

Range: East Texas, Oklahoma, Arkansas, and Louisiana; east to Florida, north to North Carolina and Virginia; and west to Ohio, Illinois, and Missouri.

Wildlife Uses: The fruit is eaten by several species of birds, especially the catbird and pileated woodpecker. White-tailed deer browse the twigs in winter.

Medicinal Uses: Native Americans used bark tea to induce vomiting; it is also a strong laxative. The fruit and bark will cause diarrhea and vomiting.

Remarks: The attractive leaves and fruit make Carolina buckthorn a good candidate for woodland plantings. The foliage turns yellow to orange-yellow in autumn and often lasts into winter.

The wood is hard, brittle, and of no value commercially because of the tree's small size.

The fruit is sweet and considered edible by some but others know it for its ability to cause vomiting. The berries use by Native Americans account for the plant's other common name, Indian cherry.

Rhamnus is an ancient Greek name; *caroliniana* refers to the state of South Carolina where it was first named.

Rhamnus caroliniana ❀ a. Growth form with fruit, b. Twig with flowers, c. Flower,
d. Winter twig

Common buckthorn

Rhamnus cathartica L.

Buckthorn family (Rhamnaceae)

Also called European buckthorn

Appearance: A profusely branched shrub or small tree to 25 feet high.

Flowers: April–June, male, female, and, sometimes, perfect flowers on the same tree; male flowers on a short branch of the new year's growth, clusters of 2 to 6; flowers small, smooth, yellowish-green; petals 4, spreading, sometimes recurved; stamens 4; female flowers 2 to 15 on a short spur (thick, slow-growing, reduced branch) of the new year's growth; calyx lobes 4, green; usually no petals, but 4 if present, linear, yellowish-brown; stamens absent.

Fruit: August–September, often remains until December; single or clustered along short spur branches; fruit black, globe-shaped, 1/4 to 3/8 inch across, smooth, semiglossy, juicy, 4 seeds per fruit, but usually only 1 to 2 mature; seeds round, slate gray, smooth, dull, a ridge along one side.

Leaves: Simple, **some leaves appearing alternate but most are opposite**, 1 1/4 to 3 inches long, 1 to 2 1/4 inches wide, longer than broad and tapering at both ends to oval or inverted egg-shaped, **tip abruptly pointed** or sometimes rounded, base rounded to wedge-shaped, margin toothed with the tip usually turned in and bearing a gland; dark green above; paler below; both surfaces smooth; **leaf blades with mostly 3 to 4 veins on each side of the central vein**; leaf stalk 1/2 to 1 1/4 inches long, slightly grooved, hairy above.

Twigs: Slightly flattened, gray to yellowish-brown, dull, smooth, pores are narrow vertical slits, numerous; **twigs often ending in a thorn instead of an end bud.**

Trunk: Bark of young trunks gray, smooth; older trunks with somewhat scaly bark and with long, horizontal pores, trunk usually blotched with light and dark gray; wood hard, fine-grained, light brown, sapwood wide, white.

Habitat: Escaping occasionally from cultivation and invading wooded thickets, along roadsides and abandoned fields. Can invade tallgrass prairie and woodland habitats.

Range: Introduced from Europe and escaping in North America, from Missouri, east to Illinois, Indiana, Ohio, and Virginia; north to Nova Scotia, and west to Minnesota, the Dakotas, and Saskatchewan.

Wildlife Uses: The fruits are eaten by several bird species, which help to spread this nuisance shrub.

Medicinal Uses: The fruits are a strong laxative.

Remarks: This is an invasive shrub and should not be planted. Once established it is difficult to eradicate. Common buckthorns and other exotic buckthorns are sold as ornamentals by nurseries and are used as hedges in many urban areas.

Rhamnus is an ancient Greek name; *cathartica* means cathartic, which refers to its ability to cause vomiting.

Rhamnus cathartica ❧ a. Growth form, b. Flower, c. Twig with fruit and thorns

Winged sumac

Rhus copallina L.

Cashew family (Anacardiaceae)

Also called dwarf sumac, shining sumac, flame-leaf sumac

Appearance: Slender-branched shrub to small tree, up to 26 feet tall, with a rounded top and forming thickets from root sprouting.

Flowers: Late May–July, both male and female flowers in dense clusters at the end of new growth, on separate plants; clusters 6 to 8 inches long, 5 to 7 inches wide; flowers numerous, both male and female flowers about 1/8 inch across; petals 5, greenish-white; stamens 5.

Fruit: September, compact clusters, erect or drooping, persistent; fruit globe-shaped, flattened, red, hairy, about 1/8 inch in diameter; seeds solitary, smooth, oval to bean-shaped, olive-brown.

Leaves: Alternate, featherlike arrangement, 5 to 12 inches long, **central stem hairy, broadly winged**; leaflets 7 to 17, sides of leaflets unequal, broadest below the middle to uniformly wide, tip pointed, base ending at a sharp angle, **margin entire or remotely toothed**; upper surface dark green, shiny, smooth to hairy; lower surface paler, hairy; leaf stalk about 3 inches long, hairy; **broken leaves and leaf stalk with white sticky sap.**

Twigs: Brittle, green to reddish-brown, **hairy at first**, smooth later; **broken twigs with white sticky sap;** pores dark. Part of the season's twig-growth often dies back over winter.

Trunk: Bark thick, greenish-brown to gray, some shallow grooves, pores red and prominent; wood soft, brittle, brown, with a white sapwood.

Habitat: Occurs in prairies, thickets, open woods, rocky sandstone, chert and igneous glades, borders of woodland generally in acid soils, abandoned fields, roadsides and along railroads.

Range: Texas, Oklahoma, Arkansas, and Louisiana; east to Florida, north to New Hampshire, and west to Michigan, Wisconsin, Iowa, southeast Nebraska, and east Kansas.

Wildlife Uses: The fruit is eaten by at least 20 species of birds, and white-tailed deer occasionally browse it, as well as the stems and foliage.

Medicinal Uses: Native Americans used bark tea to stimulate milk flow and as a wash for blisters. Berries can be used to treat bed-wetting and mouth sores. Root tea is used for dysentery.

Remarks: Winged sumac makes a desirable ornamental shrub due to its glossy, dark green leaves and brilliant red leaves in autumn. The bark and leaves contain tannin and are used in the tanning industry. The crushed, somewhat bitter, fruit was added to drinking water by Native Americans to make it more palatable.

Sumac is from the Old French language as written and spoken before 1400.

Rhus is from the ancient Latin name *rhous* for a bushy sumac; *copallina* is a Mexican name meaning "copal gum," which refers to a hard resin characteristic of some tropical trees.

Rhus copallina ❀ a. Growth form with flower clusters, b. Male flower, c. Female flower, d. Twig with fruit cluster

Smooth sumac

Rhus glabra L.

Cashew family (Anacardiaceae)

Appearance: Thicket-forming shrub or small tree attaining a height of 20 feet.

Flowers: Late May–July, both male and female flowers in dense clusters at the end of new growth, on separate plants; clusters 5 to 9 inches long, 3 to 5 inches wide; flowers numerous, both male and female flowers, about 1/8 inch across; petals 5, white; stamens 5.

Fruit: August–September, compact clusters, erect, persistent; fruit globe-shaped, about 1/8 inch in diameter, dark red with red velvety hairs; 1-seeded, stone smooth, oval, straw-colored.

Leaves: Alternate, featherlike arrangement, 12 to 16 inches long, **central stem smooth, lacking wings**; leaflets 15 to 23, longest leaflets near middle of the leaf; leaflets longer than broad to lance-shaped, tip pointed, base rounded or wedge-shaped, **margin coarsely toothed; upper surface dark green, shiny**; lower surface lighter to conspicuously white, smooth; **leaf stalk smooth**, about 3 inches long; **broken leaves and leaf stalks with white sticky sap**.

Twigs: Rigid, **smooth, with white coating**, reddish-brown to purplish, with prominent gray pores, **broken twigs with white sticky sap.** Part of the season's twig-growth often dies back during winter.

Trunk: Bark grayish-brown, roughened with raised pores; old trunks with shallow grooves; wood soft, brittle, yellowish-brown, with a white sapwood.

Habitat: Occurs in upland prairies, thickets, idle fields, borders and openings of woods, roadsides and along railroads. Throughout Missouri in every county.

Range: Very widespread; New Mexico, Texas, Oklahoma, Arkansas, and Louisiana; east to Florida, north to Maine and Quebec, and west to Utah, Montana, Oregon, Washington, and British Columbia.

Wildlife Uses: The fruit is eaten by at least 32 species of birds, including wild turkey and bob-white quail. Cottontail rabbit and white-tailed deer eat the leaves and twigs.

Medicinal Uses: Native Americans used the plant in many ways. The somewhat bitter fruits were crushed and added to water to freshen it. Various concoctions of the bark, twigs, leaves and flowers were used medicinally as astringents, (causes tissue to contract) to stop bleeding, and for renal disorders. In Appalachia, the leaves are rolled and smoked as a treatment for asthma. The fruits in infusion (boiling water poured over them) have been used as a treatment for fever. The bark, boiled in milk, has been used to treat burns.

Remarks: Smooth sumac, with its bright red clusters of fruit and brilliant autumn foliage, makes a good ornamental shrub. It has been in cultivation since 1620. The leaves are reported to have been mixed with tobacco and smoked. The twigs, leaves and roots contain tannin and were used for staining and dyeing.

Sumac is from the Old French language as written and spoken before 1400.

Rhus is from the ancient Latin name *rhous* for a bushy sumac; *glabra* refers to the plant's smoothness.

Rhus glabra ❀ a. Growth form with fruit cluster, b. Male flower, c. Female flower, d. Fruit, e. Winter twig

Black locust

Robinia pseudo-acacia L.

Bean family (Fabaceae)

Appearance: Medium-sized tree, up to 70 feet tall, with an irregular, open crown and some low branches, as well as, several large upright branches.

Flowers: May–June, **pea-shaped, showy, white, fragrant, in loose, drooping clusters, 4 to 5 inches long**; flower bonnet-shaped with five petals, 3/4 to 1 inch long, **with a yellow blotch on the inside of the uppermost petal**; stamens 10; flower stalk about 1/2 inches long.

Fruit: September–October, in flattened pods, 3 to 5 inches long, about 1/2 inches wide, smooth, reddish-brown, splitting lengthwise along both sides; seeds 4 to 8, spotted, flat, kidney-shaped; **pods often persist on the tree through winter**.

Leaves: Alternate, feather-like arrangement, 8 to 14 inches long, with leaflets 7 to 19; leaflets 1/2 to 2 inches long, 1/2 to 1 inch wide, broadest near the middle to uniformly wide, with tiny bracts at base of leaflets; margin entire, **leaf tip with a small notch and an extremely small bristle**; upper surface bluish- to dark green, dull, smooth; lower surface paler, smooth except with hairs on the veins; leaf stalk slender, 1 1/2 to 2 inches long; leaves turn yellow in autumn.

Twigs: Dark brown, stout, zigzag, brittle, **smooth, angled with a pair of small spines where the leaves attach**.

Trunk: Bark reddish-brown to almost black, with deep grooves and long, flat-topped, interlacing ridges; wood dark yellow to brown, hard, strong, heavy, durable, close-grained.

Habitat: Occurs in dry or rocky upland woods, along streams, in pastures, thickets, and disturbed sites.

Range: Native to the Ozark Mountains of Oklahoma, Arkansas, and Missouri and following the Appalachian Mountains and Piedmont Plateau of Alabama and Georgia; northeast to Pennsylvania. Introduced and naturalized elsewhere over the eastern United States; also in Oregon and other western states.

Wildlife Uses: The flowers are a good nectar source for bees. White-tailed deer browse the leaves and twigs. The seeds are eaten by bobwhite quail and squirrels.

Medicinal Uses: Native Americans chewed root bark to induce vomiting and to reduce toothaches. Flower tea has been used for rheumatism. All parts of the tree are considered toxic, including bee honey made from the flowers.

Remarks: Black locust has been planted as an ornamental in the United States and Europe since sometime between 1601 and 1636. A pioneer species, black locust easily invades disturbed sites, often developing clones from sucker sprouts. A tough tree, it is difficult to eradicate once established. The wood is ranked as the seventh hardest of any tree in North America. Highly resistant to decay, it is used for posts and for fuel. Pioneers used black locust pegs for pinning timber joints because the dense wood would not shrink on drying.

Robinia is in honor of Jean (1550–1629) and Vespasien (1579–1662) Robin, father and son, who were herbalists to Henry IV of France and first cultivated the locust tree in Europe; *pseudo-acacia* ("false-acacia") refers to its resemblance to an acacia.

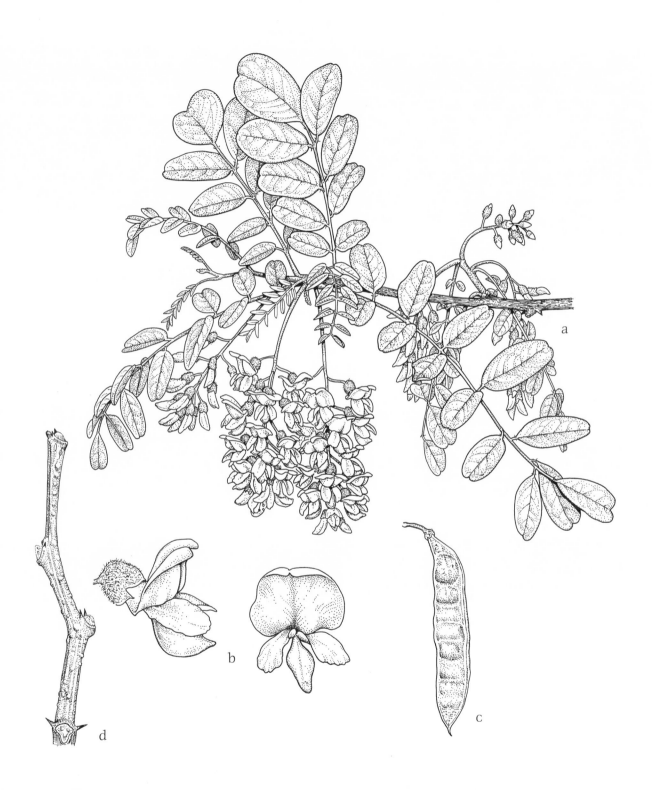

__Robinia pseudo-acacia__ ❧ a. Growth form with flowers, b. Flower, c. Fruit, d. Twig

Peach-leaved willow

Salix amygdaloides

Willow family (Salicaceae)

Appearance: Medium-sized tree, up to 50 feet tall, often with a leaning trunk and upright branches forming an open, irregular crown.

Flowers: April–June, appearing with the leaves, male and female flowers in catkins on separate trees, petals absent; male catkins 1 to 2 inches long, slender, hairy; stamens 5 to 9; female catkins 1 1/2 to 3 inches long, hairy.

Fruit: June–July, in catkins 2 to 3 inches long; capsules cone-shaped, light reddish or yellow, about 1/4 inch long, curved and splitting into 2 halves when ripe; seeds numerous, minute, with long, silky hairs at the base.

Leaves: Alternate, simple, **similar in shape to peach leaves**, 2 1/2 to 6 inches long; 3/4 to 1 1/4 inches wide, lance-shaped, broadest below the middle, thin, papery; margin finely toothed, tip tapering to a point, base often uneven; upper surface yellowish-green, shiny, smooth; lower surface paler, often with a whitish coating, smooth; **leaf stalk 1/4 to 3/4 inches long, often twisted**; leafy appendage at base of leaf stalk kidney-shaped, about 1/2 inch long, falling away early; leaves turn yellow in autumn.

Twigs: Slender, long, flexible, drooping at the tip, smooth, shiny, yellow or orange at first, darkening to reddish-brown or gray with age; pores small, scattered.

Trunk: Bark reddish-brown or darker, grooves irregular, with broad, flat ridges often becoming shaggy; wood light brown, soft, weak, close-grained.

Habitat: Occurs along muddy banks and low ground bordering the Missouri, Mississippi, and other large rivers of northern, central, and eastern Missouri.

Range: Texas and New Mexico; northeast to Vermont, Quebec, and British Columbia; west to Manitoba and Washington.

Wildlife Uses: The shoots and buds are eaten by many rodents (including muskrat and beaver), as well as cottontail rabbit. Beaver eat the bark. Bees use the nectar to produce high-grade honey.

Medicinal Uses: The original basic ingredient of aspirin, salicin, was extracted from the bark in the early 19th century. Today, the chemical (salicylic acid), derived from salicin, is synthesized rather than extracted. Native Americans used the bark tea to treat toothache, stomachache, diarrhea, dysentery, and dandruff.

Remarks: Peach-leaved willow has been in cultivation since 1895. Rapidly growing and short-lived, it is a pioneer species, colonizing newly disturbed sites, stabilizing soils, and maintaining themselves for up to 30 years before other bottomland trees shade them out. Native Americans used the stems for basketry and bow making. Today, the wood is used for charcoal and firewood. Cuttings of peach-leaved willow can be used to revegetate disturbed stream banks. Stem cuttings (slips), when driven into riverbanks, quickly establish roots and stabilize soils, allowing other plants to becoming established.

Salix is the classical Latin name; *amygdaloides* is from the Greek *amygdalus* ("peach") and refers to the peach-like leaves.

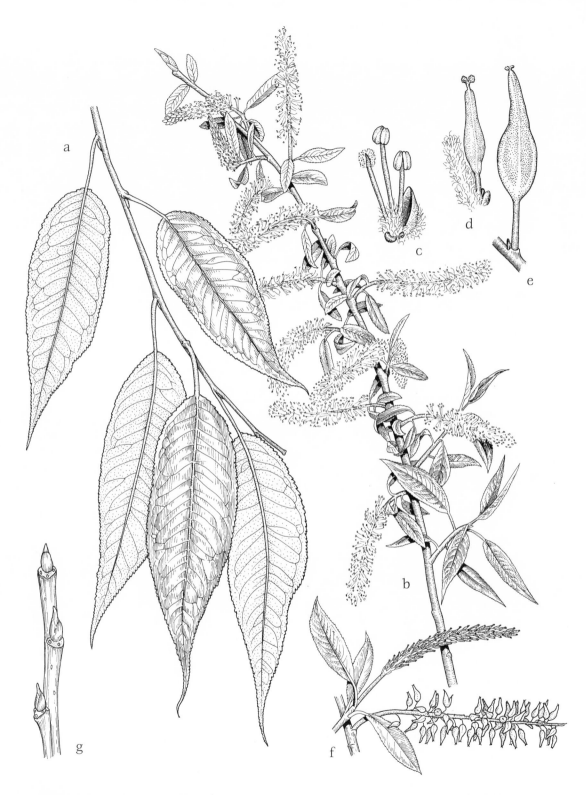

Salix amygdaloides ❧ a. Growth form, b. Twig with leaves and male catkins, c. Male flower, d. Female flower, e. Fruit, f. Fruit cluster, g. Twig

Weeping willow

Salix babylonica L.

Willow family (Salicaceae)

Appearance: Medium-sized tree, up to 60 feet tall, with a broad, rounded-crown and drooping branches (giving the tree its name).

Flowers: April–May, appearing with the leaves, male and female flowers in catkins on separate trees, petals absent; male catkins about 1 inch long, yellowish; stamens 3 to 5, hairy at the base; female catkins less than 1 inch long.

Fruit: June–July, in catkins 2 to 3 inches long; capsules cone-shaped, about 1/4-inch long, splitting into 2 parts when ripe; seeds numerous, minute, with long, silky hairs at the base.

Leaves: Alternate, simple, 3 to 7 inches long; **1/4 to 1/2 inch wide, narrowly lance-shaped**; margin finely toothed, tip tapering to a point; upper surface dark green, silky hairy when young, smooth with age; lower surface smooth; leaf stalk about 1/4 inch long, smooth, **with sticky glands at the top**; leaves turn yellow in autumn.

Twigs: Slender, long, drooping "weeping," yellowish-green at first, turning brown with age.

Trunk: Bark gray, rather smooth or with shallow grooves and interlacing ridges; wood light brown, soft, weak, close-grained.

Habitat: Commonly planted as an ornamental tree and rarely escapes. Grows best in moist sites.

Range: Native to northern China and introduced from Europe into North America in 1730. It is widely planted in the United States below an altitude of 3,500 feet.

Remarks: A fast growing, short-lived tree, weeping willow is commonly planted in cemeteries, parks, lawns, and in moist areas near streams, lakes, and ponds. It is undesirable as a lawn tree because the fragile twigs and branches easily suffer from ice damage.

Willow is from Middle English *wilghe* or *wilowe*, which is from the Old English *welig*, originating before the 12th century.

Salix is the classical Latin name; *babylonica* refers to its once-presumed West Asia origin of Babylon, but it is actually from northern China.

Weeping willow is known to hybridize with two other exotic willow species: white willow, *Salix alba* L. and crack willow, *Salix fragilis* L., both of which are also found in Missouri. Neither white willow nor crack willow have "weeping" branches or twigs. White willow lacks glands at the top of the leaf stalk; twigs are tough and not easily broken; planted in yards and sometimes naturalizes in wet ground along streams and ponds. Crack willow has sticky glands at the top of the leaf stalk; twigs are very brittle and easily broken, hence, the common name; also escapes from cultivation and found in wet ground along streams and in wet woods. Both trees were introduced into the United States during colonial times for making charcoal that was used as an ingredient for gunpowder and for medicine. A tea made from the bark was used as a substitute for quinine to treat malaria and for other fevers.

Weeping willow is commonly planted as an ornamental in Missouri but rarely escapes cultivation.

Salix babylonica ❀ a. Growth form, b. Twig with male catkins, c. Female flower, d. Fruit clusters, e. Fruit capsule with seeds, f. Twig, g. Leaf scar with bud

Carolina willow

Salix caroliniana Michaux

Willow family (Salicaceae)

Also called ward's willow, coastal plain willow

Appearance: Shrub or small tree to 30 feet. Branches spreading or drooping to form an open, irregular crown.

Flowers: April–May, male and female flowers in separate catkins on the tips of twigs, borne on separate plants; catkins slender, narrowly cylindrical, up to 4 inches long; male catkins with 4 to 7 stamens; female catkins not as full or as showy as the yellow male catkins.

Fruit: June–July, capsule about 1/4 inch long, egg- to cone-shaped, abruptly long-pointed, brown at maturity, stalk of capsule very short, almost absent; seeds minute with long, silky hairs at the base, which are 2 to 3 times as long as the seed.

Leaves: Alternate, simple, **2 to 7 inches long**, 3/8 to 3/4 inch wide, **narrowly lance-shaped**, tip pointed, base gradually narrowed on young leaves, on older ones often rounded; upper surface bright green, smooth; lower surface white to silvery-white, smooth, young leaves with matted hairs; margin finely toothed; leaf stalk 1/4 to 1/2 inch long, densely hairy, lacking glands; **stipules up to 3/4 inch across, conspicuous, margin toothed.**

Twigs: Slender, yellowish- to reddish-brown or grayish, more or less hairy, eventually smooth.

Trunk: Bark reddish-brown to gray, ridges thin to broad, grooves shallow to deep, conspicuously checkered, breaking into closely flattened scales; wood dark reddish-brown, sapwood nearly white, light, soft, not strong.

Habitat: Occurs along gravel bars, sandy gravel beds and rocky banks of streams. The most common willow along gravel bars in Ozark streams.

Range: Texas, Oklahoma, Arkansas, and Louisiana; east to Florida, north to Maryland, and west to Illinois, Missouri, and Kansas.

Wildlife Uses: Willow twigs and leaves are browsed by white-tailed deer. The shoots and buds are eaten by many rodents (including muskrat and beaver), as well as cottontail rabbits. Some ducks and water birds feed on willow catkins and leaves. Bees use willow nectar to produce high-grade honey. Dense thickets also provide cover for wildlife.

Remarks: Carolina willow is a pioneer species invading and stabilizing newly formed gravel bars. The common phrase "bend like a willow" comes from the shrub's ability to withstand the force of floods and storms by bending and being flexible.

Willow is from Middle English *wilghe* or *wilowe*, which is from the Old English *welig*, a name originating before the 12th century.

It is one of the willow species used in the Ozarks for making wickerwork for baskets, furniture and ornamental pieces.

Salix is the classical Latin name; *caroliniana* refers to the states of Carolina, where the plant was first described.

Salix caroliniana ❀ a. Growth form, b. Catkin, c. Seed capsules

Pussy willow

Salix discolor Muhlenb.

Willow family (Salicaceae)

Appearance: A large shrub to small tree to 16 feet high, the trunks single or clustered, the branches high.

Flowers: February–April, before the leaves, male and female flowers in separate catkins and on separate plants in axils on twigs of previous year; male catkins 3/4 to 1 1/2 inches long, 1/2 to 1 1/4 inches wide, densely flowered, showy; stamens 2; female catkins 3/4 to 1 1/4 inches long, about 1/2 inch wide, numerous flowers.

Fruit: June, catkins drooping, 2 1/2 to 3 1/4 inches long; capsules wide spreading, about 1/2 inch long, egg-shaped with a long neck; seeds dark green, cylindrical, blunt-tipped, a ring of short, stiff hairs and an outer ring of long, silky hairs around the base more than twice the length of the seed.

Leaves: Simple, alternate, 1 1/2 to 3 1/4 inches long, 3/4 to 1 1/4 inches wide, longer than broad, the width about 1/2 the length, tip pointed, base wedge-shaped to narrowly rounded, margin irregularly toothed and wavy; upper surface dark green, semi-shiny, smooth; **lower surface with a light, whitish coating**; leaf stalk about 3/8 inch long, hairy, the blade slightly pointing down.

Twigs: Flexible, reddish-purple to reddish-brown, dull, **smooth**; pores oval, small, yellow.

Trunk: Bark grayish-brown, tight with fine ridges along the stem, slightly grooved and ridged on old trunks; wood soft, brownish, with a wide, white sapwood.

Habitat: Along creeks and rivers in open or wooded areas; **collected only from Clark County**.

Range: Northeast Missouri, Iowa, and Illinois; east to Virginia, north to Maine and Labrador; and west to North Dakota and Alberta.

Wildlife Uses: Willow twigs and leaves are browsed by white-tailed deer. The shoots and buds are eaten by many rodents (including muskrat and beaver), as well as cottontail rabbits. Some ducks and water birds feed on willow catkins and leaves. Bees use willow nectar to produce high-grade honey. Dense thickets also provide cover for wildlife.

Remarks: Pussy willow had not been seen growing in the wild in Missouri since 1892 in Clark County, but a new site was discovered in Schuyler County bordering the Iowa state line. The species is classified as endangered in Missouri. Since pussy willow is more northern in its distribution, its occurrence in Missouri probably always was extremely rare.

The soft, silky hairs clothing the bracts of the catkins before they open give this species the name of "pussy willow," because of their similarity to the pads of cats' feet. The pussy willow sold in florists shops is a species from Europe and Asia known as goat willow *(Salix caprea* L.). It has much larger fuzzy catkins, but rarely escapes from cultivation and has not been recorded to do so in Missouri.

Salix is the classical Latin name; *discolor* means "of two different colors," probably referring to the yellow male and greenish female catkins.

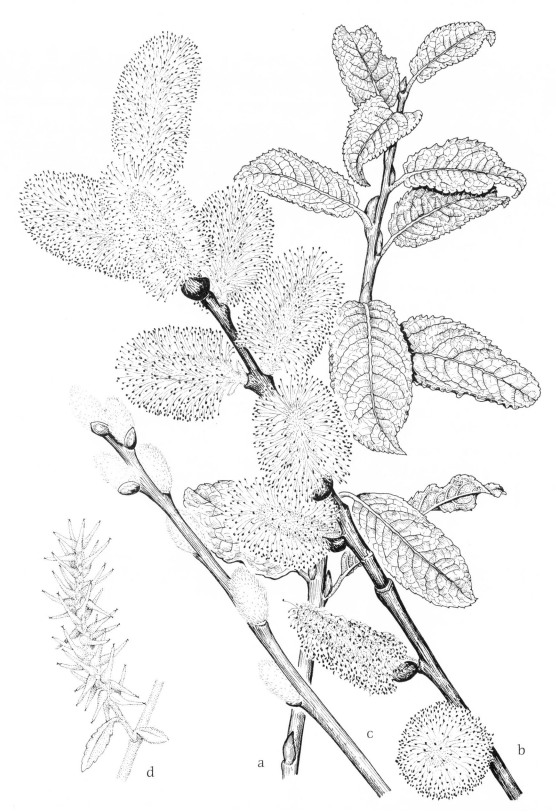

Salix discolor ❀ a. Growth form, b. Male catkins, c. Female catkins, d. Seed capsules

Missouri willow

Salix eriocephala Michaux

Willow family (Salicaceae)

Also called diamond willow, heart-leaved willow

Appearance: Shrub to small- or medium-sized tree, up to 50 feet tall, with slender branches that form a narrow crown.

Flowers: April–May, flowering with or prior to the leaves, male and female flowers in separate catkins and on separate plants in axils on twigs of previous year; male catkins 1 1/2 to 2 3/4 inches, cylindrical; flowers clustered; stamens 2; female catkins 1 to 3 inches long.

Fruit: May–June, catkins 2 to 3 inches long; capsules about 3/8 inch long, egg-shaped with a long neck, yellowish-brown; seeds cylindrical, surrounded by a ring of long, white, silky hairs at the base.

Leaves: Simple, alternate, 1 1/2 to 3 inches long, 1/4 to 3/4 inch wide, blade lance-shaped, broadest in the middle, tip pointed, base rounded or heart-shaped, **margin finely toothed, equally and closely spaced, 13 to 25 to an inch**; upper surface dark green to yellowish-green, smooth; lower surface pale to lightly covered with a white, waxy coating, smooth to hairy; **leaf stalk 1/8 to 3/4 inch long; stipules (leafy appendages) persistent on vigorous shoots, heart- to kidney-shaped surrounding the stem.**

Twigs: Gray-brown to dark brown, smooth to somewhat hairy, branchlets reddish-brown, smooth.

Trunk: Bark thin, smooth, light gray with a slight tinge of red, pores; large; older bark shallowly grooved, the ridges wide, flat and tightly flattened; wood durable, dark brown, with a narrow, pale sapwood.

Habitat: Occurs in floodplains along the Missouri and Mississippi Rivers and their larger tributaries; also as shrubs in wet ground along streams, spring branches and in fens.

Range: Kansas, Missouri, and Arkansas; east to North Carolina, north to Newfoundland, and west to Ontario, Minnesota, and the Dakotas.

Wildlife Uses: Willow twigs and leaves are browsed by white-tailed deer. The shoots and buds are eaten by many rodents (including muskrat and beaver), as well as cottontail rabbits.

Remarks: Some authors refer to smaller plants of Missouri willow as heart-leaved willow, *Salix rigida* Muhl., which occur as shrubs in wet ground along streams, spring branches, and in fens in the Ozarks.

Missouri willow is rather fast-growing and longer-lived than most other willows. Prized among craftsmen for its straight limbs, this willow is used to make walking sticks.

The name Missouri is used because the willow once had the scientific name of *Salix missouriensis* Bebb (P & S).

Salix is the classical Latin name; of the willows; probably from the Celtic *sal* (near) and *lis* (water); *eriocephala* is from *erios* ("woolly") and *cephala* ("head"), possibly referring to the fuzzy male catkins.

Salix eriocephala ❀ a. Growth form, b. Male catkins, c. Seed capsules

Sandbar willow

Salix exigua Nutt.

Willow family (Salicaceae)

Appearance: A slender, upright shrub forming thickets by spreading roots, or a small tree to 30 feet.

Flowers: May–June, flowering with leaves present, male and female flowers in separate catkins in axils on twigs, borne on separate plants; catkins slender, cylinder-shaped; male catkins 3/4 to 2 inches long, about 1/4 to 3/4 inch broad; many-flowered, stamens 2; female catkins loosely flowered, 2 to 3 inches long, about 1/4 inch broad.

Fruit: June–July, catkins 1 1/2 to 2 inches long; capsules about 1/4 inch long, oval with a beaklike point, pale brown, smooth; seeds minute, attached to long white silky hairs at the base 2 to 3 times the length of the seed.

Leaves: Simple, alternate, 2 to 6 inches long, 1/8 to 3/8 inch wide, narrow lance-shaped, thin, tip pointed, base gradually narrowed to a short leaf stalk, **margin with scattered and unevenly spaced, gland-tipped teeth, only 3 to 12 to an inch**; upper surface dark green, smooth or hairy along the main vein; lower surface paler, hairy; **leaf stalk 1/8 inch or less**, hairy; stipules (leafy appendages where the leaf meets the stem) small or absent. Young leaves silky hairy beneath.

Twigs: Slender, erect, green to brown or red, smooth or hairy and sometimes with a white, waxy coating.

Trunk: Slender, straight, with small branches; bark green to gray or brown, smooth; on older trunks furrowed and broken into closely flattened scales; pores sometimes large and abundant; wood soft, light-weight, close-grained, weak, brittle, light brown, with a pale brown sapwood.

Habitat: Occurs on sand bars, mud flats and alluvial muddy banks of streams, oxbow lakes, ponds and ditches of river bottoms and floodplains throughout Missouri; absent from four counties of the southeastern lowlands.

Range: Occurs over a wide range; Arizona, New Mexico, Texas, Oklahoma, Arkansas, and Louisiana; north to Canada and Alaska; also northern Mexico.

Wildlife Uses: Willow twigs and leaves are browsed by white-tailed deer. The shoots and buds are eaten by many rodents (including muskrat and beaver), as well as cottontail rabbits. Some ducks and water birds feed on willow catkins and leaves. Bees use willow nectar to produce high-grade honey.

Remarks: Sandbar willow is also known as *Salix interior* Rowlee. Sandbar willow often forms dense thickets that can be hard to penetrate. A pioneer species, it is one of the first woody plants to inhabit a newly made sandbar in a river. It is associated with silver maple (*Acer saccharinum*) and cottonwood (*Populus deltoides*) on the river flats of the Missouri and Mississippi rivers. Sandbar willow is a good soil binder and bank stabilizer, and prevents washing and erosion of alluvial soil.

Salix is the classical Latin name; *exigua* is Latin for "small," referring to the size of the leaves.

Salix exigua ❋ a. Growth form, b. Twig with seed capsules, c. Open capsule

Black willow

Salix nigra Marsh.

Willow family (Salicaceae)

Appearance: Medium to large-sized tree, up to 100 feet tall, with a straight trunk and a broadly irregular, open crown on productive sites.

Flowers: April–May, appearing with the leaves, male and female flowers in catkins on separate trees, petals absent; male catkins 1 to 2 inches long, slender, hairy; stamens 3 to 7; female catkins 3/4 to 2 inches long, hairy.

Fruit: May–June, in catkins about 2 inches long; capsules narrowly coned-shaped, light brown, about 1/4 inches long, splitting into 2 halves when ripe; seeds numerous, minute, with long, silky hairs at the base.

Leaves: Alternate, simple, 3 to 6 inches long, 1/4 to 3/4 inches wide, **narrowly lance-shaped**, thin, papery; margin finely toothed, **very long pointed, often curved toward the tip**; upper surface dark green, somewhat shiny, smooth; lower surface paler, smooth; leaf stalk short, hairy, less than 1/4 inches long; leafy appendage at base of leaf stalk may or may not be present; leaves turn yellow in winter.

Twigs: Slender, **brittle**, smooth, reddish-brown.

Trunk: Bark light brown to **black, rough, deeply grooved**, ridges broad, flat with shaggy scales; wood light brown, soft, light weak, not durable, close-grained.

Habitat: Occurs along streams, swamps, sloughs, marshes, and ponds in wet bottomland soil.

Range: Texas, Arkansas, Oklahoma, and Louisiana; east to Florida, north to Maine and New Brunswick; west to Wisconsin, Iowa, southeastern Nebraska, and Kansas.

Wildlife Uses: Twigs and leaves are browsed by white-tailed deer. The shoots and buds are eaten by many rodents (including muskrat and beaver), as well as cottontail rabbit. Beaver eat the bark.

Some ducks and water birds feed on the catkins and leaves. Bees use the nectar to produce high-grade honey. Dense thickets also provide cover for wildlife.

Medicinal Uses: The original basic ingredient of aspirin, salicin, was extracted from the bark in the early 19th century. Today, the chemical (salicylic acid), derived from salicin, is synthesized rather than extracted. Native Americans used the bark tea to treat toothache, stomach ache, diarrhea, dysentery, and dandruff.

Remarks: Black willow was first cultivated in 1809. A rapidly growing but short-lived tree (less than 85 years), black willow ranks as one of the largest willow species in the world; reaching heights of over 120 feet in southern states. Black willow is very tolerant of flooding for long periods of time and can withstand being buried by sediments that accompany floods. The branching root system forms dense networks and helps to stabilize the tree in shifting soil and makes a good choice for reducing soil erosion along riverbanks. Also, stem cuttings (slips), driven into riverbanks, quickly establish roots and stabilize soils, allowing other plants to becoming established.

The soft, light, springy wood is used for wickerwork baskets and furniture; also for pulp, charcoal, veneer, flooring, boxes, and crates.

Salix is the classical Latin name; *nigra* refers to the black bark.

Salix nigra ❧ a. Leaves, b. Twig with leaves and male catkins, c. Male flower, d. Female flower, e. Fruit cluster, f. Fruit capsule with seeds, g. Seed, h. Twig, i. Leaf scar with bud

Silky willow

Salix sericea Marshall

Willow family (Salicaceae)

Appearance: A shrub to small tree to 15 feet, with clustered stems and dark green leaves that are brightly silvered beneath with close, silky hairs.

Flowers: March–May, numerous catkins appear in the spring before the leaves, male and female flowers in separate catkins and on separate plants in axils on twigs of previous year; male catkins are 1/4 to 3/4 inch long, oval to egg-shaped; flowers several; stamens 2; female catkins are 1/2 to 1 inch long; flowers several.

Fruit: June, catkins up to 1 1/4 inches long, narrow, cylindrical; capsules about 1/8 inch long, egg-shaped, tip blunt, with silvery hairs.

Leaves: Simple, alternate, 2 to 3 inches long, 1/2 to 3/4 inch wide, narrowly lance-shaped, tip pointed, base narrowing sharply to rounded, margin finely toothed; upper surface dark green, hairy to smooth; lower surface with dense shiny-silvery hairs; the small veins becoming finely netted with age; leaf stalk slender, 1/4 to 3/4 inch long, light to dark brown, hairy to smooth; **stipules (leafy appendages where the leaf meets the stem) linear- to lance-shaped, dropping early.**

Twigs: Slender, **easy to break, brittle**; light to dark brown, hairy to smooth.

Habitat: Occurs in fens, swampy ground around springs, and spring branches in the eastern part of the Ozarks.

Range: Northern Arkansas, southeast Missouri, Tennessee, and northern Alabama; east to South Carolina, north to Maine and Quebec; and west to Wisconsin and east Iowa.

Wildlife Uses: Willow twigs and leaves are browsed by white-tailed deer. The shoots and buds are eaten by many rodents (including muskrat and beaver), as well as cottontail rabbits. Bees use willow nectar to produce high-grade honey. Dense thickets also provide cover for wildlife.

Remarks: A characteristic inhabitant of Ozark fens, silky willow can be found growing with other unique plants, many of which are found more commonly in northern states. Called ice age relicts, these plants migrated south with glacial advances and found refuge in the unglaciated Ozarks. As the climate warmed, some populations died because of changing habitat, others migrated north, and some remained in pockets of cool, moist soils.

These special areas, called Ozark fens, provide continuous moisture as water percolates down through ancient broken-down rocks in nearby hills. At some point, the water meets an impenetrable bedrock deep in the hill and seeps out, usually at the base of a slope. This seepage is continuous, even during drought years, because of the water working its way through the hills. This concentration of fens in the Ozarks is found nowhere else in unglaciated North America.

Salix is the classical Latin name; of the willows; probably from the Celtic *sal* (near) and *lis* (water); *sericea* means "silky," and refers to the underside of the leaves.

Salix sericea ❀ a. Growth form, b. Male catkins, c. Catkins with open seed capsules, d. Seed capsule

Red-berried elder

Sambucus racemosa L.

Honeysuckle family (Caprifoliaceae)

Also called red-berried elderberry, stinking elder, scarlet elder

Appearance: A shrub or small tree to 24 feet, not forming colonies.

Flowers: April–May, **in pyramidal clusters**, longer than broad, on new growth, clusters 2 to 4 inches long, 1 1/4 to 2 inches wide; cluster stalk 3/4 to 2 1/2 inches long; flowers white, about 1/8 inch across; petals 5, rounded, spreading; stamens 5, extending beyond the flower.

Fruit: June–August, **in pyramidal clusters** at the ends of branches, berrylike fruit about 1/8 inch diameter, egg-shaped, **red**, semi-glossy, juice yellowish; seeds 3, yellow, less than 1/8 inch long, flattened on the sides, minutely roughened.

Leaves: Opposite, featherlike arrangement, 3 to 7 inches long; leaflets 5 to 7, blades 2 to 4 inches long, 3/4 to 1 1/4 inches wide, broadly lance-shaped to egg-shaped, tip pointed, base narrowed or rounded, blade often with uneven sides, margin sharply toothed; upper surface dark green, smooth; lower surface paler, hairy but smooth later; end leaflet stalk 1/4 to 1 inch long, side leaflet stalks short or absent, hairy.

Twigs: Young ones hairy, gray to reddish- or yellowish-brown, smooth later; pores prominent.

Trunk: Bark tight, greenish-brown or grayish-brown, smooth; pores raised; wood a narrow ring of soft, greenish-white material around the brown pith.

Habitat: Occurs on shaded, north- to northeast-facing wooded limestone bluffs and ledges; found only in Marion County in Missouri.

Range: Georgia and Tennessee, north to Newfoundland, and west to Ohio, Indiana, Illinois, Missouri, South Dakota, Colorado, Oregon, and Alaska.

Wildlife Uses: The fruit is eaten by at least 23 species of birds, and by raccoons and squirrels.

Medicinal Uses: The leaves have been used to treat sores and tumors. The berries, bark and leaves have been used as a laxative.

Remarks: Red-berried elder also is known as *Sambucus pubens* Michx., an older reference. There are several varieties that occur across its range. Once established, it is known as a fast grower. The striking, large purple buds stand out in the winter against a background of snow.

Red-berried elder is more commonly found in northern climates and in the mountains of the Appalachians. In Missouri, it is an ice age relict, a term used to describe plants that migrated south, ahead of glacial advances. As the climate warmed, some populations died because of changing habitat, others migrated north with retreating glaciers, and some remained in pockets of cool, moist sites such as north-facing bluffs.

The name elder is from the Old English (450–1100 A.D.) *elloen*, its origin unknown, perhaps related to *alder*.

Sambucus is the classical Latin name; *racemosa* is for the racemelike (cluster) of flowers and fruits.

Sambucus racemosa ❧ a. Growth form with flower cluster, b. Flower, c. Growth form with fruit cluster

Soapberry

Sapindus drummondii Hook. & Arn.

Soapberry family (Sapindaceae)

Also called western soapberry, chinaberry

Appearance: Medium-sized tree, up to 50 feet tall (in Missouri, commonly 10 to 20 feet tall), with upright branches and a broad, rounded crown.

Flowers: Late May–July, **in large, branched clusters, 5 to 10 inches long, 4 to 6 inches wide**, branching hairy; flowers small, numerous, about 1/4 inch across; petals 5, white; sepals 5, shorter than the petals, yellow-green; stamens 8.

Fruit: September–October, smooth turning wrinkled and leathery with age, berry-like, round to globe-shaped, yellow, fleshy, about 1/2 inch in diameter; seed solitary, black, smooth but minutely pitted with soft, short, white hairs at the base; **fruit eventually turns black and persists into winter**.

Leaves: Alternate, **feather-like arrangement, 5 to 18 inches long; leaflets 7 to 19, arranged alternately on the central stalk**, 1 1/2 to 4 inches long, 1/2 to 3/4 inch wide, lance-shaped, **curved, sides uneven**; margin entire, tip long-pointed, **base with unequal sides**; upper surface pale yellow-green, smooth; lower surface light green, with soft hairs or smooth with hairs along the veins; leaf stalk slender, hairy, 1 1/2 to 2 inches long; leaves turn yellow-gold in autumn.

Twigs: Yellowish-green to gray, finely hairy; pores small.

Trunk: Bark gray-brown, with shallow grooves and narrow ridges with scaly plates, bitter and astringent; wood light brown or yellowish, hard, strong, heavy, close-grained.

Habitat: Occurs at the base or on the ledges of south and west-facing limestone or dolomite bluffs along streams and on limestone and dolomite glades in extreme southwestern Missouri.

Range: Arizona, New Mexico, Texas, and Louisiana; north to Arkansas and southwestern Missouri; and west to Kansas and Oklahoma; also into northern Mexico.

Wildlife Uses: The tree provides cover for birds.

Medicinal Uses: The fruit is used in Mexico as a remedy for renal disorders, rheumatism, and fevers. The fruit contains the substance saponin, which is considered to have a low toxicity level if eaten.

Remarks: Soapberry has been in cultivation since 1800. It is an attractive tree with its feathery yellow-green leaves, broadly rounded crown, and beautiful fall color. Even with these attributes, few nurseries seem to carry it. The wood is used for baskets and frames. The fruit contains saponin and, when mashed in water, produces soapy suds used to wash clothes in some Latin American countries. Some individuals develop dermatitis when handling the fruits.

Soapberry is a species of concern in Missouri. Classified as rare, it was probably never very common, being on the edge of its range, but land clearing has certainly reduced its numbers.

Sapindus is from the Latin *sapo* ("soap") and *Indus* ("Indies"), referring to related species of the West Indies that are used for soap; *drummondii* is in honor of the botanist Thomas Drummond (1807–1835).

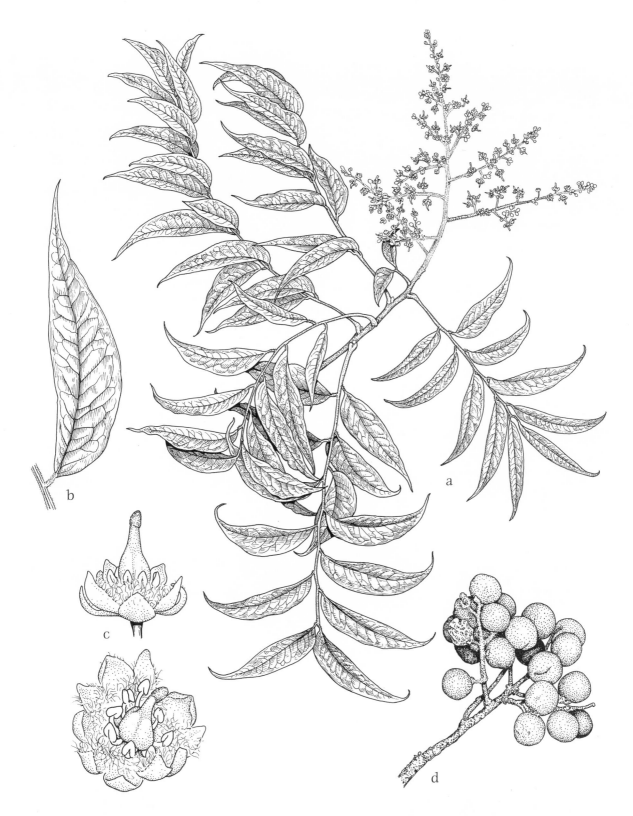

Sapindus drummondii ❧ a. Growth form with flowers, b. Leaflet, c. Flower, d. Twig with fruit

Sassafras

Sassafras albidum (Nutt.) Nees

Laural family (Lauraceae)

Appearance: Short to medium-sized tree, up to 60 feet tall, often forming colonies from root sprouts, with a column-shaped canopy, a flattened crown, and **contorted branches that turn upwards at their ends**.

Flowers: April–May, before the leaves emerge, male and female flowers occurring on separate trees in stalked, branched clusters about 2 inches long, at the tips of twigs; flowers small, about 1/2 inch across, yellow; **petals absent; sepals 6**, spreading; male flowers with 9 stamens; female flowers with 6 sterile stamens.

Fruit: Late August–October, berry-like, widest at the middle, about 1/2 inch long, **dark blue, shiny, attached to a swollen stalk; stalk about 1 1/2 inches long, red**; seed solitary, light brown, granular surface, ridged on two sides; dispersed mainly by birds.

Leaves: Alternate, simple, thin, **aromatic when crushed**, 4 to 6 inches long, 2 to 4 inches wide, broadest at the middle; **margin with 3 shapes (entire, with a 1-sided lobe, or 3-lobed)**, tip pointed or rounded, base tapered; upper surface bright green to blue-green, smooth, somewhat shiny; lower surface paler, smooth, sometimes hairy along the veins; leaf stalk slender, about 1 inch, hairy; leaves turn orange, yellow, red, or scarlet in early autumn.

Twigs: Moderately stout, **curved upward at tips**, yellowish-green becoming greenish-brown with age; **broken twig with spicy odor and taste**.

Trunk: Bark aromatic, reddish-brown to gray with deep grooves and firm, long, flat-topped ridges; wood light brown to dull orange, soft, weak, brittle, close-grained.

Habitat: Occurs on the border of dry woods, glades, prairies, and in bottomland soils in valleys; also along roadsides, railroads, idle fields, pastures, fencerows, and thickets.

Range: East Texas, Oklahoma, Arkansas, and Louisiana; east to Florida, north to Maine, and west to Ontario, Michigan, Illinois, Iowa, and Missouri.

Wildlife Uses: The fruit is known to be eaten by at least 28 species of birds. The leaves are browsed by woodchuck, white-tailed deer, cottontail rabbit, and black bear. The leaves also serve host to a variety of spectacular moths and butterflies.

Medicinal Uses: Root bark tea is a well-known spring blood tonic and "blood purifier;" also a folk remedy for a variety of internal ailments. However, safrole, the oil found in sassafras, has been found to cause liver cancer in laboratory animals. In 1976, the Federal Drug Administration listed it as carcinogenic and officially banned the sale of sassafras tea, roots, and oil.

Remarks: Sassafras has been in cultivation since 1630. Requiring full sun for best growth, it is one of our most striking and aromatic trees. The wood is used for posts, rails, buckets, carving, canoe paddles, cabinets, and interior finish.

Sassafras is derived from the word *salsafras*, a name which was given by early French settlers, with reference to its medicinal properties; *albidum*, which is Latin for "white," refers to the light-colored wood.

Sassafras albidum ❀ a. Growth form, b. Flower clusters, c. Flower, d. Fruit, e. Twig

Bladdernut

Staphylea trifolia L.

Bladdernut family (Staphyleaceae)

Also called American bladdernut

Appearance: A thicket-forming shrub or small tree to 25 feet, the branches near the top.

Flowers: April–May, in **drooping clusters** 2 to 4 inches long from twigs of the previous year; flowers small, white, about 1/4 inch long; petals 5, about 1/4 inch long, tip blunt; stamens 5, extending beyond the petals.

Fruit: August, **persistent until midwinter**, fruits solitary or in drooping clusters of 2 to 5; **capsule bladderlike**, 1 1/4 to 2 1/2 inches long, 3-lobed, inflated, net-veined, green to brown, opening at the tip; seeds 1 to 4, about 1/4 inch long, rounded, somewhat flattened, yellowish- to grayish-brown, hard, shiny.

Leaves: Opposite, **compound with 3 leaflets**, the 3 leaflets 1 1/2 to 4 inches long, 1 1/4 to 2 inches wide, egg-shaped to broadest at the middle, tip pointed, base tapering, margin sharply toothed; upper surface bright green, hairy on the veins; lower surface slightly paler, hairy; end leaflet stalk 1/2 to 1 1/2 inches long, much longer than side leaflet stalks, hairy; main petioles 2 to 4 inches long, hairy.

Twigs: Flexible, smooth, reddish-brown to greenish-brown, often striped, curved, ascending.

Trunk: Bark grayish-brown, smooth on young shrubs and slightly grooved and flaky on older trunks; wood hard, nearly white, with no definite line of sapwood.

Habitat: Occurs in rich wooded valleys, and north- or east-facing wooded slopes—especially of limestone or dolomite, along streams, and in thickets.

Range: Oklahoma and Arkansas; east to Georgia, north to New Hampshire and Quebec; and west to Ontario, Michigan, Wisconsin, Minnesota, east Nebraska, and east Kansas.

Medicinal Uses: An infusion of the powdered bark has been used as a wash for sore faces.

Remarks: Bladdernut sometimes is cultivated for ornament. Its attractive drooping flower clusters, dark green leaves, and interesting pods are worthy of planting in partial shade, especially along a border. It has a habit of suckering from the roots, so allow plenty of room.

The foliage remains green late into autumn, but eventually turns a yellowish-green. The fruit, which becomes inflated and bladderlike at maturity, makes a popping sound when crushed between the fingers. It is reported that the seeds from an Old World species taste like pistachio nuts, and that bladdernut is similar in taste. Another source says that the seeds can be used in place of walnuts in making chocolate chip cookies. Also, a sweet edible oil is obtained from the seed and is used for cooking purposes.

Staphylea is from the Greek word meaning "cluster of grapes," in reference to the drooping clusters of flowers; *trifolia* denotes the 3 leaflets.

Staphylea trifolia ❀ a. Growth form with seed capsules, b. Twig with flower cluster

Saltcedar

Tamarix ramosissima Ledeb.

Tamarisk family (Tamaricaceae)

Also called tamarisk

Appearance: Shrub to small-sized tree, up to 20 feet tall, **often with several twisted trunks and many slender, contorted branches**.

Flowers: May–September, borne in clusters at the tips of twigs of the current season's growth; clusters about 2 inches long, narrow, cylindrical; **flowers very small, 20 to 60 in a cluster**, white or pink; petals 5; stamens 5.

Fruit: July–October, small, dry capsules, broadest near the base, tip gradually tapering, about 1/8 inch long, splitting open at the tip; seeds minute, yellow, tipped by a tuft of white hair.

Leaves: Alternate, **scale-like, sparse, delicate, up to 1/8 inch long**, lance-shaped, broadest at the base, pressed against the stem; margin entire, tip pointed; leaf surface green to grayish-green, smooth.

Twigs: Very slender, less that 1/4 inch in diameter, flexible, smooth, red, becoming grayish with age; **upper twigs break off easily**.

Trunk: Bark of young stems red-brown, smooth, on older trees dark brown, with grooves and ridges that peel off in thin strips; wood whitish, soft, often twisted or knotty, close-grained.

Habitat: Establishes along borders of streams and rivers; also in tailings of mine spoils.

Range: Native to Asia and southeastern Europe. Planted and spreading across the southwestern United States and Mexico; also from Texas, Oklahoma, Arkansas, and Louisiana; east to Florida, north to Massachusetts, and west to Indiana, Missouri, Kansas, Nebraska, the Dakotas, and western United States.

Wildlife Uses: Some species of birds nest in saltcedar. The flowers are a nectar source for bees.

Remarks: Saltcedar was first introduced and escaped from cultivation in the early 1800s. It has been used as an ornamental, for erosion control, and for windbreaks. Its aggressive nature has eliminated a diversity of plants along numerous stream and river corridors throughout the Southwest. Government agencies are working to eliminate saltcedar on public land but the task is monumental. Dense populations of this exotic species on private lands are also a major concern. Difficult to control, saltcedar is fire-adapted and resprouts after burning. Its tap roots allow it to intercept deep water tables and interfere with aquatic systems by monopolizing limited sources of moisture. Mass groves of saltcedar degrade habitat by eliminating plant diversity that is so important for a variety of wildlife. Although not a problem in Missouri yet, saltcedar has the ability to adapt to new conditions and begin spreading throughout stream and river corridors. Management is a long-term commitment using mechanical removal and herbicide.

Saltcedar is so named for its high salt content and its cedar-like foliage. Tamarisk is a derivation of the genus *Tamarix*.

Tamarix is the ancient name, possibly in reference to the Tamaracine people of southern Europe, where the plant grows; *ramosissima* is from *ramosus* ("with many branches") and *issimus* ("to the greatest degree"), which combined means "with many branches."

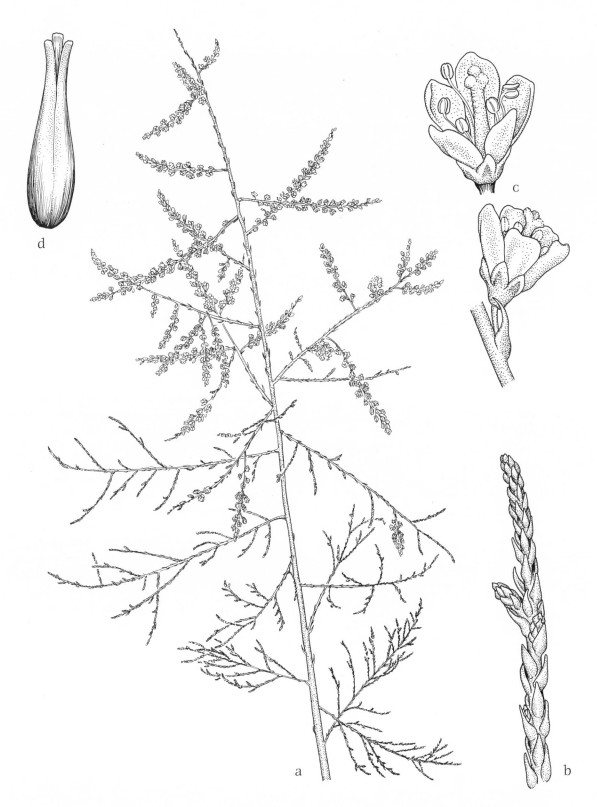

Tamarix ramosissima ✤ a. Growth form with flowers, b. Twig with leaves, c. Flower, d. Fruit

Bald cypress

Taxodium distichum (L.) Rich.

Cypress family (Cupressaceae) which now includes the bald cypress family (Taxodiaceae)

Appearance: Large-sized tree, up to 130 feet tall, **with a swollen base**, pyramid-shaped or open, flat-topped crown and **cone-shaped "knees" emerging from roots of the tree if it is growing in water**.

Flowers: March–April, emerging before or with the leaves, both male and female cones found on the same tree; male cones hanging in many-branched flower clusters 4 to 6 inches long; cones scaly, brown; stamens 6 to 8; female cones solitary, or 2 to 3 together, clustered in the leaf axils, scaly, rounded, brown, composed of several spirally arranged scales, about 1/2 inches long.

Fruit: October–November, **cones** solitary, or 2 to 3 together, round to globe-shaped, about 1 inch in diameter, **green changing to purple**, with resin; scales shield-shaped, woody, thick, brown, opening at maturity and disintegrating; seeds 3-sided with 3 wings, about 1/3 long.

Leaves: Alternate, **needle-like, in 2 rows on opposite sides of the small twigs**; leaves 1/2 to 3/4 inch long, flat, linear; margin entire, tip pointed; surface light green, shiny; leaves turn golden to reddish-brown in autumn and are shed with the small twigs in late November. Note: An uncommon form of bald cypress has the leaves pressed against the small twigs, rather than spreading from the twigs, as in the common form.

Twigs: Light green on new growth, turning reddish-brown with age, smooth flexible; **side twigs green, falling with leaves still attached**.

Trunk: Cinnamon-brown to gray, thick, with long, narrow grooves and **flat, long ridges that peel off in fibrous, narrow strips**; trunk swollen at the base; wood reddish-brown, light, soft, very durable, decay-resistant, close-grained.

Habitat: Occurs in swamps, sloughs, and wet bottomland forests in the lowlands of south-eastern Missouri's Bootheel. In other parts of the state, some trees have naturalized where planted.

Range: Texas, Oklahoma, Arkansas, and Louisiana; east to Florida, and north along the coastal plain to Massachusetts; also the middle Mississippi and lower Ohio River floodplains in Missouri, Illinois, Indiana, Kentucky, and Tennessee.

Wildlife Uses: The seeds are eaten by a number of bird species including wood ducks.

Remarks: Bald cypress was planted as an ornamental in Europe beginning in 1640. It is a magnificent tree and often planted around pond margins and even in yards and on campuses. Cypress wood has been used for barrels, caskets, boats, shingles, railroad ties, fence posts, and bridge beams. The largest remaining stand of old-growth bald cypress trees in the state can be seen along the edge of Allred Lake Natural Area, in Butler County. Here, trees range from 500 to 1,000 years old.

Cypress is from the Greek *kyparissos*; the name was first recorded in 1175 from an unknown Mediterranean language. "Bald" refers to the loss of leaves in autumn; other conifers are evergreen.

Taxodium is from the Greek and means "yew-like," in reference to the leaves; *distichum* means "two-ranked," and also refers to the leaves.

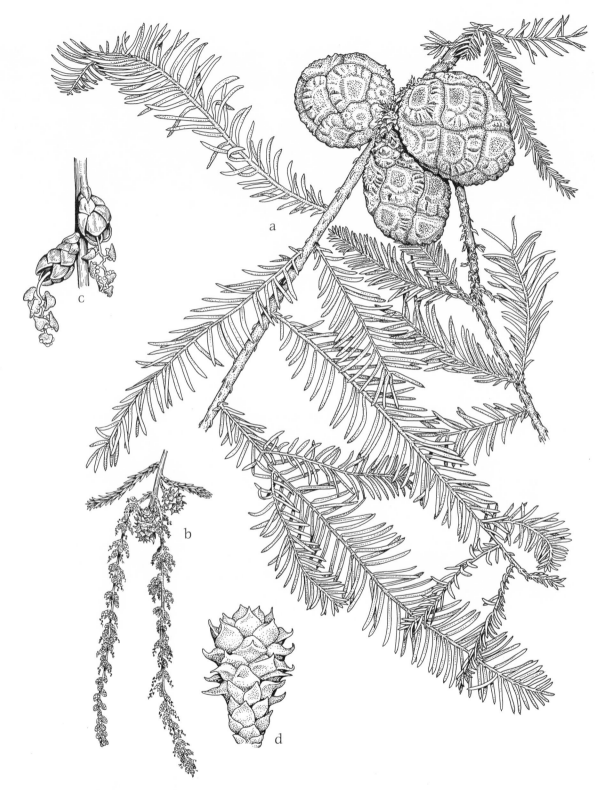

Taxodium distichum ❀ a. Growth form with fruit cones, b. Male and female flower cones,
c. Male flower cones, d. Female flower cone

American basswood

Tilia americana L.

Linden family (Tiliaceae)

Also called basswood, linden, American linden

Appearance: Medium-sized tree, up to 60 feet tall, with small, horizontal, often drooping, branches forming a broad, round-topped head.

Flowers: Late May–July, from 6 to 15 flowers borne on a drooping, stalk; stalk slender, *smooth*, 1 1/2 to 4 inches long, attached to a **strap-shaped, reduced leaf**, 2 to 5 inches long, 3/4 to 1 1/2 inches wide, **smooth**, strongly veined, narrow; flowers pale yellow to whitish, fragrant, about 1/2 inch in diameter; petals 5; sepals 5, small, narrow; stamens numerous.

Fruit: August–October, dry, persistent, nearly round, about 1/4 inch long, covered with dense brown hairs; seeds 1 to 2, dark brown, about 1/8 inch long.

Leaves: Alternate, simple, 5 to 6 inches long, 3 to 5 inches wide, broadest near the base; margin coarsely toothed, gland-tipped; tip pointed, base unequal, rounded; upper surface dark green, smooth, shiny; **lower surface paler, smooth with tufts of hair in the vein axils**; leaf stalk 1 1/2 to 2 inches long, smooth; leaves turn yellow in autumn.

Twigs: Slender, smooth, green to brown turning gray with age; pores numerous; **winter buds dark red, egg-shaped, about 1/4 inch long**.

Trunk: Bark light brown to gray, with deep furrows and narrow, flat-topped, long ridges, which shed small, thin scales; wood light brown to reddish-brown, soft, light, straight-grained. Often with sprouts around the base of older trees.

Habitat: Occurs in moist woods on lower slopes, at the base of bluffs, and along streams.

Range: Texas, Oklahoma, Arkansas, and Louisiana; east to Florida, north to Maine and New Brunswick; and west to Ontario, Minnesota, the Dakotas, Nebraska, and Kansas.

Wildlife Uses: The fruit is eaten by a number of species of birds and rodents. Cottontail rabbits and white-tailed deer browse the leaves and foliage.

Remarks: American basswood is also known as *Tilia americana* var. *americana*. American basswood has been cultivated as an ornamental since 1730. In Eastern states, with better soils and increased rainfall, basswood can attain a height of 130 feet. It is a fast-growing, relatively long-lived tree. American basswood is commonly planted in lawns, parks, and along city streets in Eastern towns. The tree has a tendency to sprout from its roots often forming clumps in the wild. Although widely distributed in the state, large populations are rarely encountered. The flower nectar is known for making high quality bee honey, and the wood is used for carving, musical instruments, woodenware, toys, pulp, furniture, and boxes.

Native Americans utilized the fibrous inner bark for making strong, tangle-free rope; also thongs, baskets, and mats.

The "bass" in basswood is from the Latin *bassus* ("low"), referring to the often-drooping limbs. Linden is a name given to it by horticulturists for its similarity to the European lindens.

Tilia means "wing," referring to the strap-shaped, reduced leaf; *americana*, refers to its distribution.

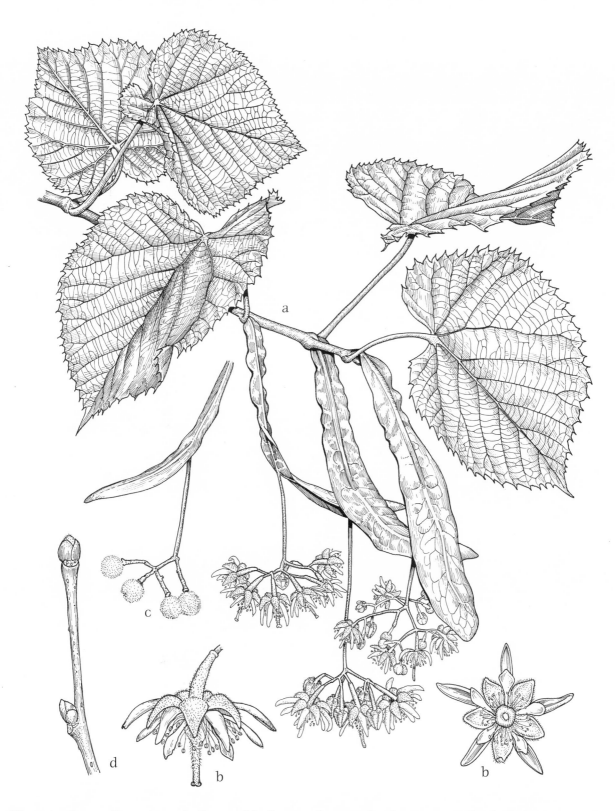

Tilia americana ❧ a. Growth form with flower clusters, b. Flower, c. Fruit, d. Twig

White basswood

Tilia heterophylla Vent.

Linden family (Tiliaceae)

Also called white linden, silver-leaved linden, bee-tree linden

Appearance: Medium-sized tree, up to 60 feet tall, with a long, clear trunk ending in a full spreading, rounded crown.

Flowers: May–July, from 6 to 15 flowers borne on a drooping stalk; **stalk slender, hairy**, 2 to 4 inches long, attached to a **strap-shaped, reduced leaf**, 4 to 6 inches long, 1 to 1 1/2 inches wide, **hairy** above, narrow; flowers pale yellow to whitish, fragrant, about 1/3 inches wide; petals 5, hairy; sepals 5 small, hairy, narrow; stamens numerous.

Fruit: August–October, dry, persistent, nearly round, about 1/4 to 1/3 inch long, covered with dense, brown hairs; seeds 1 to 2, reddish-brown, about 1/8 inches long.

Leaves: Alternate, simple, 3 to 5 inches long, 2 1/2 to 4 inches wide, broadest near the base; margin toothed, gland-tipped; tip pointed, base unequal, rounded; upper surface dark green, smooth; **lower surface covered with white or brown matted, woolly hairs or with brown hair tufts in the vein axils**; leaf stalk 1 1/2 to 13/4 long, smooth or somewhat hairy; leaves turning yellow in autumn.

Twigs: Slender, yellowish- to reddish-brown, smooth; pores numerous; **winter buds dark red, egg-shaped, about 1/4 inches long**.

Trunk: Bark brown to gray, with deep grooves and flat-topped, long ridges, which shed small, thin scales; wood pale brown to reddish-brown, light, soft, straight-grained.

Habitat: Occurs mainly along rocky woods and bluffs bordering streams.

Range: Northern Arkansas, east to Mississippi, Alabama, Georgia, and Florida; north to New York, and west to Ohio, Indiana, Illinois, and Missouri.

Wildlife Uses: The fruit is eaten by a number of species of birds and rodents. Cottontail rabbits and white-tailed deer browse the leaves and foliage.

Remarks: White basswood is also known as *Tilia americana* var. *heterophylla*. White basswood has been in cultivation since 1800. Planted in Europe as an ornamental, it was first identified as a separate species in the gardens of the French emperor Napoleon. A fast-growing, relatively long-lived tree, white basswood reaches its largest growth (around 100 feet) in the Appalachian Mountains, where it is often dominant on moist, well-drained soils in coves or along mountain streams. Similar to basswood in landscape qualities, it is planted in urban areas in the eastern states and also has a tendency to root sprout. The flower nectar is known for making high quality bee honey and the soft, light wood is used for cabinetwork, woodenware, furniture, plywood, interior trim, caskets, crates, and pulp.

The "bass" in basswood is from the Latin *bassus* ("low"), referring to the often-drooping limbs. Linden is a name given to it by horticulturists for its similarity to the European lindens. White refers to the color of the lower surface of the leaf.

Tilia means "wing," referring to the strap-shaped, reduced leaf; *heterophylla* means "diversely-leaved," which refers to the differences between the upper and lower leaf surfaces.

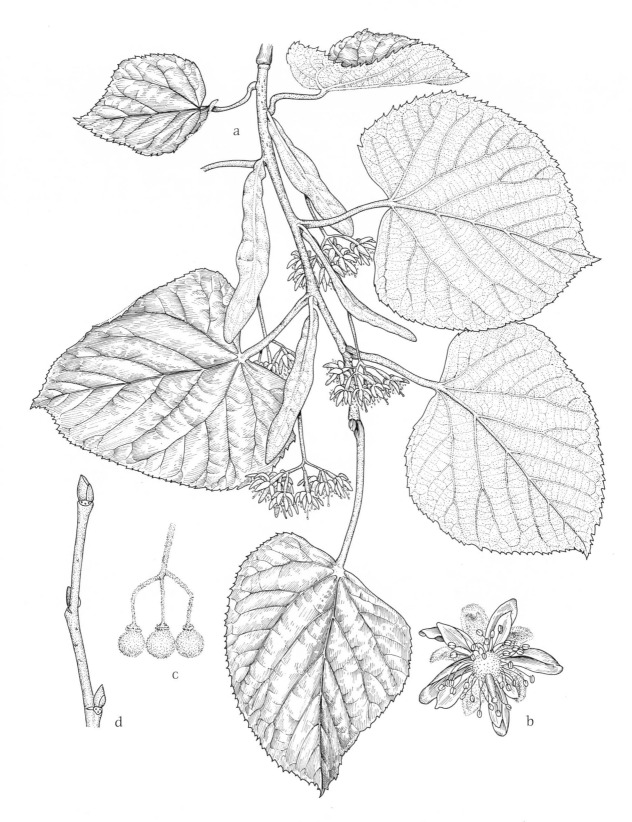

Tilia heterophylla ❀ a. Growth form with flower clusters, b. Flower, c. Fruit, d. Twig

Winged elm

Ulmus alata Michaux

Elm family (Ulmaceae)

Appearance: Small to medium-sized tree, up to 60 feet tall, with a short trunk and a spreading, open, round-topped crown.

Flowers: February–March, before the leaves in spring, in drooping clusters; flowers small, greenish, hairy, 1/8 inch long, petals absent; stamens 5.

Fruit: March–April, in drooping clusters on long stalks; **fruit about 1/4 inch across**, seed surrounded by a thin wing; wing greenish or reddish, broadest in the middle, notched at the tip, with a fringe of silvery hairs along the margin; seed solitary, egg-shaped, brown, surface wrinkled.

Leaves: Alternate, simple, stiff to almost leathery, 1 1/2 to 3 inches long, 3/8 to 1 1/4 inches wide, narrow, broadest at the base or towards the middle, often slightly curved; margin with smaller teeth along the lower side of the larger teeth; tip pointed, base uneven; upper surface dark green, smooth to somewhat rough; lower surface paler, smooth to hairy, especially along the veins; **leaf stalk 1/8 inch long, stout, hairy**; leaves turn a dull yellow in autumn.

Twigs: Slender, reddish-brown, hairy at first becoming smooth with age, **often with thin, corky wings on young branches, up to 1/2 inch wide on each side of the twig; buds smooth (without hairs)**.

Trunk: Bark reddish-brown to gray, grooves irregular and shallow, ridges flat with flattened scales; wood brown, heavy, hard, difficult to split, close-grained.

Habitat: Occurs in dry rocky uplands and borders of glades; also in low ground of valleys, ravine bottoms, and along streams.

Range: Texas, Oklahoma, Arkansas, and Louisiana; east to Florida, north to Virginia, and west to Ohio, Indiana, Missouri, and the very southeastern corner of Kansas.

Wildlife Uses: The seeds are eaten by some birds, cottontail rabbit, opossum, squirrels, and other rodents. The leaves and twigs are eaten by white-tailed deer in the spring.

Remarks: Winged elm is frequently used as a street and shade tree in the South. It grows rapidly when young and is relatively pest free, although there are reports that it may be susceptible to Dutch elm disease. On dry, rocky sites, the tree is stunted and gnarly but it attains its greatest size on rich, moist, loamy soils.

The wood is used for furniture, flooring, boxes, and crates. Winged elm's resistance to splitting makes it a choice wood for the manufacture of high quality hockey sticks. The fibrous inner bark has been used for baling twine to fasten together the covers of cotton bales.

Elm is the Old English (450 to 1100) name.

Ulmus is the ancient Latin name; *alata* is Latin for "winged," and refers to the corky wings on the twigs.

Ulmus alata ❊ a. Growth form, b. Twig with corky wings, c. Flower clusters, d. Flower, e. Fruit, f. Twig

American elm

Ulmus americana L.

Elm family (Ulmaceae)

Also called white elm

Appearance: Medium to large-sized tree, up to 70 feet tall, **with spreading branches to form a broad spreading, fan-shaped crown**.

Flowers: February–April, before the leaves in spring, in drooping clusters, **with flower stalks originating from the same point**; flowers small, red to green, 1/8 inch long, hairy, petals absent; stamens 5 to 9.

Fruit: March–May, in drooping clusters **on long stalks, which originate from the same point**; fruit about 1/2 inch long, seed surrounded by a thin wing; wing red to green, broadest in the middle, notched at the tip, with a fringe of silvery hairs along the margin; seed solitary, flat, egg-shaped, brown, surface wrinkled.

Leaves: Alternate, simple, 4 to 6 inches long, 2 to 3 inches wide, often broadest near or above the middle; margin with smaller teeth along the lower side of the larger teeth; tip pointed, base uneven; **upper surface dark green, shiny, mostly smooth** to somewhat rough; lower surface paler, smooth to softly hairy; leaf stalk stout, smooth to slightly hairy, 1/4 inch long; leaves turn bright yellow in autumn.

Twigs: Slender, reddish-brown turning ash gray with age, hairy at first, smooth later.

Trunk: Bark light to dark gray, cross-section with alternating brown and white layers, grooves deep, ridges flattened with thin, closely pressed scales; wood light to dark brown, tough, heavy, hard, strong, difficult to split, close-grained.

Habitat: Occurs in low moist ground in valleys and along streams.

Range: Texas, Oklahoma, Arkansas, and Louisiana; east to Florida, north to Newfoundland, west to Ontario, North Dakota, Montana, and Saskatchewan; and south to Nebraska and Kansas.

Wildlife Uses: The seeds are eaten by some birds, cottontail rabbit, opossum, squirrels, and other rodents. White-tailed deer eat the leaves and twigs in the spring.

Remarks: American elm has been in cultivation since 1752. Its gently spreading limbs and vase-shaped crown made American elm a popular ornamental planting along city streets and it was known as the all-American shade tree. Unfortunately, the Asian fungus, *Ophiostoma ulmi*, which was imported on logs shipped from Europe around 1930, quickly spread and began killing hundreds of thousands of these magnificent trees. Dutch elm disease is spread by North American and European elm bark beetles that fly from tree to tree, feeding on the twigs and spreading the disease. The fungus enters the tree's sapwood, eventually blocking the water flow and causing the branches to wilt and die. Hot temperatures appear to control the spread of the disease so the problem is not as serious in the Deep South as it is in the North. Research is ongoing to find completely disease resistant trees for future sustainable populations of the American elm. In the meantime, individual trees can be treated with fungicide injections every three years to kill or block the fungus at a fairly reasonable price.

Ulmus is the ancient Latin name; *americana* refers to its native range.

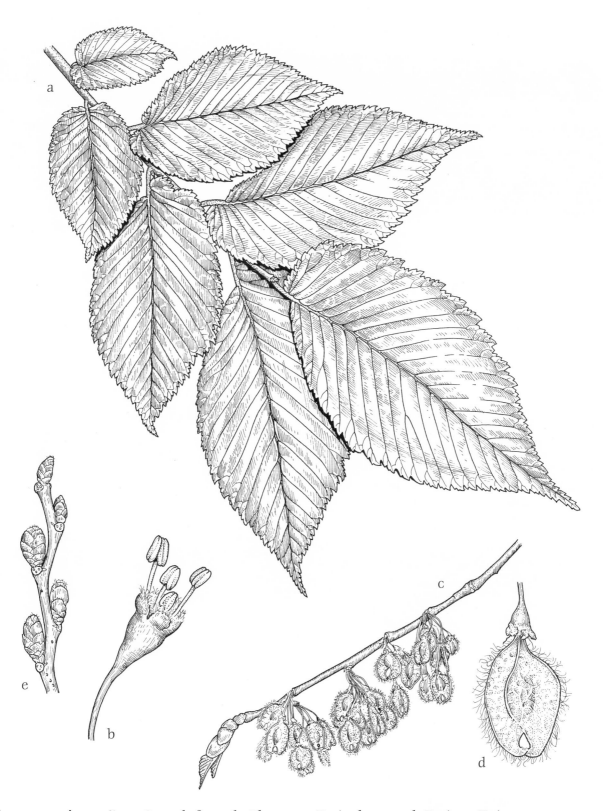

Ulmus americana ❧ a. Growth form, b. Flower, c. Fruit clusters, d. Fruit, e. Twig

Cedar elm

Ulmus crassifolia Nutt.

Elm family (Ulmaceae)

Appearance: Medium to large-sized tree, up to 80 feet tall, **with the base of the trunk swollen and fluted**, and a crown of long, some-what drooping branches forming a narrow or rounded head.

Flowers: August–September, in small, 3 to 5 flowered clusters; flowers small, green to red, 1/8 inch long, hairy, petals absent; stamens 5 to 6.

Fruit: October–November, about 1/4 to 1/2 inch long, seed surrounded by a thin wing; wing green, broadest at the middle, notched at the tip, with a fringe of white hairs along the margin; seed solitary, flattened.

Leaves: Alternate, simple, stiff, leathery, 1 to 2 inches long, 3/4 to 1 inch wide, broadest at the base or near the middle; margin with smaller teeth along the lower side of the larger teeth; tip round or pointed, base uneven; upper surface dark green, very rough, shiny; lower surface hairy; leaf stalk short, 1/4 to 1/2 inches long, hairy; leaves turn bright yellow in autumn with many remaining on the tree into winter.

Twigs: Slender, reddish-brown, hairy, often with brown, **thin corky wings on each side of the twig**.

Trunk: Bark light gray to brownish-gray, with deep grooves separating the broad, flat ridges; **base of the trunk often swollen and fluted**; wood is brown, heavy, hard, compact, difficult to split, close-grained.

Habitat: Occurs in low, bottomland woods and borders of swamps in the southeast Missouri Bootheel.

Range: Texas, Oklahoma, Arkansas, Louisiana, and western Mississippi; north to southeastern Missouri; also adjacent northeastern Mexico.

Wildlife Uses: The seeds are eaten by some birds, cottontail rabbit, opossum, squirrels, and other rodents. White-tailed deer eat the leaves and twigs in the spring.

Remarks: Cedar elm is most abundant in Texas where it grows on moist, limestone soils along watercourses, but it is also commonly found on dry limestone hills of the Edwards Plateau. The tree is often planted as an ornamental shade tree. In Missouri, it was discovered in the 1980s, grow-ing in Dunklin County, just north of the bound-ary with Arkansas. Since then, the tree has been found at Hornersville Swamp and Warbler Woods Conservation Areas, both in Dunklin County, and Big Cane Conservation Area and Allred Lake Natural Area, both in Butler County. All locations are in wet bottomland forests with populations ranging from one to eight trees. Cedar elm is a species of conservation concern and classified as endangered in the state. Although cedar elm was probably never in great numbers, deforestation and ditching of most of the Bootheel has con-tributed to the tree's decline.

In the South, the wood is used to make boxes, crates, baskets, and barrels.

Elm is the Old English (450 to 1100) name. The name "cedar" is used to describe the tree's similar-ity to the cone-shaped, thin-branched red cedar.

Ulmus is the ancient Latin name; *crassifolia* combines the Latin *crass* ("thick") and *folia* ("leaf"), which refers to cedar elm's thick leaves.

Ulmus crassifolia ❀ a. Growth form, b. Flowers, c. Fruit, d. Twig

Siberian elm

Ulmus pumila L.

Elm family (Ulmaceae)

Also called dwarf elm

Appearance: Medium-sized tree, up to 60 feet tall, with somewhat drooping branches and a rounded canopy.

Flowers: March–April, **stalk short or absent**, appearing with or before the leaves emerge, in tight clusters along the twig, **not drooping**; flowers greenish; petals absent; stamens 4 to 5.

Fruit: April–May, in tight clusters along the twig; fruit 1/4 to 1/2 inches long, seed surrounded by a thin wing; wing light brown, round, notched at the tip, **smooth (without hairs)**; seed solitary, about 1/8 inch across, thin, surface wrinkled.

Leaves: Alternate, simple, 1 to 2 inches long, 1/2 to 1 inch wide, broadest near the middle; **margin evenly, simply toothed (without any smaller teeth on each tooth)**, tip pointed, **base with sides nearly equal**; upper surface dark green, shiny, smooth, veins indented; lower surface paler, smooth with some hairs in the vein axils; leaf stalk short, up to 1/2 inch long; leaves turn yellow in autumn.

Twigs: Very slender, flexible, greenish-brown and hairy when young, turning brown to gray and smooth with age, drooping.

Trunk: Bark dark gray, becoming deeply grooved, with long, flat ridges that form a broad interlacing network; wood red-brown, hard, heavy, tough, difficult to split.

Habitat: Occasionally planted and escaped from cultivation.

Range: Native to East Asia, namely China, East Siberia, and Turkestan; escaped throughout the central United States.

Wildlife Uses: Of little value to wildlife.

Remarks: Siberian elm was introduced to the United States as an ornamental around 1860. Although a fast growing tree, the wood is fairly brittle and subject to storm damage, creating considerable branch and twig litter on lawns. Also, large limbs are subject to splitting from the crotches of older trees. It is often heavily attacked by the elm leaf beetle, *Pyrrhalta luteola*, which gives the tree a continually unattractive appearance throughout most of the season.

In its homeland, the inner bark of Siberian elm is dried and made into noodles. The dried inner bark can also be ground into a powder and then used as a thickener in soups or added to cereal flours when making bread. The seeds are eaten raw or cooked. Used when immature, they can be made into a sauce and a wine.

Siberian elm is often incorrectly called Chinese elm, *Ulmus parvifolia*, a species that flowers in autumn. To date, Chinese elm has not been known to escape from cultivation in Missouri.

Elm is the Old English (450 to 1100) name. Siberia denotes its origin.

Ulmus is the ancient Latin name; *pumila* is Latin for "dwarf," referring to the small leaves.

Ulmus pumila ❀ a. Growth form, b. Twig with flowers, c. Flower, d. Twig with fruit clusters,
e. Fruit, f. Leaf scar and bud

Slippery elm

Ulmus rubra Muhlenb.

Elm family (Ulmaceae)

Also called red elm

Appearance: Medium-sized tree, up to 60 feet tall, with a long trunk, dividing into large branches that form a spreading, open, flat-topped crown.

Flowers: February–April, before the leaves emerge, in dense clusters on short stalks; flower about 1/4 inch long, green, hairy, petals absent; stamens 5 to 9.

Fruit: April–June, in clusters on short stalks; fruit 1/4 to 3/4 inch long, seed surrounded by a thin wing; wing reddish-brown, broadest in the middle, notched at the top, smooth; seed solitary, flattened, hairy, brown, broadest in the middle.

Leaves: Alternate, simple, 4 to 8 inches long, 2 to 3 inches wide, broadest at or near the middle; margin with smaller teeth along the lower side of the larger teeth; **tip abruptly tapering into a long, narrow point**, base uneven; **upper surface dark green, very rough, sandpapery; with stiff, erect hairs; lower surface paler with soft hairs**; leaf stalk stout, hairy, 1/4 to 1/2 inches long; leaves turn dull yellow in autumn.

Twigs: Stout, gray, densely hairy when young, smooth with age; inner surface slippery when chewed; buds dark purplish- to reddish-brown, hairy.

Trunk: Bark reddish-brown to gray, grooves shallow, ridges long, flattened, inner bark slippery when chewed; wood reddish-brown, strong, tough, hard, heavy, compact, durable, easy to split, close-grained.

Habitat: Occurs in dry upland or rocky woods and along streams.

Range: Texas, Oklahoma, Missouri, Arkansas, and Louisiana; east to Florida, north to Maine and Quebec, west to Ontario, Minnesota, the Dakotas, Nebraska, and Kansas.

Wildlife Uses: The seeds are eaten by some birds, cottontail rabbit, opossum, squirrels, and other rodents. White-tailed deer eat the leaves and twigs in the spring.

Medicinal Uses: Native Americans used various parts of the tree for a wide range of medicines. Inner bark tea was traditionally used by settlers for sore throats, coughs, stomach ulcers, indigestion, and upset stomachs. Externally, the tea was applied to fresh wounds, burns, and scalds. The inner bark is still used in some throat lozenges.

Remarks: Slippery elm has been in cultivation since 1830. Although the shape is not as graceful as American elm, it is still attractive, moderately fast growing, relatively long-lived (150 to 200 years), and provides excellent, heavy shade. Like American elm, it is susceptible to Dutch elm disease and elm phloem necrosis, another destructive disease that affects the nutrient flow through the tissues.

Native Americans in northern states and into Canada used its bark for canoe shells when paper birch, *Betula papyrifera*, was not available.

The name "slippery" refers to the inner bark, which is very mucilaginous when chewed.

Ulmus is the ancient Latin name; *rubra* is Latin for "red," which refers to the color of the wood.

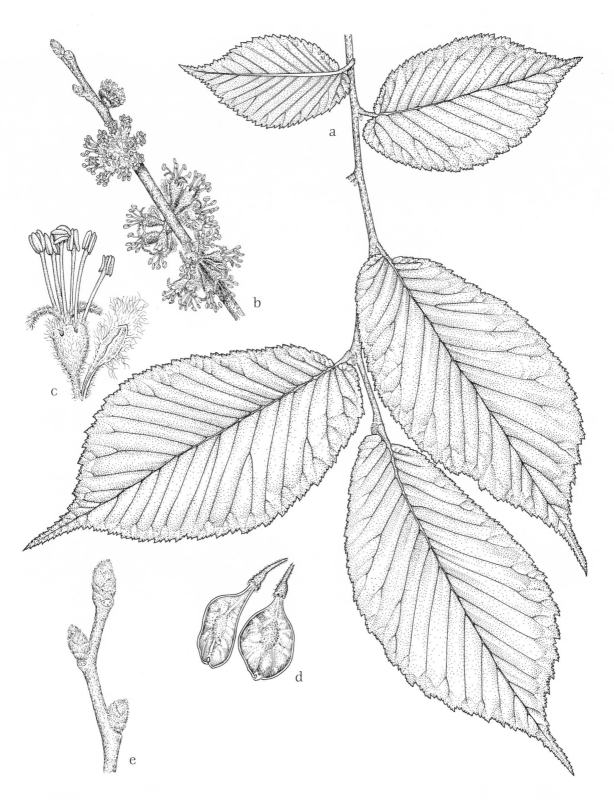

Ulmus rubra ✼ a. Growth form, b. Twig with flower clusters, c. Flower, d. Fruit, e. Twig

Rock elm

Ulmus thomasii Sarg.

Elm family (Ulmaceae)

Also called cork elm

Appearance: Medium to large-sized tree, up to 90 feet tall, with a tall trunk, a short, narrow crown, and drooping branches.

Flowers: March–April, appearing before the leaves emerge, in drooping clusters; flowers small, greenish, about 1/8 inch long, petals absent; stamens 5 to 8.

Fruit: April–May, in clusters; **fruit 1/2 inch long, 3/8 to 5/8 inch across**; seed surrounded by a thin wing; wing green, flattened, broadest near the middle, covered with silver-white hairs, deeply divided at the tip; seed solitary, flat, yellowish, widest near the base, about 1/4 inch long, surface wrinkled; seed easily separating from the wing.

Leaves: Alternate, simple, 3 to 6 inches long, 1 1/4 to 3 1/2 inches wide, broadest near or above the middle; margin with smaller teeth along the lower side of the larger teeth; tip abruptly pointed, base somewhat uneven; upper surface dark green, shiny, smooth; lower surface paler, hairy; leaf stalk smooth, 1/8 to 3/8 inch long; leaves turn bright yellow in autumn.

Twigs: Slender, gray to gray-brown, smooth or slightly hairy, usually with brown **corky wings on branches 2 to 5 years old, up to 1/2 inch long and irregularly interrupted along the twig; buds hairy.**

Trunk: Bark gray to gray-brown, grooves shallow, ridges wide, separating into flat scales; wood light reddish-brown, heavy, hard, strong, tough, difficult to split, close-grained.

Habitat: Occurs on lower slopes of rocky woods, and floodplain forests in valleys and along streams.

Range: Northwestern Arkansas; east to Tennessee, north to New York, Vermont and Quebec; and west to Minnesota, and south to Iowa, southeastern South Dakota, eastern Kansas, and Missouri.

Wildlife Uses: The seeds are eaten by some birds, cottontail rabbit, opossum, squirrels, and other rodents. White-tailed deer eat the leaves and twigs in the spring.

Remarks: Rock elm has been in cultivation since 1875. Like most other elms, it is susceptible to Dutch elm disease and elm phloem necrosis. It is a moderately fast growing and long-lived tree.

With its interlaced fibers, rock elm is difficult to shatter, which made it favorable for use in the days of wooden battleships and sailing vessels. Considered as tough as hickory, it was favored by lumberman in northern states and into Canada for ax handles. More recently, it is used in the manufacture of furniture, containers, crates, veneer, and for general construction.

In Missouri, rock elm is a species of conservation concern and is classified as rare.

Unlike American elm and slippery elm, rock elm can be found on somewhat drier, rocky slopes, hence the name. The other name, cork elm, is for its corky wings occurring on the twigs and small branches.

Ulmus is the ancient Latin name; *thomasii* honors its discoverer, David Thomas (1776–1859), an American civil engineer and horticulturist.

Ulmus thomasii ✿ a. Growth form with fruit, b. Flower cluster, c. Fruit, d. Twig

Farkleberry

Vaccinium arboreum Marshall

Heath family (Ericaceae)

Also called highbush blueberry, sparkleberry

Appearance: Stiff branched shrub or small crooked tree attaining a height of 20 feet.

Flowers: May–June, in loose clusters in the axils of leaves; flowers hanging, about 1/2 inch long, white or pinkish, bell-shaped, 5-lobed, curled at the tip; stamens 10, not extending beyond the flower.

Fruit: July–October, about 3/8 inch across, globe-shaped, black, shiny, sweet, mealy, dry, persistent; seeds many, of various shapes, flattened sides, golden-brown, glossy, deeply pitted.

Leaves: Alternate, simple, **sometimes evergreen**, 1 to 3 inches long, about 1 inch wide, oval to broadest above the middle, **tip mostly rounded, or with a short abrupt point**, base wedge-shaped, margin entire or slightly toothed; **leathery, glossy above**; duller green and slightly hairy below; leaf stalk almost absent, hairy.

Twigs: Slender, light brown to dark or reddish-brown, spreading apart, smooth or hairy.

Trunk: Bark dark brown or grayish-brown, with fine grooves exposing the reddish inner bark; younger branches reddish, with brown outer bark peeling off in flat, thin plates; wood hard, fine-grained, light reddish-brown.

Habitat: Occurs in acid soils overlying sandstone, chert or igneous bedrock, rocky open woods on dry slopes and ridges, along bluffs and glades, occasionally in low woods along creeks and near swamps.

Range: East Texas, Oklahoma, Arkansas, and Louisiana; east to Florida, north to Virginia, and west to Missouri.

Wildlife Uses: The edible fruit is eaten by several bird species.

Medicinal Uses: The leaves and the bark of the root have been used in a tea to treat sore throat and diarrhea. The fruit has been used to make a drink for treating chronic dysentery.

Remarks: The dark green foliage, which is partially evergreen, together with the white flowers, give this shrub a very ornamental appearance. It does well in full sun, but, like the azalea, needs acid soil.

Some of the plants are tall, with rounded crowns, and others are somewhat flat-topped and have crooked, zigzag branches. Cut or burned stems will produce uncharacteristic straight shoots the first year with thinner, less glossy leaves. It flowers abundantly, but is sparsely fruited; the fruits ripen throughout a long period. Fruits are edible, but their dryish, mealy texture makes them less palatable than deerberry or lowbush blueberry. The plant usually is found in loose thickets.

The origin and meaning of the name farkleberry is unknown.

Vaccinium is the classical Latin name for an Old World species; *arboreum* refers to the treelike habit.

Vaccinium arboreum ❧ a. Growth form with fruit and lichens, b. Twig with flowers, c. Stem with bark and lichens

Black haw

Viburnum prunifolium L.

Honeysuckle family (Caprifoliaceae)

Appearance: A shrub or small tree to 18 feet, with stiff spreading branches forming an irregular crown near the top.

Flowers: April–May, in round-topped clusters 2 to 4 inches wide; flowers numerous, white, about 1/4 inch wide; petals 5, spreading; stamens 5, extending beyond the petals.

Fruit: September–October, stalks red, bluish-black with a white coating, about 1/2 inch long, globe-shaped to half as broad as long, flesh thin and dry but edible, sweet; seed solitary, encased in a hard covering that is grooved on one side, oval, flat, dark brown.

Leaves: Opposite, simple, blades 1 1/2 to 3 inches long, 1 to 1 3/4 inches wide, thin, oval to egg-shaped or half as broad as long, tip pointed to blunt or rounded, base blunt to rounded, margin finely toothed, **pointing inward or upward; upper surface dull green, not shiny,** smooth; lower surface paler, smooth; leaf stalk green to red, slender, 1/4 to 3/4 inches long, **not winged**, broadly grooved.

Twigs: Slender, rigid, green to reddish or brown, some with short lateral spurs (shortened or compressed twig).

Trunk: Bark dark gray to brown, appears checkered with shallow grooves and flat squarish ridges; wood reddish-brown, hard, heavy, with a wide white sapwood.

Habitat: Occurs in low woods along streams, at the base and edge of bluffs, dry upper slopes of ravines and thickets. Throughout Missouri and probably in every county.

Range: Texas, Oklahoma, Arkansas, and Louisiana; east to Florida, north to Connecticut, and west to New York, Ohio, Michigan, Illinois, Iowa, and east Kansas.

Wildlife Uses: Viburnums form a minor, but important, segment of the diet of many birds and mammals. The fruits are eaten by many species of birds including cardinal, cedar waxwing, robin, ruffed grouse and wild turkey, and mammals such as white-tailed deer, cottontail rabbit, chipmunk, squirrel, skunk and mice. The twigs, bark and leaves are eaten by white-tailed deer and beaver.

Medicinal Uses: The bark of viburnums has been used to treat uterine infections and malaria. The bark also is used as an astringent, nerve tonic and antispasmodic. Native Americans made a tea from the bark to increase urine flow.

Remarks: The plant has been in cultivation as an ornamental since 1727. The fall colors are deep lavender or maroon-purple to finally deep rose-red.

Viburnum is the classical Latin name of the wayfaring-tree, *Viburnum lantana* L., of Eurasia, which is often cultivated; *prunifolium* means "plum-leaved" which refers to its leaves resembling those of plum.

Viburnum prunifolium ❀ a. Growth form with flower cluster, b. Flower, c. Fruit cluster

Southern black haw

Viburnum rufidulum Raf.

Honeysuckle family (Caprifoliaceae)

Also called rusty nannyberry, rusty black haw, wild raisin

Appearance: An irregularly branched shrub to 18 feet.

Flowers: April–May, in flat clusters 2 to 6 inches across; flowers numerous, white, about 1/4 inch in diameter; petals 5, spreading, tips rounded; stamens 5, extending beyond the petals.

Fruit: September, in drooping clusters, stalks red, fruit about 3/8 inch long, bluish-black, smooth, oval, the skin smooth and tough, the flesh mealy, sweet and edible; seeds solitary, oval, flat, dark brown.

Leaves: Opposite, simple, blades 1 1/2 to 4 inches long, 1 to 2 1/2 inches wide, broadest at or above the middle tip rounded to pointed, base heart-shaped or rounded, margin finely toothed; upper surface dark green, leathery, **glossy**, smooth; **lower surface paler with scattered rust colored hairs especially on the veins**; leaf stalk about 1/4 inch long, with or without a wing, smooth, broadly grooved above and often with scattered rust-colored hairs.

Twigs: Fairly rigid, gray-brown, smooth, **lightly to densely matted with rust-colored hairs at first**, becoming nearly smooth later.

Trunk: Bark rather rough, ridges narrow and rounded, grooves narrow, breaking into dark reddish-brown or black squarrish plates; wood hard, heavy, brownish, with a wide white sapwood.

Habitat: Occurs in rocky or dry woods, rich moist valleys and alluvial ground along streams, rocky glades and thickets.

Range: Texas, Oklahoma, Arkansas, and Louisiana; east to Florida, north to Virginia, and west to Ohio, Indiana, Illinois, Missouri, and southeast Kansas.

Wildlife Uses: Viburnums form a minor, but important, segment of the diet of many birds and mammals. The fruits are eaten by many species of birds including cardinal, cedar waxwing, robin, ruffed grouse and wild turkey, and mammals such as white-tailed deer, cottontail rabbit, chipmunk, squirrel, skunk and mice. White-tailed deer and beaver eat the twigs, bark and leaves.

Medicinal Uses: The bark of viburnums has been used to treat uterine infections and malaria. Native Americans made a tea from the bark to increase urine flow.

Remarks: The shrub is worthy of cultivation because of the dark green shiny leaves, clusters of white flowers, bluish-black fruit and autumn colors. The foliage turns a deep rose-purple to rose-red or bright red.

Viburnum is the classical Latin name of the wayfaring-tree, *Viburnum lantana* L., of Eurasia, which is often cultivated; *rufidulum* refers to the rusty-red hairs on young leaves, petioles and twigs.

Viburnum rufidulum ❧ a. Growth form with flower cluster, b. Flower, c. Twig with fruit cluster

Oak Leaves
White Oak Group

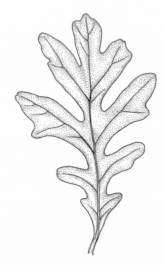

White oak
Quercus alba
p. 274–275

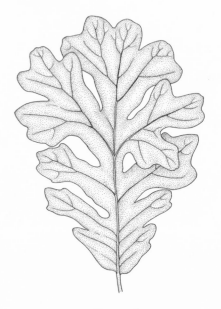

Bur oak
Quercus macrocarpa
p. 286–287

Swamp white oak
Quercus bicolor
p. 276–277

Post oak
Quercus stellata
p. 308–309

Overcup oak
Quercus lyrata
p. 284–285

Chinkapin oak
Quercus muehlenbergii
p. 292–293

Dwarf chinkapin oak
Quercus prinoides
p. 302–303

Swamp chestnut oak
Quercus michauxii
p. 290–291

Oak Leaves
Red Oak Group

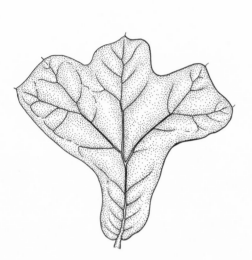

Black jack oak
Quercus marilandica
p. 288–289

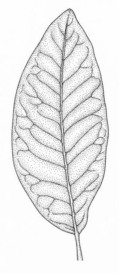

Shingle oak
Quercus imbricaria
p. 282–283

Willow oak
Quercus phellos
p. 300–301

Water oak
Quercus nigra
p. 294–295

Sawtooth oak
Quercus acutissima
p. 272–273

Southern red oak
Quercus falcata
p. 280–281

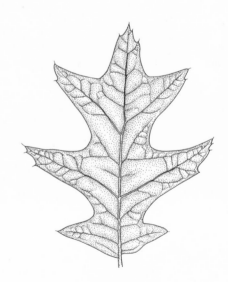

Cherrybark oak
Quercus pagoda
p. 296–297

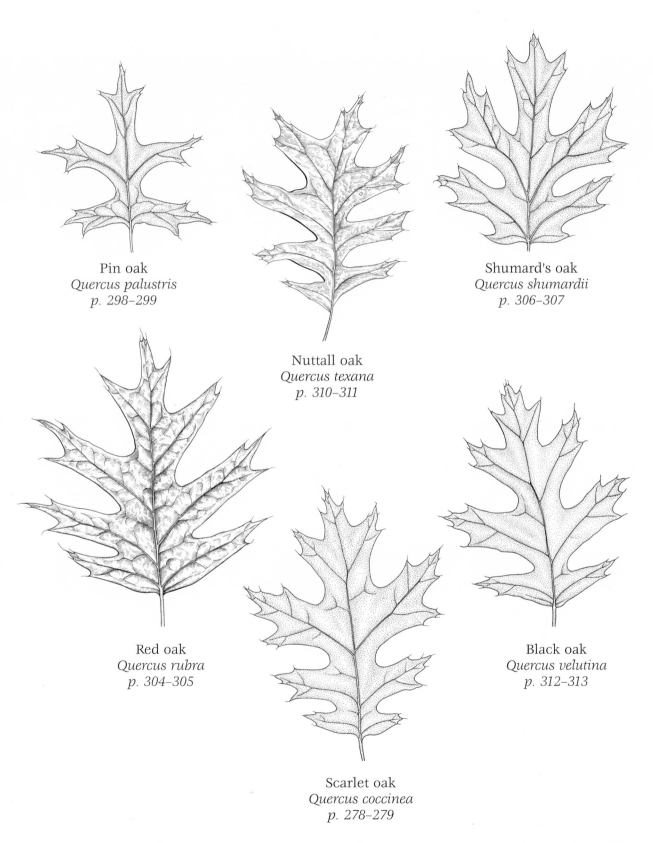

Pin oak
Quercus palustris
p. 298–299

Nuttall oak
Quercus texana
p. 310–311

Shumard's oak
Quercus shumardii
p. 306–307

Red oak
Quercus rubra
p. 304–305

Scarlet oak
Quercus coccinea
p. 278–279

Black oak
Quercus velutina
p. 312–313

Oak Acorns
White Oak Group

White oak
Quercus alba
p. 274–275

Swamp white oak
Quercus bicolor
p. 276–277

Overcup oak
Quercus lyrata
p. 284–285

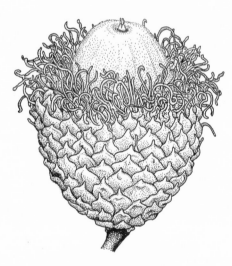

Bur oak
Quercus macrocarpa
p. 286–287

Swamp chestnut oak
Quercus michauxii
p. 290–291

Chinkapin oak
Quercus muehlenbergii
p. 292–293

Dwarf chinkapin oak
Quercus prinoides
p. 302–303

Post oak
Quercus stellata
p. 308–309

Oak Acorns
Red Oak Group

Sawtooth oak
Quercus acutissima
p. 272–273

Scarlet oak
Quercus coccinea
p. 278–279

Southern red oak
Quercus falcata
p. 280–281

Shingle oak
Quercus imbricaria
p. 282–283

Black jack oak
Quercus marilandica
p. 288–289

Water oak
Quercus nigra
p. 294–295

Cherrybark oak
Quercus pagoda
p. 296–297

Pin oak
Quercus palustris
p. 298–299

Willow oak
Quercus phellos
p. 300–301

Red oak
Quercus rubra
p. 304–305

Shumard's oak
Quercus shumardii
p. 306–307

Nuttall oak
Quercus texana
p. 310–311

Black oak
Quercus velutina
p. 312–313

Oak Reproductive Cycle

Oaks are divided into two groups: red oaks and white oaks. The red oak group is characterized by having acorns that take two years to mature. The acorns do not germinate until they have made it through winter with a moist, cold treatment. The inner surface of the acorn shell is usually coated with wooly hair; the kernels are usually bitter; and the acorn cap scales are relatively thin. The leaves have bristles at the tips of teeth or lobes, or if the margin is smooth, there is a distinct bristle at the tip of the leaf. The bark is typically dark-colored and furrowed.

The white oak group has acorns maturing at the end of their first growing season. The acorns do not need a cold treatment to germinate and usually sprout in late autumn; the inner surface of the acorn shell is smooth; the kernels are sweet (relative to the red oak group); and the acorn cap scales are relatively thickened ("knobby"). The leaves typically have rounded teeth or lobes, but never bristle-tipped. The bark is typically grayish and usually scaly.

Oak flowers appear in early spring as the new leaves are emerging. The male flowers occur in cylindrical drooping clusters called catkins, which emerge from the previous year's twig. Female flowers are small and few in numbers, emerging from the axils of leaves on the current year's growing twig. The female flowers are wind-pollinated by pollen from the male flowers.

Red Oak Group

Quercus acutissima	Sawtooth oak
Quercus coccinea	Scarlet oak
Quercus falcata	Southern red oak
Quercus imbricaria	Shingle oak
Quercus marilandica	Black jack oak
Quercus nigra	Water oak
Quercus pagoda	Cherrybark oak
Quercus palustris	Pin oak
Quercus phellos	Willow oak
Quercus rubra	Northern red oak
Quercus shumardii	Shumard's oak
Quercus texana	Nuttall oak
Quercus velutina	Black oak

White Oak Group

Quercus alba	White oak
Quercus bicolor	Swamp white oak
Quercus lyrata	Overcup oak
Quercus macrocarpa	Bur oak
Quercus michauxii	Swamp chestnut oak
Quercus muehlenbergii	Chinkapin oak
Quercus prinoides	Dwarf chinkapin oak
Quercus stellata	Post oak

Oak Reproductive Cycle demonstrated by black oak, *Quercus velutina* ❦ a. Twig with young leaves, catkins with male flowers, young fruit below, and female flowers along the upper twig in the leaf axils b. Male catkin, c. Male flowers, d. Female flower, e. Twig with young fruit, f. Acorn, g. Cup with nut

Hickory Reproductive Cycle

Hickory flowers appear in the spring with the leaves. The male flowers occur on cylindrical drooping clusters called catkins. The catkins are usually three-branched with several catkins appearing at the base of the current season's growth. The female flowers are few in number and relatively inconspicuous, appearing near the end of the new growth. The female flowers are wind-pollinated by pollen from the male flowers.

The fruits are bony-shelled nuts, which are enclosed in a four-parted husk. In some hickory species, the husk is thick and splits to the base at maturity, while in others it is thin and splits late and only part way.

Missouri hickories:

Carya aquatica	Water hickory
Carya cordiformis	Bitternut hickory
Carya glabra	Pignut hickory
Carya illinoinensis	Pecan
Carya laciniosa	Shellbark hickory
Carya ovata	Shagbark hickory
Carya pallida	Sand hickory
Carya texana	Black hickory
Carya tomentosa	Mockernut hickory

Hickory Reproductive Cycle demonstrated by shagbark hickory, *Carya ovata* ❀ a. Twig with young leaves, catkins with male flowers, and female flowers toward the tip, b. Male catkin, c. Male flowers, d. Female flowers, e. Husk splitting open, f. Nut

List of Families, Genera, and Species

Aceraceae (maple family)
Acer ginnala, Amur maple
Acer negundo, box elder
Acer rubrum var. *drummondii*, Drummond's red maple
Acer rubrum var. *rubrum*, red maple
Acer saccharinum, *silver maple*
Acer saccharum spp. *floridanum*, Southern sugar maple
Acer saccharum spp. *nigrum*, black maple
Acer saccharum spp. *saccharum*, sugar maple
Acer saccharum spp. *schneckii*, Schneck's sugar maple

Annonaceae (custard apple family)
Asimina triloba, pawpaw

Anacardiaceae (cashew tree)
Cotinus obovatus, smoke tree
Rhus copallina, winged sumac
Rhus glabra, smooth sumac

Aquifoliaceae (holly family)
Ilex decidua, possum haw
Ilex opaca, American holly
Ilex verticillata, winterberry

Araliaceae (ginseng family)
Aralia spinosa, Devil's walking stick

Betulaceae (birch family)
Alnus serrulata, alder
Betula nigra, river birch
Carpinus caroliniana, musclewood
Ostrya virginiana, hop hornbeam

Bignoniaceae (trumpet creeper family)
Catalpa bignonioides, Southern catalpa
Catalpa ovata, Chinese catalpa
Catalpa speciosa, Northern catalpa

Caesalpiniaceae (senna family)
Cercis canadensis, redbud
Gleditsia aquatica, water locust
Gleditsia triacanthos, honey locust
Gymnocladus dioica, Kentucky coffee tree

Caprifoliaceae (honeysuckle family)
Sambucus racemosa, red-berried elder
Viburnum prunifolium, black haw
Viburnum rufidulum, Southern black haw

Cornaceae (dogwood family)
Cornus alternifolia, alternate-leaved dogwood
Cornus amomum ssp. *obliqua*, swamp dogwood
Cornus drummondii, rough-leaved dogwood
Cornus florida, flowering dogwood
Cornus foemina, stiff dogwood
Cornus racemosa, gray dogwood

Cupressaceae (cypress family)
Juniperus ashei, Ashe's juniper
Juniperus virginiana, red cedar

Taxodium distichum, bald cypress

Ebenaceae (ebony family)
Diospyros virginiana, persimmon

Elaeagnaceae (oleaster family)
Elaeagnus angustifolia, Russian olive

Ericaceae (heath family)
Vaccinium arboreum, farkleberry

Fabaceae (bean family)
Cladrastis kentukea, yellow-wood
Robinia pseudo-acacia, black locust

Fagaceae (oak family)
Castanea dentata, American chestnut
Castanea mollissima, Chinese chestnut
Castanea pumila var. *ozarkensis*, Ozark chinquapin
Castanea pumila var. *pumila*, Allegheny chinquapin
Fagus grandifolia, American beech
Quercus acutissima, sawtooth oak
Quercus alba, white oak
Quercus bicolor, swamp white oak
Quercus coccinea, scarlet oak
Quercus ellipsoidalis, Northern pin oak
Quercus falcata, Southern red oak

Quercus imbricaria, shingle oak
Quercus lyrata, overcup oak
Quercus macrocarpa, bur oak
**Quercus margaretta*, sand post oak
Quercus marilandica, black jack oak
Quercus michauxii, swamp chestnut oak
Quercus muehlenbergii, chinkapin oak
Quercus nigra, water oak
Quercus pagoda, cherrybark oak
Quercus palustris, pin oak
Quercus phellos, willow oak
Quercus prinoides, dwarf chinkapin oak
Quercus rubra, Northern red oak
Quercus shumardii, Shumard's oak
Quercus stellata, post oak
Quercus texana, Nuttall oak
Quercus velutina, black oak

Hamamelidaceae (witch hazel family)
Hamamelis vernalis, Ozark witch hazel
Hamamelis virginiana, Eastern witch hazel
Liquidambar styraciflua, sweet gum

Hippocastanaceae (horse chestnut family)
Aesculus glabra, Ohio buckeye
Aesculus pavia, red buckeye

Juglandaceae (walnut family)
Carya aquatica, water hickory
Carya cordiformis, bitternut hickory
Carya glabra, pignut hickory
Carya illinoinensis, pecan
Carya laciniosa, shellbark hickory
Carya ovata, shagbark hickory
Carya pallida, sand hickory
Carya texana, black hickory

Carya tomentosa, mockernut hickory
Juglans cinerea, butternut
Juglans nigra, black walnut

Lauraceae (laural family)
Sassafras albidum, sassafras

Leitneriaceae (corkwood family)
Leitneria floridana, corkwood

Magnoliaceae (magnolia family)
Liriodendron tulipifera (tulip tree)
Magnolia acuminata, cucumber magnolia

Moraceae (mulberry family)
**Broussonetia papyrifera*, paper mulberry
*Maclura pomifera, Osage orange
*Morus alba, white mulberry
Morus rubra, red mulberry

Mimosaceae (mimosa family)
**Albizia julibrissin*, mimosa

Nyssaceae (tupelo family)
Nyssa aquatica, water tupelo
Nyssa biflora, swamp black gum
Nyssa sylvatica, black gum

Oleaceae (olive family)
Chionanthus virginicus, fringe tree
Forestiera acuminata, swamp privet
Fraxinus americana, white ash
Fraxinus biltmoreana, Biltmore ash
Fraxinus pennsylvanica, green ash
Fraxinus profunda, pumpkin ash
Fraxinus quadrangulata, blue ash

Pinaceae (pine family)
Pinus echinata, short-leaf pine
*Pinus nigra, Austrian pine
*Pinus strobus, Eastern white pine
*Pinus taeda, loblolly pine
*Pinus virginica, scrub pine

Platanaceae (plane tree)
Platanus occidentalis, sycamore

Rhamnaceae (buckthorn family)
Rhamnus caroliniana, Carolina buckthorn
Rhamnus cathartica, common buckthorn

Rosaceae (rose family)
Amelanchier arborea, service berry
**Amelanchier humilis*, low service berry
Crataegus calpodendron, urn-tree hawthorn
Crataegus coccinioides, Kansas hawthorn
Crataegus crus-galli, cockspur thorn
Crataegus engelmanii, barberry-leaved hawthorn
Crataegus intricata, thicket hawthorn
Crataegus marshallii, parsley haw
Crataegus mollis, downy hawthorn
Crataegus phaenopyrum, Washington thorn
Crataegus pruinosa, frosty hawthorn
Crataegus punctata, dotted hawthorn
Crataegus rotundifolia, round-leaved hawthorn
Crataegus spathulata, littlehip hawthorn
Crataegus succulenta, red haw
Crataegus uniflora, one-flower hawthorn
Crataegus viridis, green haw

Malus angustifolia, narrow-leave crab apple
Malus coronaria, sweet crab apple
Malus ioensis, prairie crab apple
**Malus pumila*, apple
Prunus americana, wild plum
Prunus angustifolia, Chickasaw plum
**Prunus cerasus*, sour cherry
Prunus hortulana, Hortulan plum
**Prunus mahaleb*, perfumed cherry
Prunus mexicana, big tree plum
Prunus munsoniana, wild goose plum
**Prunus persica*, peach
Prunus serotina, black cherry
Prunus virginiana, choke cherry
**Pyrus communis*, pear

Rutaceae (citrus family)
Ptelea trifoliata, hop tree

Salicaceae (willow family)
**Populus alba*, silver poplar
Populus deltoides, cottonwood
Populus grandidentata, bigtooth aspen
Populus heterophylla, swamp cottonwood
**Populus nigra*, Lombardy poplar
**Populus tremula*, European aspen
Populus tremuloides, quaking aspen
**Salix alba*, white willow
Salix amygdaloides, peach-leaved willow
**Salix babylonica*, weeping willow
Salix caroliniana, Carolina willow
Salix discolor, pussy willow
Salix eriocephala, Missouri willow
Salix exigua, sandbar willow

**Salix fragilis*, crack willow
Salix nigra, black willow
**Salix purpurea*, basket willow
Salix sericea, silky willow

Sapindaceae (soapberry family)
Koelreuteria paniculata, golden-rain tree
Sapindus drummondii, soapberry

Sapotaceae (sapodilla family)
Bumelia lanuginosa, woolly buckthorn
Bumelia lycioides, Southern buckthorn

Scrophulariaceae (figwort family)
**Paulownia tomentosa*, princess tree

Simaroubaceae (quassia family)
**Ailanthus altissima*, tree-of-heaven

Staphyleaceae (bladdernut family)
Staphylea trifolia, bladdernut

Tamaricaceae (tamarisk family)
**Tamarix ramosissima*, saltcedar

Tiliaceae (linden family)
Tilia americana, American basswood
Tilia heterophylla, white basswood

Ulmaceae (elm family)
Celtis laevigata, sugar berry
Celtis occidentalis, hackberry
Celtis tenuifolia, dwarf hackberry
Planera aquatica, water elm
Ulmus alata, winged elm

Ulmus americana, American elm
Ulmus crassifolia, cedar elm
**Ulmus pumila*, Siberian elm
Ulmus rubra, slippery elm
Ulmus thomasii, rock elm

*Not native to Missouri

Other Tree Species

Amelanchier humilis Wieg., low service berry. Native from South Dakota and Minnesota; east to Ohio and Pennsylvania; north to Quebec and Ontario; planted in Missouri and escaped from cultivation in Lawrence, Pettis, and Stoddard counties; see p. 36, couplet #146, for characteristics that separate it from service berry, *Amelanchier arborea*

Fraxinus biltmoreana Beadle, biltmore ash. Twigs and leaf stalks hairy, lower surface of leaflets white or gray-green, main body of fruit (containing seed) winged no more than 1/3 its length, fully grown fruit 1 to 2 inches long; known from Dunklin, Jackson, Mississippi, and St. Louis counties.

Malus baccata (L.) Borkh., Siberian crab apple. A small to medium tree, up to 50 feet tall, forming a rounded, wide-spreading crown of branches; flowers pink in bud, opening white, 1 1/2 inches across, very fragrant; fruit bright red or yellow, 3/8 inch in diameter; native to Siberia and planted as an ornamental; escaped from cultivation in Jackson and St. Louis counties.

Nyssa biflora Walter, swamp black gum. Also called *Nyssa sylvatica* var. *biflora* (Walter) Sarg.; similar to black gum, *Nyssa sylvatica* var. *sylvatica*, but with a swollen buttress like water tupelo, *Nyssa aquatica*, with leaves smaller than black gum, 2 to 4 inches long, 1 to 2 1/2 inches wide; fruit 2 per stalk; stone of fruit prominently ribbed; a medium-sized tree, up to 60 feet tall; occurs in swamps; there is a historic record from Dunklin County; range is from southeast Missouri to four counties in southern Arkansas, southeastern Texas; east along the coastal plain of Louisiana to Florida; and north along the coast from Georgia to Maryland and Delaware.

Pinus banksiana Lamb., jack pine. A small-sized evergreen tree, up to 35 feet tall; needles are 2 per bundle, stiff, 3/4 to 1 1/2 inches long; cones are curved or arched to the side; cone scales mostly lacking spines; native to Canada and the northeastern states to Wisconsin and Minnesota; planted and reproducing locally around plantings throughout Missouri; a scrubby, irregular growth form, mainly planted as an ornamental or for erosion control.

Pinus nigra Arnold, Austrian pine. A medium-sized evergreen tree, up to 60 feet tall; needles are 2 per bundle, stiff, 3 1/2 to 6 inches long; cone scales are thickened and ridged on the front and armed with a short spine; native to Europe; planted for a screen or as an ornamental; not known to escape from cultivation; very susceptible to the pine wilt nematode that can spread to other pines.

Prunus spinosa L., blackthorn. A thorny shrub to small tree, up to 20 feet tall; leaves blunt at the tip, 3/4 to 2 inches long, less than 3/4 inch wide; fruit purple, about 1 inch across; native to Eurasia and Africa, used as an ornamental with a record of its naturalizing in Jasper County; fruit a vital ingredient of sloe gin.

Quercus ellipsoidalis E. Hill, Northern pin oak. A small to medium-sized tree, up to 60 feet tall, with branches much divided and drooping, persistent on trunk; appearance is similar to pin oak, *Quercus palustris* and scarlet oak, *Q. coccinea*; leaves are similar to black oak, *Q. velutina*, but lack tufts of hairs in the leaf axils or nearly so; inner surface of acorn cup smooth (lacking hairs); and cup scales tightly appressed. Recorded from Harrison County in dry upland woods but its occurrence in Missouri is in question based on collected specimens, which appear to be black oak. Northern pin oak ranges from southeastern North Dakota, Manitoba, Minnesota, and Iowa; east to northern Ohio and Michigan.

Quercus margaretta Ashe ex Small, sand post oak. Shrub to small tree, up to 20 feet tall, often clonal, spreading by long rhizomes (runners); leaves variable in size and shape, 1 1/2 to 4 inches long, usually 5-lobed with the upper pair of lobes broad and blunt; upper surface smooth, lower surface brownish-downy; smaller size and smaller leaves distinguish sand post oak from post oak, *Quercus stellata*; a state record collection from Lawrence County was determined to be a hybrid between post oak and dwarf chinkapin oak, *Q. prinoides*. Another collection from Jasper County has yet to be resolved. Sand post oak ranges from Oklahoma, Texas, and Louisiana; east to Virginia.

Quercus prinus L., rock chestnut oak. Also known as *Quercus montana* Willd. Medium-sized tree, up to 70 feet tall, with a rounded, dense, broad crown; leaves similar in size and shape to swamp chestnut oak, *Q. michauxii*, but smooth on the lower surface; bark is dark brown, deeply grooved; occurs on rocky upper slopes; range is from Maine, south to Georgia and Mississippi; west to southern Illinois. Not known from Missouri but its westernmost occurrence is on Atwood Ridge, Union County, Illinois, the first line of hills above the Mississippi River; a distance of about 1 mile from the hills on the Missouri side. The author was unsuccessful in searching for rock chestnut oak at Trail of Tears State Park, Missouri, but it still may occur in the vicinity due to its close proximity to the Illinois population.

Rhus typhina L., staghorn sumac. A thicket-forming large shrub to small tree, up to 30 feet tall, with a dense covering of velvety hairs on the twigs; native to the northeastern United States; planted as an ornamental in Missouri but rarely escaping; one record is from St. Louis County, collected along a bridge embankment by Viktor Mühlenbach in 1956.

Salix purpurea L., basket willow. A large shrub to small tree, up to 18 feet tall; planted as an ornamental, this tree was brought from Europe during colonial times to be used for basket making. It was collected in Ralls County in 1912 and 1913. The best recognizable feature is the purple-tinged leaves covered by a silvery or gray color. Basket willow rarely escapes from cultivation.

Nursery Sources
for Native Trees

Insist that nurseries purchase or grow trees from this region so that they are better adapted; also, make sure the trees are nursery-propagated and not dug from the wild.

ArborVillage
PO Box 227
Holt MO 64048
816-264-3911

Cascade Forestry Nursery
22033 Fillmore Road
Cascade IA 52035
319-852-3042

Country Blooms
9625 Manchester Road
Rock Hill MO 63119
314-961-7840

Eureka Nursery
1421 W Fifth Street
Eureka MO 63343
636-938-9040

Forrest Keeling Nursery
88 Keeling Land
Elsberry MO 63343
573-898-5571

Garden Heights
1605 South Big Bend
St Louis MO 63117
314-645-7333

George O. White State Nursery
14027 Shafer Road
Licking MO 65542
573-674-3229

Gilberg Perennial Farms
2906 Ossenford Road
Wildwood MO 63038
314-458-2033

Hartke Nursery
1030 N Warson Road
St Louis MO 63132
314-997-6678

Hillerman Nursery & Florist
4100 Southpoint Road
Washington MO 63090
636-239-6729

Keller's Flowerhaus
15640 East 40 Hwy
Kansas City MO 64136
816-373-6223

Longfellow's Garden
12007 Hwy 50
Centertown MO 65023
573-584-9611

McGinnis Tree & Seed
309 East Florence
Glenwood IA 51534
712-527-4308

Missouri Wildflowers Nursery
9814 Pleasant Hill Road
Jefferson City MO 65109
573-496-3492
mowldflrs@socket.net
www.mowildflowers.net

Moffett Nurseries
6451 State Route 6 NE
St Joseph MO 64507
816-233-1223

Native Gardens
5737 Fisher Lane
Greenback TN 37742
865-856-0220
sales@native-gardens.com
www.native-gardens.com

Nolin River Nut Tree Nursery
797 Port Wooden Road
Upton KY 42784
270-369-8551
nolinriver@hotmail.com
www.nolinnursery.com

Parkview Gardens
1925 Randolph
St. Charles MO 63301
636-946-7641

Pine Ridge Gardens
832 Sycamore Road
London AR 72847
501-293-4359
pineridg@cswret.com
www.pineridgegardens.com

Prestige Landscape
108 North Eatherton Road
Chesterfield MO 63005
636-519-8700

Ridgecrest Nursery
3347 Highway 64
Wynne AR 72396
870-238-3763
ridgecrest@crosscountybank.com

Soil Service Nursery Inc
7125 Troost Avenue
Kansas City MO 64131
816-333-3232

St Michaels Nursery
Howell County Road 8860
Brandsville MO 65688

Sunlight Gardens
174 Golden Lane
Andersonville TN 37705
865-494-8237
sungardens@aol.com

Sunny Hill Gardens and Florist
206 North Kingshighway
Cape Girardeau MO 63701
573-335-5785

Ten Acre Gardens
8853 East Cloud
Salina KS 76401
785-536-4672

Town & Country Nursery
Box 132 7984 South
Hwy 94
Dutzow MO 63342
636-433-2234

Trees by Touliatos
2020 Brooks Road
Memphis TN 38116
901-345-7361

Troy Nursery
1158 Bueneman Lane
Troy MO 63379
636-366-4550

Waldbart Nursery
5517 North Hwy 67
Florissant MO 63034
314-741-3121

Wholesale Only:
Bowood Farms Inc
Fox Creek Lane
RR1 Box 90
Clarksville MO 63336
573-242-3840

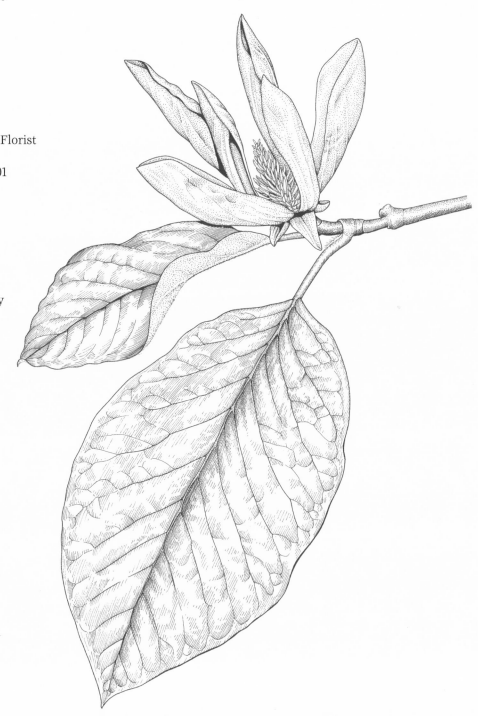

Selected References

Barnes, B.V. and W.H. Wagner, Jr. 1981. Michigan Trees: A Guide to the Trees of Michigan and the Great Lakes Region. University of Michigan Press, Ann Arbor, Michigan. 383 pp.

Brown, C.L. and L.K. Kirkman. 1990. Trees of Georgia and Adjacent States. Timber Press, Portland, Oregon. 292 pp.

Crawford, H.S., C.L. Kucera, and J.H. Ehrenreich. 1969. Ozark Range and Wildlife Plants. Forest Service, U.S. Dept. of Agriculture, Washington, D.C. 236 pp.

Cullina, W. 2002. Native Trees, Shrubs, & Vines: A guide to Using, Growing, and Propagating North American Woody Plants. Houghton Mifflin Company, New York. 354 pp.

Dirr, M. 1998. Manual of Woody Landscape Plants: Their Identification, Ornamental Characteristics, Culture, Propagation, and Uses, Fifth Edition. Stipes Publishing, Champaign, Illinois. 1187 pp.

Duncan, W.H. and M.B. Duncan. 1988. Trees of the Southeastern United States. University of Georgia Press, Athens, Georgia. 322 pp.

Elias, T.S. 1980. Trees of North America. Van Nostrand Reinhold Company, New York. 948 pp.

Farrar, J.L. 1995. Trees of the Northern United States and Canada. Iowa State University Press, Ames, Iowa. 502 pp.

Fernald, M.L. 1950. Gray's Manual of Botany, 8th ed. American Book Co., New York. 1632 pp.

Gleason, H.A. 1952. The New Britton and Brown Illustrated Flora of the Northeastern United States and Adjacent Canada, 3 vols. New York Botanical Garden, New York.

Henderson, C.L. 1987. Landscaping for Wildlife. Minnesota Department of Natural Resources, St. Paul. 149 pp.

Hunter, C.G. 1989. Trees, Shrubs, & Vines of Arkansas. The Ozark Society Foundation, Little Rock, Arkansas. 207 pp.

Kurz, D. 1997. Shrubs and Woody Vines of Missouri. Missouri Department of Conservation, Jefferson City. 387 pp.

Ladd, D. 1988. A Preliminary Revision of the Genus Crataegus in Missouri. Unpublished manuscript. The Nature Conservancy, St. Louis, Missouri. 13 pp.

Leopold, D.J., McComb, W.C., and Muller, R.N. 1998. Trees of the Central Hardwood Forests of North America. Timber Press, Portland, Oregon. 468 pp.

Martin, A.C., H.S. Zim, and A.L. Nelson. 1951. American Wildlife & Plants. Dover Publications, Inc., New York, 500 pp.

Mohlenbrock, R.H. 1986. Guide to the Vascular Flora of Illinois, revised ed. Southern Illinois University Press, Carbondale, Illinois. 507 pp.

Nelson, P. 1985. The Terrestrial Natural Communities of Missouri. Missouri Dept. of Natural Resources, Jefferson City. 197 pp.

Palmer, B. 1995. Missouri Conservation Trees and Shrubs. Missouri Department of Conservation, Jefferson City. 37 pp.

Peattie, D.C. 1950. A Natural History of Trees of Eastern and Central North America. Houghton Mifflin, New York. 606 pp.

Sargent, C.S. 1965. Manual of the Trees of North America, Vols.1 and 2. Dover Publications, New York.

Stephens, H.A. 1973. Woody Plants of the North Central Plains. University Press of Kansas, Lawrence, Kansas. 530 pp.

Sternberg, G. and J. Wilson. 1995. Landscaping with Native Trees. Chapters Publishing Ltd., Shelburne, Vermont. 288 pp.

Steyermark, J.A. 1963. Flora of Missouri, Iowa State University Press. Ames, Iowa. 1725 pp. (Pp. 1726–1728 [errata] added at second printing, 1968)

Tylka, D. 2002. Native Landscaping for Wildlife and People. Missouri Dept. of Conservation, Jefferson City. 181 pp.

Vines, R.A. 1960. Trees, Shrubs, and Woody Vines of the Southwest. University of Texas Press, Austin, Texas. 1104 pp.

Yatskievych, G. 1999. Steyermark's Flora of Missouri, Vol. 1, revised ed. Missouri Dept. of Conservation, Jefferson City, MO, and Missouri Botanical Garden Press, St. Louis, Missouri 991 pp.

Yatskievych, G. and J. Turner. 1990. Catalogue of the Flora of Missouri. Missouri Botanical Garden, St. Louis, Missouri. 344 pp.

Electronic Sources

Grow Native! Information on growing native plants
www.grownative.org

680 Tree Fact Sheets
http://hort.ifas.ufl.edu/trees

Forests of Illinois
www.museum.state.il.us/muslink/forest

Plants for a Future
www.comp.leeds.ac.uk/pfaf/D_search.html

Silvics of North America
www.na.fs.fed.us/spfo/pubs/silvics_
manual/table_of_contents.htm

Tree Guide, Inc.
www.treeguide.com

Champion Trees and Ancient Forests
www.championtrees.org

Fire Effects Information
www.fs.fed.us/database/feis

The Meanings of Latin Names
www.cnr.vt.edu/dendro/dendrology/
syllabus/meanings.htm

Online Etymology Dictionary
www.etymonline.com

National Register of Big Trees
www.americanforests.org/resources/
bigtrees/register.php

Missouri Department of Conservation (MDC)
www.conservation.state.mo.us

Forestry Section
www.conservation.state.mo.us/forest

Missouri State Champion Trees
www.conservation.state.mo.us/forest/
IandE/statetre.htm

MDC Nature Section
www.conservation.state.mo.us/nathis

Missouri Natural Areas System
www.conservation.state.mo.us/nathis/
naturalareas

Directory of Missouri Natural Areas
www.conservation.state.mo.us/areas/
natareas/index.shtml

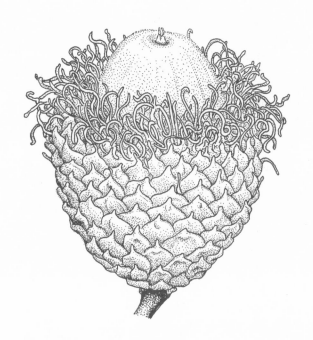

Index to Scientific and Common Names

Acer
  ginnala, 40
  negundo, 42
  negundo var. *texanum*, 42
  nigrum, 48
  rubrum, 44
  rubrum var. *drummondii*, 44
  saccharinum, 46
  saccharum ssp. *floridanum*, 50
  saccharum ssp. *nigrum*, 48
  saccharum ssp. *saccharum*, 50
  saccharum ssp. *schneckii*, 50
Aesculus
  glabra, 52
  pavia, 54
Ailanthus altissima, 56
Albizia julibrissin, 58
Alder, 60
  Black, 182
  Common, 60
  Smooth, 60
  Tag, 60
Allegheny chinquapin, 98
Alnus serrulata, 60
Althaea, shrubby, 176
Alternate-leaved dogwood, 116
Amelanchier
  arborea, 62
  humilis, 387
American basswood, 352
American beech, 154
American bladdernut, 346
American chestnut, 96
American elm, 358
American holly, 180
American linden, 352
American plum, 248
American smoke tree, 128
American sycamore, 234
American yellowwood, 114
Amur maple, 40
Angelica tree, 64
Apple, 210
  Common, 210

Hedge, 200
Narrow-leaved crab, 204
Prairie crab, 208
Siberian crab, 387
Southern crabapple, 204
Sweet crab, 206
Turkey crab, 134
Wild, 210
Aralia spinosa, 64
Ash
  Biltmore, 387
  Blue, 164
  Green, 160
  Pumpkin, 162
  Red, 160
  Stinking, 268
  Wafer, 268
  White, 158
Ash-leaved maple, 42
Ashe's juniper, 188
Asimina triloba, 66
Aspen,
  Bigtooth aspen, 240
  European, 246
  Large-toothed, 240
  Quaking, 246
  Trembling, 246
Austrian pine, 387
Bald cypress, 350
Barberry-leaved hawthorn, 146
Basket
  Oak, 290
  Willow, 388
Basswood, 352
  American, 352
  White, 354
Beard, old man's, 112
Beech
  American, 154
  Blue, 76
Bee-tree linden, 354
Berry
  June, 62
  Low service, 387

Pigeon, 116
  Sarvice, 62
  Service, 62
Betula nigra, 68
Big tree plum, 258
Bigtooth aspen, 240
Biltmore ash, 387
Birch, river, 68
Bitternut hickory, 80
Black alder, 182
Black cherry, 264
Black gum, 218
  Swamp, 387
Black haw, 370
  Rusty, 372
  Southern, 372
Black hickory, 92
Black jack oak, 288
Black locust, 322
Black maple, 48
Black oak, 312
Black tupelo, 218
Black walnut, 186
Black willow, 336
Blackthorn, 387
Bladdernut, 346
  American, 346
Blue ash, 164
Blue beech, 76
Blue dogwood, 116
Blueberry, highbush, 368
Bois-d'arc, 200
Bowwood, 200
Box elder, 42
Broussonetia papyrifera, 70
Buckeye
  Ohio, 52
  Red, 54
Buckthorn
  Carolina, 74, 314
  Common, 316
  European, 316
  False, 72
  Southern, 74

Woolly, 72
Bumelia, smooth, 74
Bumelia
   lanuginosa, 72
   lycioides, 74
Bur oak, 286
Burning bush, 152
Bush, burning, 152
Butternut, 184
Buttonwood, 234
Carpinus caroliniana, 76
Carolina buckthorn, 74, 314
Carolina willow, 328
Carya
   aquatica, 78
   cordiformis, 80
   glabra, 82
   illinoinensis, 84
   laciniosa, 86
   ovalis, 82
   ovata, 88
   pallida, 90
   texana, 92
   tomentosa, 94
Castanea
   dentata, 96
   mollissima, 96
   pumila var. *ozarkensis*, 98
   pumila var. *pumila*, 98
Catalpa
   Chinese, 102
   Common, 100
   Northern, 102
   Southern, 100
Catalpa
   bignonioides, 100
   ovata, 102
   speciosa, 102
Catawba tree, 100, 102
Cedar
   Eastern red, 190
   Ozark white, 188
   Red, 190
Cedar elm, 360
Celtis
   laevigata, 104
   occidentalis, 106
   tenuifolia, 108
Cercis canadensis, 110
Cherry
   Black, 264

Choke, 266
Ground, 252
Indian, 62, 314
Mahaleb, 256
Perfumed, 256
Rum, 264
Sour, 252
Sweet, 252
Wild, 264
Wild black, 264
Cherrybark oak, 296
Chestnut
   American, 96
   Ozark, 98
Chestnut oak, 290
   Chinese, 96
   Dwarf, 302
   Rock, 388
   Yellow, 292
Chickasaw plum, 250
Chinaberry, 342
Chinese catalpa, 102
Chinese chestnut, 96
Chinese elm, 362
Chinkapin oak, 292
   Dwarf, 302
Chinquapin
   Allegheny, 98
   Dwarf, 302
   Oak, 292
   Ozark, 98
Chionanthus virginicus, 112
Chittim wood, 72
Choke cherry, 266
Cigartree, 100, 102
Cladrastis
   lutea, 114
   kentukea, 114
Club, Hercules, 64
Coastal Plain willow, 328
Cockspur thorn, 132
Coffee tree, Kentucky, 170
Common alder, 60
Common apple, 210
Common buckthorn, 316
Common catalpa, 100
Common hop tree, 268
Cork elm, 366
Corkwood, 194
Cornus
   alternifolia, 116

   amomum ssp *obliqua*, 118
   drummondii, 120
   florida, 122
   foemina, 124
   obliqua, 118
   racemosa, 126
Cotinus
   coggygria, 128
   obovatus, 128
Cotton gum, 216
Cottonwood, 238
   Eastern, 238
   Southern, 238
   Swamp, 242
Cow oak, 290
Crab, wild, 204, 206, 208,
Crab apple
   Narrow-leaved, 204
   Prairie, 208
   Siberian, 387
   Southern, 204
   Sweet, 206
   Turkey, 134
Crack willow, 326
Crataegus
   calpodendron, 130
   coccinioides, 146
   collina, 146
   crus-galli, 132
   engelmannii, 146
   intricata, 146
   margaretta, 146
   marshallii, 146
   mollis, 134
   phaenopyrum, 136
   pruinosa, 138
   sicca, 146
   spathulata, 140
   succulenta, 146
   uniflora, 142
   viridis, 144
Cucumber magnolia, 202
Cucumber tree, 202
Cypress, bald, 350
Deciduous holly, 178
Devil's walking stick, 64
Diamond willow, 332
Diospyros virginiana, 148
Dogwood
   Alternate-leaved, 116
   Blue, 116

Flowering, 122
Gray, 126
Pagoda, 116
Pale, 118
Rough-leaved, 120
Silky, 118
Stiff, 124
Swamp, 118
Dotted hawthorn, 146
Downy hawthorn, 134
Drummond's red maple, 44
Dwarf chestnut oak, 302
Dwarf chinkapin oak, 302
Dwarf chinquapin oak, 302
Dwarf elm, 362
Dwarf hackberry, 108
Dwarf hawthorn, 142
Dwarf sumac, 318
Eastern cottonwood, 238
Eastern red cedar, 190
Eastern redbud, 110
Eastern wahoo, 152
Eastern white pine, 226
Eastern witch hazel, 174
Elaeagnus angustiflolia, 150
Elder
    Box, 42
    Red-berried, 340
    Scarlet, 340
    Stinking, 340
Elderberry, red-berried, 340
Elm
    American, 358
    Cedar, 360
    Cork, 366
    Dwarf, 362
    Red, 364
    Rock, 366
    Siberian, 362
    Slippery, 364
    Water, 232
    White, 358
    Winged, 356
Empress tree, 222
Euonymus atropurpureus, 152
European aspen, 246
European buckthorn, 316
European smoke tree, 128
Fagus grandifolia, 154
False buckthorn, 72
False shagbark hickory, 82

Farkleberry, 368
Flame-leaf sumac, 318
Flowering dogwood, 122
Forestiera acuminata, 156
Fraxinus
    americana, 158
    biltmoreana, 387
    pennsylvanica, 160
    profunda, 162
    quadrangulata, 164
    tomentosa, 162
Fringe tree, 112
Frosty hawthorn, 138
Gleditsia
    aquatica, 166
    triacanthos, 168
Goat willow, 330
Gobbler oak, 272
Goldenrain tree, 192
Graney graybeard, 112
Gray dogwood, 126
Graybeard, graney, 112
Green ash, 160
Green haw, 144
Green osier, 116
Ground cherry, 252
Gum
    Black, 218
    Bully, 72
    Cotton, 216
    Sour, 218
    Swamp black, 387
    Sweet, 196
    Tupelo, 216
Gum-elastic, 72
Gymnocladus dioica, 170
Hackberry, 106
    Dwarf, 108
    Northern, 106
Hamamelis
    vernalis, 172
    virginiana, 174
Hard maple, 50
Haw
    Black, 370
    Green, 144
    Parsley, 146
    Possum, 178
    Red, 134, 146
    Rusty black, 372
    Southern black, 372

Summer, 134
Hawthorn, 146
    Barberry-leaved, 146
    Dotted, 146
    Downy, 134
    Dwarf, 142
    Frosty, 138
    Kansas, 146
    Littlehip, 140
    One-flower, 142
    Pasture, 140
    Pear, 130
    Round-leaved, 146
    Thicket, 146
    Urn-tree, 130
Hazel
    Eastern witch, 174
    Ozark witch, 172
    Vernal witch, 172
Heart-leaved willow, 332
Hedge apple, 200
Hercules club, 64
Hibiscus syriacus, 176
Hickory
    Black, 92
    Bitternut, 80
    False shagbark, 82
    Kingnut, 86
    Mockernut, 94
    Ozark pignut, 92
    Pignut, 82
    Red, 82
    Sand, 90
    Shagbark, 88
    Shellbark, 86
    Water, 78
    White, 94
Highbush blueberry, 368
Holly
    American, 180
    Deciduous, 178
Honey locust, 168
Hop hornbeam, 220
Hop tree, 268
Hornbeam, 76
    Hop, 220
Hortulan plum, 254
Ilex
    decidua, 178
    opaca, 180
    verticillata, 182

Indian cherry, 62, 314
Ironwood, 74, 220
Jack oak, black, 288
Jack pine, 387
Juglans
   cinerea, 184
   nigra, 186
June berry, 62
Juniper, Ashe's, 188
Juniperus
   ashei, 188
   virginiana, 190
Kansas hawthorn, 146
Kingnut hickory, 86
Kinnikinnik, 118
Kentucky coffee tree, 170
Koelreuteria paniculata, 192
Large-toothed aspen, 240
Laurel oak, 282
Leitneria floridana, 194
Linden, 352
   American, 352
   Bee-tree, 354
   Silver-tree, 354
   White, 354
Liquidambar styraciflua, 196
Liriodendron tulipifera, 198
Littlehip hawthorn, 140
Loblolly, 228
Locust
   Black, 322
   Honey, 168
   Water, 166
Lombardy poplar, 244
Maclura pomifera, 200
Magnolia
   Cucumber, 202
   Southern, 202
Magnolia
   acuminata, 202
   grandiflora, 202
Mahaleb cherry, 256
Malus
   angustifolia, 204
   baccata, 387
   coronaria, 206
   ioensis, 208
   pumila, 210
Manitoba maple, 42
Maple
   Amur, 40

Ash-leaved, 42
Black, 48
Drummond's red, 44
Hard, 50
Manitoba, 42
Red, 44
Schneck's sugar, 306
Silver, 46
Soft, 46
Southern sugar, 50
Sugar, 50
Mexican plum, 258
Mimosa, 58
Missouri willow, 332
Mockernut hickory, 94
Morus
   alba, 212
   rubra, 214
Mossy cup oak, 286
Mulberry
   Paper, 70
   Red, 214
   Silkworm, 212
   White, 212
Musclewood, 76
Nannyberry, rusty, 372
Narrow-leaved crab apple, 204
Nettle tree, 106
Northern catalpa, 102
Northern hackberry, 106
Northern pin oak, 387
Northern red oak, 304
Nuttall oak, 310
Nyssa
   aquatica, 216
   biflora, 387
   sylvatica, 218
   var. *biflora*, 387
Oak
   Basket, 290
   Black, 312
   Black jack, 288
   Bur, 286
   Cherrybark, 296
   Chinkapin, 292
   Chinquapin, 292
   Cow, 290
   Dwarf chestnut, 302
   Dwarf chinkapin, 302
   Dwarf chinquapin, 302
   Gobbler, 272

Laurel, 282
Mossy cup, 286
Northern pin, 387
Northern red, 304
Nuttall, 310
Overcup, 284
Pin, 298
Post, 308
Red, 304
Rock chestnut, 388
Sand post, 387
Sawtooth, 272
Scarlet, 278
Scrub, 302
Shingle, 282
Shumard, 306
Southern red, 280
Spanish, 280
Swamp chestnut, 290
Swamp white, 276
Water, 294
White, 274
Willow, 300
Yellow chestnut, 292
Ohio buckeye, 52
Old man's beard, 112
Oleaster, 150
Olive, Russian, 150
One-flower hawthorn, 142
Orange, Osage, 200
Osage orange, 200
Osier, green, 116
Ostrya virginiana, 220
Overcup oak, 284
Ozark chestnut, 98
Ozark chinquapin, 98
Ozark pignut hickory, 92
Ozark white cedar, 188
Ozark witch hazel, 172
Pagoda dogwood, 116
Pale dogwood, 118
Paper mulberry, 70
Parsley haw, 146
Pasture hawthorn, 140
Paulownia, 222
   Royal, 222
Paulownia tomentosa, 222
Pawpaw, 66
Peach, 262
Peach-leaved willow, 324
Pear, 270

Hawthorn, 130
Pecan, 84
Perfumed cherry, 256
Persimmon, 148
Pigeon berry, 116
Pignut hickory, 82
    Ozark, 92
Pin oak, 298
    Northern, 387
Pine
    Austrian, 387
    Eastern white, 226
    Jack, 387
    Loblolly, 228
    Scrub, 230
    Short-leaf, 224
    Virginia, 230
    White, 226
Pinus
    banksiana, 387
    echinata, 224
    nigra, 387
    strobus, 226
    taeda, 228
    virginiana, 230
Plane tree, 234
Planer tree, 232
Planera aquatica, 232
Platanus occidentalis, 234
Plum
    American, 248
    Big tree, 258
    Chickasaw, 250
    Hortulan, 254
    Mexican, 258
    Sugar, 62
    Wild, 248, 258
    Wild Goose, 254, 260
Poplar
    Lombardy, 244
    Silver, 236
    Tulip, 198
    White, 236
    Yellow, 198
Populus
    alba, 236
    deltoides, 238
    grandidentata, 240
    heterophylla, 242
    nigra var. *italica*, 244
    tremula, 246

tremuloides, 246
Possum haw, 178
Post oak, 308
    Sand, 387
Prairie, crab apple, 208
Princess tree, 222
Privet, swamp, 156
Prunus
    americana, 248
    angustifolia, 250
    avium, 252
    cerasus, 252
    fruticosa, 252
    hortulana, 254
    mahaleb, 256
    mexicana, 258
    munsoniana, 260
    persica, 262
    serotina, 264
    spinosa, 387
    virginiana, 266
Ptelea trifoliata, 268
Pumpkin ash, 162
Pussy willow, 330
Pyrus
    communis, 270
    malus, 210
Quaking aspen, 246
Quercus
    acutissima, 272
    alba, 274
    bicolor, 276
    borealis, 304
    coccinea, 278
    ellipsoidalis, 387
    falcata, 280
    falcata var. *falcata*, 280
    falcata var. *pagodaefolia*, 296
    imbricaria, 282
    lyrata, 284
    macrocarpa, 286
    margaretta, 387
    marilandica, 288
    michauxii, 290
    montana, 388
    muehlenbergii, 292
    nigra, 294
    nuttallii, 310
    pagoda, 296
    palustris, 298
    phellos, 300

    prinoides, 302
    prinus, 388
    rubra, 304
    shumardii, 306
    var. *schneckii*, 306
    var. *shumardii*, 306
    stellata, 308
    texana, 310
    velutina, 312
Raisin, wild, 372
Red ash, 160
Red buckeye, 54
Red cedar, 190
Red elm, 364
Red haw, 134, 146
Red hickory, 82
Red maple, 44
Red mulberry, 214
Red oak, 304
    Northern, 304
    Southern, 280
Redbud, 110
    Eastern, 110
Red-berried elder, 340
Red-berried elderberry, 340
Rhamnus
    caroliniana, 314
    cathartica, 316
Rhus
    copallina, 318
    glabra, 320
    typhina, 388
River birch, 68
Robinia pseudo-acacia, 322
Rock chestnut oak, 388
Rock elm, 366
Rose of Sharon, 176
Rough-leaved dogwood, 120
Round-leaved hawthorn, 146
Royal paulownia, 222
Rum cherry, 264
Russian olive, 150
Rusty black haw, 372
Rusty Nannyberry, 372
Salix
    alba, 326
    amygdaloides, 324
    babylonica, 326
    caprea, 330
    caroliniana, 328
    discolor, 330

eriocephala, 332
exigua, 334
fragilis, 326
interior, 334
nigra, 336
purpurea, 388
rigida, 332
sericea, 338
Saltcedar, 348
Sambucus
   pubens, 340
   racemosa, 340
Sand hickory, 90
Sand post oak, 387
Sandbar willow, 334
Sapindus drummondii, 342
Sarvice berry, 62
Sarviss tree, 62
Sassafras, 344
Sassafras albidum, 344
Sawtooth oak, 272
Scarlet elder, 340
Scarlet oak, 278
Schneck's sugar maple, 306
Scrub oak, 302
Scrub pine, 230
Service berry, 62
   Low, 387
Shadblow, 62
Shadbush, 62
Sharon, Rose of, 176
Shagbark hickory, 88
   False, 82
Shellbark hickory, 86
Shingle oak, 282
Shining sumac, 318
Short-leaf pine, 224
Shrubby althaea, 176
Shumard oak, 306
Siberian crab apple, 387
Siberian elm, *362*
Sideroxylon
   lanuginosum, 72
   lycioides, 74
Silktree, 58
Silkworm mulberry, 212
Silky dogwood, 118
Silky willow, 338
Silver maple, 46
Silver poplar, 236
Silver-leaved linden, 354

Slippery elm, 364
Smoke tree, 128
   American, 128
   European, 128
Smooth alder, 60
Smooth bumelia, 74
Smooth sumac, 320
Soapberry, 342
   Western, 342
Soft maple, 46
Sour cherry, 252
Sour gum, 218
Souther blackhaw, 372
Southern buckthorn, 74
Southern catalpa, 100
Southern cottonwood, 238
Southern crab-apple, 204
Southern magnolia, 202
Southern red oak, 280
Southern sugar maple, 50
Spanish oak, 280
Sparkleberry, 368
Staghorn sumac, 388
Staphylea trifolia, 346
Stiff dogwood, 124
Stinking ash, 268
Stinking elder, 340
Sugar maple, 50
   Schneck's, 50
   Southern, 50
Sugar plum, 62
Sugarberry, 104
Sumac
   Dwarf, 318
   Flame-leaf, 318
   Shining, 318
   Smooth, 320
   Staghorn, 388
   Winged, 318
Summer haw, 134
Swamp black gum, 387
Swamp chestnut oak, 290
Swamp cottonwood, 242
Swamp dogwood, 118
Swamp privet, 156
Swamp tupelo, 216
Swamp white oak, 276
Sweet cherry, 252
Sweet crab apple, 206
Sweet gum, 196
Sycamore, 234

American, 234
Tag alder, 60
Tamarisk, 348
Tamarix ramosissima, 348
Taxodium distichum, 350
Tearblanket, 64
Thicket hawthorn, 146
Thorn
   Cockspur, 132
   Washington, 136
Tilia
   americana, 352
   americana var. *americana*, 352
   americana var. *heterophylla*, 354
   heterophylla, 354
Tree,
   American smoke, 128
   Angelica, 64
   Catawba, 102
   Common hop, 268
   Cucumber, 202
   Empress, 222
   European smoke, 128
   Fringe, 112
   Goldenrain, 192
   Hop, 268
   Kentucky coffee, 170
   Nettle, 106
   Plane, 234
   Planer, 232
   Princess, 222
   Sarviss, 62
   Smoke, 128
   Tulip, 198
Tree-of-heaven, 56
Trembling aspen, 246
Tulip poplar, 198
Tulip tree, 198
Tupelo, 216, 218
   Black, 218
   Swamp, 216
   Water, 216
Tupelo gum, 216
Turkey crab apple, 134
Ulmus
   alata, 356
   americana, 358
   crassifolia, 360
   parvifolia, 362
   pumila, 362
   rubra, 364

thomasii, 366
Urn-tree hawthorn, 130
Vaccinium arboreum, 368
Vernal witch hazel, 172
Viburnum
    prunifolium, 370
    rufidulum, 372
Virgilia, 114
Virginia pine, 230
Wafer ash, 268
Wahoo, 152
    Eastern, 152
Walking stick, devil's, 64
Walnut,
    Black, 186
    White, 184
Ward's willow, 328
Washington thorn, 136
Water elm, 232
Water hickory, 78
Water locust, 166
Water oak, 294
Water tupelo, 216
Weeping willow, 326
Western soapberry, 342
White ash, 158
White basswood, 354
White cedar, 188
White elm, 358
White hickory, 94
White linden, 354
White mulberry, 212
White oak, 274
    Swamp, 276
White pine, eastern, 226
White poplar, 236
White walnut, 184
White willow, 326
Wild apple, 210
Wild black cherry, 264
Wild cherry, 264
Wild crab, 204, 206, 208
Wild goose plum, 254, 260
Wild plum, 248, 258
Wild raisin, 372
Willow
    Basket, 388
    Black, 336
    Carolina, 328
    Coastal plain, 328
    Crack, 326

Diamond, 332
Goat, 330
Heart-leaved, 332
Missouri, 332
Oak, 300
Peach-leaved, 324
Pussy, 330
Sandbar, 334
Silky, 338
Wards, 328
Weeping, 326
White, 326
Winged elm, 356
Winged sumac, 318
Winterberry, 182
Witch hazel
    Eastern, 174
    Ozark, 172
    Vernal, 172
Wood, chittim, 72
Woolly buckthorn, 72
Yellow chestnut oak, 292
Yellow poplar, 198
Yellow-tree, 114
Yellowwood, 114, 128
    American, 114

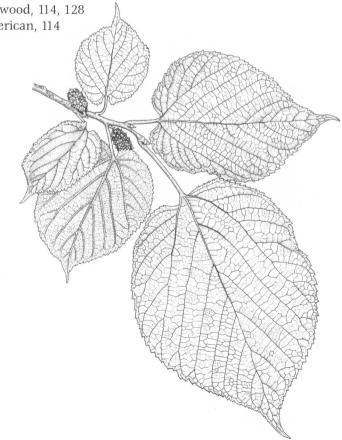

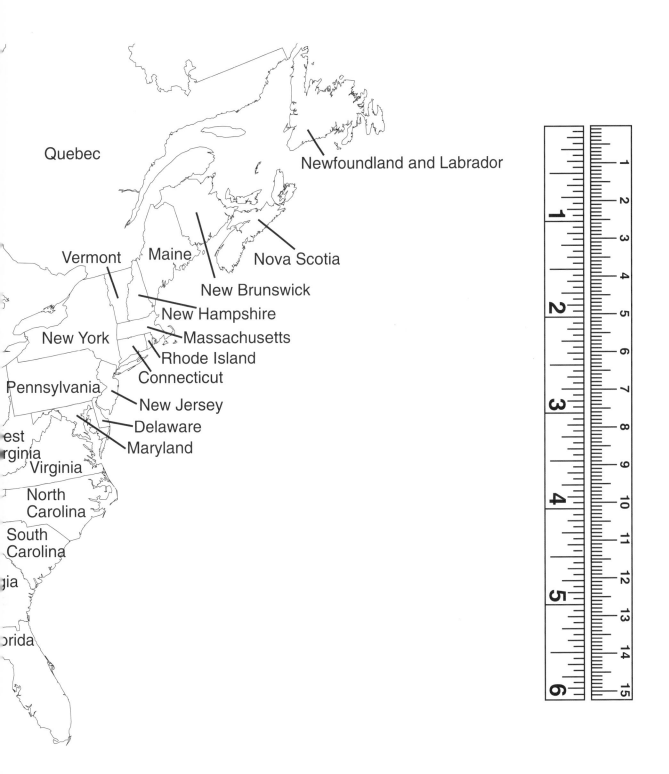

Quebec

Newfoundland and Labrador

Vermont   Maine

Nova Scotia

New Brunswick

New Hampshire

New York   Massachusetts

Rhode Island

Connecticut

Pennsylvania

New Jersey

Delaware

Maryland

est
rginia

Virginia

North
Carolina

South
Carolina

jia

orida